I Can't ~~Go On...~~

by

Eileen Swan

Bound Biographies

Life is not cured, it is managed

Please seek medical advice before implementing any of the strategies discussed in this book, especially if you have any pre-existing conditions.

Dedication

This book is dedicated to the memory of Ronald Swan,
love of my life and twin of my soul.

Acknowledgements

The writing of this book has been governed by a wonderful synchronicity which I attribute to Divine Intelligence and I thank this Power for bringing the following people into my life at the right time.

Ken Smith who inspired me to keep a record of our talks together and without whom I would never have dreamed of writing a book.

Lionel Holmes for his painstaking transcription of the manuscript.

Christine Holmes who contributed to the editing and led me to Tony Gray who cut my original huge volume of words to a more manageable size, in a comparatively painless operation.

Sandra Bolton for her clear illustrations of the yoga poses and her first perceptive interpretation of my idea for a cover design, later developed by John Everett.

Clive Wright for his generous support and for introducing me to Tim Miller who designed the final cover which so clearly portrays my original vision.

Nightingale Conant for their enlightening self-realisation programmes which have changed my life.

These people came into my life at the right time in the right place and I am deeply grateful to them.

Prologue

From 1957 to 1974 I taught Home Economics in a mixed grammar school, newly built in a fold of the Sussex Downs, which seemed to me to epitomise education at its finest. There was a well-chosen youthful staff and four hundred reasonably eager, responsive and cheerful pupils with mostly co-operative and caring parents.

Even in those halcyon days, there were times, usually at the end of term, when the staff felt unduly pressured – by exam-marking, reports, various dramatic performances and the ever-rising end-of-term exuberance of the pupils.

Such was our comradeship however, that as we passed one another in a seething corridor of delirious children, we would clap a quivering hand to our brow and cry dramatically, 'I can't go on!!'

We would then collapse in a giggling heap in the Staff Room, all tension would disappear, and we could proceed to the next mind-crumbling task in a state of apparent sanity.

Now that I have the experience of fourscore years on which to ponder, including over twenty years of psychotherapy and counselling, I realise what a wonderful prophylactic those little bits of drama in the corridor were. For they worked on a truly holistic level: we knew we had a problem which we faced and accepted – we shared it with someone who really understood – we exploded physically and verbally, and the result was a complete letting-go into the total release of laughter.

I know now that most of us are quietly shrieking 'I can't go on!' a fair proportion of the time; but seek in vain the understanding friend in the corridor.

There are many acquaintances but few true friends, and they are only lent to us. People change, people die, we outgrow our friends and they outgrow us. This book is intended to be such a friend; to share with true humility the various coping skills I have learned along the way, from nutrition and exercise to meditation and the growth of spiritual awareness.

Eileen Swan

2008

Contents

Book Two - I Can't Go On...Yes I Can!

Book One

I Can't Go On

Chapter 1

Tales of my birth have proved revealing: my mother gave birth to me with great difficulty and danger to herself, and my father had to choose whether mother or child should be saved – I was left for dead while attention was given to my mother. This meant that, however unconscious of it I was at the time, my first memory was of total rejection – of lying on a cold slab naked and alone. I believe this created an experience of terrifying abandonment, laying down a pattern which was to recur throughout my life. However, I survived to live a long and amazing life, rich in opportunities to find out what it was all about, and to develop various techniques for survival.

The consequences of that memory – of lying on a cold, hard slab, completely vulnerable and threatened with total annihilation – were with me for many years, until in 1975 I had the good fortune to be led to a man called Edward Barker who was a psychotherapist in Hove. Under hypnosis, he took me back to the time of my birth, and I was able to recognise the frightening feelings which I was experiencing in my daily life. These feelings were manifesting themselves as palpitations, sickness and diarrhoea, panic attacks, insomnia, sweating, constant upper respiratory infections, and a general paralysing feeling of not being able to go on, sometimes verging on the suicidal. For many years, I had moaned, 'It's not fair – everyone's all right but me – why me? – don't talk to me about God – how can there be a god – if there is I hate him?' And so on and so on, as if life were generally easy – as if life should be easy.

I realise now that life presents us with a series of problems, causing us grief, sadness, loneliness, fear, anxiety, anguish, frustration and pain. But it is in the meeting and solving of problems that we are helped to develop our courage and our wisdom. Wise people learn to welcome problems in order to encourage their spiritual growth. As Benjamin Franklin said, 'Those things that hurt, instruct.'

For most of my life, I avoided my problems. I knew that solving them would be painful, so I ignored them, hoping they would go away – or I encouraged the belief that if I met the ideal man, he would solve them for me, or that, by deadening the pain with alcohol, flirtation, tranquillisers or the perfect therapist, I could forget them. I tried to go round the problems rather than suffer through them. So I didn't grow – I stayed stuck.

My mother recovered from my birth, only to die of septicaemia when I was three weeks old. There were no antibiotics in 1921. For the next nine months I was passed round, rather like a parcel, between nine different women, one of whom would wrap me up in numerous woollen garments and place me in front of the fire, and another who would leave me outside in November wearing nothing but a vest! How did a baby survive such treatment? Traumatic birth, a total lack of bonding, the wrong food, inadequate clothing, extremes of temperature, and most importantly, a total lack of love and security. God moves in a mysterious way indeed! It is only now that I can look back with such a philosophical view. Most of my life has been spent as a total neurotic – either railing against fate, denying God, or retreating into psychosomatic illness.

I was taken from the foster-mothers by my father's sister, Aunt Alice, who insisted on my father signing a legal document, relinquishing all parental rights. Being only 26, and maybe blaming me for the death of my mother, I understand he was eager to get me out of his life and go his own way unburdened by a child, although I found out later that my grandmother was strongly opposed to this arrangement. Apparently she said, "Let him be responsible for her: he brought her into the world and he should look after her!"

Aunt was a schoolmarm of the early 1920s. That is to say, a keen supporter of the stern and relentless suppression of children, the 'Speak when you are spoken to,' the 'Do this – do that – sit down – be quiet– go to your room!' brigade. Had she not been bringing in the money to maintain this imposing house, I believe my grandmother would have forbidden my presence there.

My younger aunt – Auntie Annie – was too dependent on her mother and sister, both financially and psychologically, to voice any opinion of her own, but I believe that, like their brother Leonard whom she adored, she had a certain amount of sympathy for me.

I was to have a reprieve. Initially, it was impossible for Aunt Alice to look after me and at the same time run the concentration camp of mixed infants which she terrified into submission from 9 to 4 each day, so I was put in the care of a wonderful woman whom I called Grandma Manton. Grandma Manton had been a midwife for many years in the picture postcard village of Cropston in Leicestershire. She lived in a romantic-looking cottage with roses round the door, but no electricity or gas – and an extremely primitive and malodorous privy, where nobody even bothered to cut up the newspaper.

What bliss to grow up in such a place – you don't succumb to germs if you are totally surrounded by love and security. And I was – from Grandma Manton herself, her two daughters, her granddaughter and Grandpa Manton, a quiet, wise man in his early sixties. There was also a dog (Gyp), and a tomcat called Vera, whom nobody could be bothered to rename, even when his amorous yowlings left no doubt of his evident sexuality. I had this total security until I was three years old – playing in the dirt, paddling in puddles, and allowed to do anything that wasn't threatening me with actual danger. Cosseted at night with warm baths and cuddled in front of the fire – all the things that are so important to a growing child – not just physically, but also emotionally.

But when I was three, a terrifying break occurred: Grandma Manton, her daughter and her granddaughter dressed me up in my best clothes and took me to Leicester to an enormous house belonging to my father's mother. I had never seen such an overwhelming place before, in which people actually lived; it seemed to be the sort of forbidding edifice from my story books in which the wicked witch or giant lived... I found it very threatening as, after the small cottage, this place seemed so big. We went into a magnificent room for afternoon tea and I knew something was wrong – I can recall the feeling even now – a fearful feeling, that something terrible was about to happen. Grandma Manton, her daughter and granddaughter were all crying – and this filled me with foreboding. I remember that for tea we had tinned peaches with juice like tears, and I remember my tears rolling down and mingling with this juice. I have hated tinned peaches ever since!

I know now that I was handed over like a circus animal whose early training has been completed and was now ready for the ringmaster to whip into its final, docile performance. Eventually, the Cropston contingent quietly disappeared; the three of them just went and left me there, and I remember this as the second really terrifying experience of my life. I felt unable to move or speak, but I suppose I accepted, as a child has to: after all, you're small and helpless – there is nothing you can do – you have no resources. I was only three and apparently accepted the situation, making no comment at the time, but underneath was a perception of the world as a very dangerous place. I felt I wouldn't survive – that one day I would just fall apart and not exist any more.

I wasn't cared for as I had been, even in the physical sense. The day after my arrival, while both aunts and my uncle were at work, my Grandmother was responsible for me, but, rather as one might deal with an irritating puppy, she left me out in the garden. There was a heat wave at the time, and because I had red hair and a very fair skin, I had sunstroke extremely badly. I was very ill, with a high temperature, and my skin was badly burned, which further confirmed my feelings about this house – that it was some sort of witch's lair. Whatever had I done to the people at Cropston that they had left me here?

This became part of my programme, that if anything goes wrong, it's always my fault. These days I can work through it, but it's still there. Experiments have been done which show that furrows in the brain actually deepen when we keep thinking the same thoughts like, 'I'm ugly – no one wants/loves/understands/cares about me,' and so on. Consequently, it becomes increasingly easy for repetitive negative thoughts to recur.

My aunt had decided that I was old enough to attend a small private nursery school during the day time while she herself was teaching, so that I could live with her, her brother and sister and their mother. She made it quite clear right from the beginning that my father had signed me away. "Don't think you are ever going back to him – he doesn't want you. He's signed this paper. Look! And I have only taken you in order to have someone to look after me when I am old." The implication being, 'so don't make any plans for having a life.' At that age, the fact that my father had gone away and left me was very frightening – but the implication of these statements grew as time went on – that I had been bought as a possession and therefore I had no rights whatsoever. In the 1920s, older people had authority which was unquestioned.

The uncertainty of my situation – was I really wanted? – left me with a heaving stomach and a terrible fear of being cast out at any time. I kept asking if I could go back to Cropston, but this request was met with stern disapproval, and with my being locked in my room for hours on end. At first I cried, but when I did, I was held between my aunt's knees and shaken violently, to a refrain of 'no tears, no tears'.

However, there's always been an angel around. And the angel then was an uncle called Leonard. I never called him Uncle – I called him Len because we were friends from the beginning. There had been five children in my father's family and he was the youngest. He must have been in his early twenties. He lived at home as he was never very strong, and he worked in the office of a boot and shoe factory. He didn't have any girlfriends – or any men friends, for that matter. When he went out, he went with his sister Annie. I absolutely adored him. I adored him so much that when he went to the loo, I sat outside the door and waited for him to come out! I used to pretend that I was his dog, 'Bruce', named after a dog along the avenue.

Len loved me like a mother and a father – but it all came to a very abrupt end when I was eight. I used to go into his bedroom in the mornings and sometimes lie in his bed while he was dressing. One morning, I said, "Len, is your bottom different from mine?" And that did it! He picked me up and put me forcibly outside the door. And I was never allowed in his room again. This was a terrible blow. I didn't know what I had done, but I knew I had done something wrong which had caused Len, of all people, to literally eject me from his room. However, we remained very close; he always stuck up for me, and when Aunt Alice was at her worst, would say, "For heaven's sake, leave her alone – she's only a child."

My father used to make 'duty' visits to the family from time to time. Although he had abrogated responsibility for me, I think his conscience pricked him. He had lots of affairs with women as he was a real charmer, always the life and soul of the party, drinking copiously and attracting women, like flies round a honey pot. He had taken a job as a travelling salesman with a shoe manufacturer and quickly rose to become sales manager and a director of the firm. He had a big company car, which in those days was a source of admiration and envy. And he had a very attractive personality, but with no depth, and absolutely no sensitivity. I always sensed his understandable uneasiness with me, and I suppose he was jealous of my complete adoration of Len, who, so far as I was concerned, was my father, mother, brother, sister, and total family. The three of us went to the cinema, The Olympia on the Narborough Road in Leicester one night when I was about six. When we came out, I was dragging my feet as I was tired. Len picked me up and put me on his shoulders to carry me the rest of the way. My father turned to him with a face of absolute fury and said, "Put her down! Put her down! She's a spoilt child."

When I was eleven, and Len was 33, he became very ill with cancer of the pancreas. He lingered on for a year, and then he died. I was sent to stay with a cousin for the weekend, and at some point an uncle came and told me that Len had died – the actual words were, "Your Uncle has died and *you've* lost a jolly good friend." Again, this awful abyss opened up for me – like leaving Cropston. I was devastated and yearned for some support and comfort. But all my aunt said was, "It's a pity you turned out to be such a disappointment to him during the last few years of his life." I remember the terrible pain of this further confirmation of my utter worthlessness was almost unbearable.

My father's family were very smart – part of the jet set of the day. The aunts and my grandmother used to have lots of continental holidays, going off to Nice, Cannes, Paris, The Dorchester in London, and so forth – always places where children were not welcome. So, because it suited them, I was allowed to go back to Cropston whilst they were away.

I used to stay with Grandma Manton's married daughter and her husband, whom I called Auntie Edie and Uncle Tom. They had four children of their own and very little money. Uncle Tom was out of work, and in the thirties there wasn't any social security as we know it, so Auntie Edie had to take in washing in order to keep the family housed, fed and clothed. She had an old-fashioned kitchen with a dolly tub, a brick copper heated by a coal fire, and a miasma of steam surrounding the wet clothes that were strung around the kitchen and the living room. But I was deliriously happy there – it reinforced a message that you need money for food, warmth and shelter, but not a vast amount to be happy. In fact, the people I was coming into contact with who made me happy were finding it very difficult to survive, money wise, but the people who had money for continental holidays and so on, made me very unhappy: a most valuable lesson.

I lived with this ambivalence throughout my childhood, and had at least a glimpse of what real caring was: love was being accepted for myself, and being praised and cuddled.

The Cropston family provided me with many insights into human behaviour in general, and relationships in particular. The three boys and one girl used to fight and push each other around, have pillow fights and get into terrible trouble. When, inevitably, I became involved in this, I learned about the rough and tumble of family life, the loyalty of siblings, and the general feeling of invincibility which a family bestows – such a contrast with the bleak isolation of my life in Leicester.

Aunt Alice used to force me to learn poetry, and then hire me out to various functions to stand up and recite – a five-year-old prodigy. I was her property so I had to reflect well on her. Only once did I forget a line and she said, 'They won't ask you again, because you made a mistake.' But there was never any praise – but I realise now that this has stood me in good stead, as I particularly love the metaphysical poets and find quotations comparatively easy to recall when public speaking. People at Cropston thought my recitation was amazing and said, 'Isn't she wonderful? And only five years old.' However, in terms of general spiritual progress, it was good that I knew both the heights and the depths of childhood experience.

I was eleven when Leonard died. He left some money to Aunt Alice with which she bought some land in Cropston at the bottom of the Manton's garden, and built a weekend bungalow on an acre of ground. This was the end of an era, as from now on, even if I was with Auntie Edie and Uncle Tom, there was always the possibility that Aunt Alice would appear without warning. Uncle Tom used to swear, and get very uptight about the way I was treated. I learned my first four-letter words from him! It would have made it worse for me if they had said anything, because she would have stopped me seeing them altogether. I used to go up there in floods of tears, and Auntie Edie used to say to me, "Never mind, me duck; it's your little cross. We've all got one; and Aunt Alice is yours."

Aunt Alice was a very unpredictable woman – manic and violent, and probably depressive. She would put me across her knee, beating the hell out of me, then someone would call, and she would suddenly cuddle me, regardless of the tears on my cheeks. I would be absolutely tense, because I didn't want any contact at all with this frightening creature. Certainly she was a very disappointed woman. She had been engaged to be married five times, and all five men had ended their liaisons with her. Perhaps they all found her out? There was always a man around whom she treated like dirt – I remember one whom I called Uncle Bert. He used to stay at the bungalow at Cropston; there was only one bedroom in which she and I slept, and he slept on the settee in the living room, so they didn't appear to sleep together. Aunt Alice was 34 when I was born but she always seemed terribly old to me. Women dressed in a rather 'elderly' way in those days – very discreet make-up, if any, with hair in corrugated waves, surrounded by sausage curls. I always felt she was a witch, and when I talked about this to Auntie Edie and the family, she and her daughter cried and said they had begged Aunt Alice to let them bring me up. They didn't want any money for my keep – but she regarded me as a possession, to look after her like a slave of some kind. She told me I could never ever have a boyfriend or get married, that I belonged to her, and could not have a future of my own. I was never allowed any sense of personal identity; I had to dress and speak as she told me. I'd been brought up in my early years with a very lazy, broad Leicestershire accent which she couldn't stand. She was a great one for pretending that she belonged to the upper classes. She had money, but certainly not breeding.

So I had the advantage of living intimately within these different levels of society. As a child, you just accept people – not for what they have but for what they are, their innate goodness or badness. You can see this knowing awareness in the eyes of babies and very young children: they are unerring in their estimation of those about them.

As Wordsworth says in Intimations of Immortality:

> Our birth is but a sleep and a forgetting:
> The Soul that rises with us, our life's Star,
> Hath had elsewhere its setting,
> And cometh from afar:
> Not in entire forgetfulness,
> And not in utter nakedness,
> But trailing clouds of glory do we come
> From God, who is our home:
> Heaven lies about us in our infancy!
> Shades of the prison-house begin to close
> Upon the growing boy.

Chapter 2

Leonard had been my rock and my salvation. When my aunt built the new bungalow at Cropston I was caught between heaven and hell. In Auntie Edie and Uncle Tom's house, I had love, security, warmth and support, and yet I was bound by duty and fear to the bungalow at the bottom of their garden, where my unhappiness was intensified because I was so near, and yet so far away, from all that I most wanted and needed. It was a strange experience and one that has repeated itself in my life many times, in the sense that there's always been something that could be better but has been taken away, and it wasn't until I went into deep analysis that I realised I was doing what we all do – repeating the attitudes and patterns of behaviour laid down in childhood as a result of upbringing. This is what makes psychotherapy and analysis so valuable, even at the superficial levels of counselling: how can you possibly understand yourself if you don't look back at the conditioning of your childhood experiences?

These experiences have been invaluable in the practice of psychotherapy; I find experiential knowledge of life far more helpful than the academic input from conventional study.

Since I believe that life is a place in which we go through many experiences, we can choose to learn our lessons or to play truant. So what good could possibly come from such a life?

Whereas we are told that heaven has many mansions, it seems to me that hell has, too. Many of you will have had difficult and painful childhoods. Parents, being people, are human beings, and with the best will in the world, none of them can be the loving, protecting, caring, cuddling Mummy and Daddy of our fairy stories 24 hours a day, seven days a week. Therefore, as adults, it is important to analyse the painful events of childhood – to understand their effects upon us, so we can become stronger, mentally and emotionally, and also grow spiritually.

I realise that the pattern of the illnesses which I have suffered throughout my life was laid down during my childhood because I was quite often ill with upper respiratory diseases, particularly around my sinuses – caused by unshed tears. When I was ill, I was cosseted, as I so desperately longed to be; I was kept in a warm bed, fed delicacies, wrapped up and placed in front of the fire, and was asked how I felt. Since I was never asked how I felt on any other occasion, and my opinions and feelings were assumed for me, I suddenly realised – as many children, and indeed adults subconsciously do – that, 'This is great, so I'll be ill some more'.

I succumbed to some infection or another about every three months or so: whenever life became too much for me, and I just couldn't cope with it any more, I was ill. There was no doubt about my symptoms – I had a temperature which could be recorded, the doctor would come and listen to my chest and say it was clogged with mucus, or I would have a very visible sore throat. The pattern was so regular that it had to be psychosomatic.

Because of the pattern of my childhood illnesses I was prevented from going as far as I could in worldly terms. I had ambitions to go on the stage when I was young; I did some dramatic work and sang in the choir and often took a principal part in school plays. I was often voted form prefect in my grammar school, and a school prefect in the sixth form. I obviously had a certain charisma and, looking back, I think my career has been effective, but not on a worldly level. When I was teaching, I was constantly being urged to become an area organiser of Home Economics and possibly go on to be an HMI. But I was always held back by a physical feeling of weakness and inability to cope. Whenever I had an interview for this kind of job, I would be ill and unable to attend.

The deep emotion underlying all this inability to progress was fear, and its proven effect on the immune system – these are the 'psychosomatic illnesses' to which I refer earlier. As a child, instead of being able to say, 'I am afraid,' I said to myself, 'I must not acknowledge that I am afraid because I am helpless and no one here will help me.' I converted my fear into a bodily solution – a primitive, obscure language which seemed to have no solutions other than medical ones. Changing language from words to pain and bodily discomfort is as effective as closing our eyes and sticking our fingers in our ears. It is now a proven, scientific fact that when we are overwhelmed by strong, negative emotions such as grief and fear, the immune system can indeed be considerably weakened and our ability to fight infection greatly reduced. As we are a wonderfully interactive mystery of body, mind and spirit, we can in fact 'manufacture' an illness when we are exhausted physically or mentally, and thus gain a respite from extreme stress.

When Leonard died, life was really tough. I had just started grammar school which I found really frightening. Most of the girls came from more literate professional family homes where there was good conversation and good food – and the social niceties which I did not possess. My family had money but this had been made by my grandparents who built up and ran a painting and decorating business very successfully for a number of years. Being in 'trade', we did not have people to the house for a meal – there was no conversation as such, no music, no books other than cheap novelettes. It was a very tough period, and I felt the loss of my uncle very deeply. It was another in the succession of bereavements which has run through my life, starting with the death of my mother so early, and the 'bereavement' of my father leaving me. There seemed to be a pattern of people or situations being very important to me, and then either being taken away or somehow the relationship coming to an end. And this inculcated in me a great feeling of unfairness.

Grammar school was very difficult indeed, because I was constantly under pressure to be the best of any group in which I found myself. The work itself was more than enough to cope with. But I was also pushed into extra-curricular activities like the Girl Guides – and naturally not to be anything less than a Patrol Leader! I finally attained sufficient marks to be top of my form and rushed home full of glee, thinking, 'Now she will love me, make a fuss of me, and be pleased that she adopted me.' My aunt put on her specs, read the report, looked over the top of it, and said, "Well, you could have got a higher mark." The resultant feeling was like being a balloon into which someone has stuck a particularly vicious pin. It is a feeling which easily resurfaces when I am criticised but one which I can now recognise and manage.

So my schooldays were pretty horrendous and there were many little things going on which would appear not to matter too much, but which were very important to an adolescent girl. All my friends had smart, casual clothes into which they could change from uniform when they arrived home. But I had to wear my uniform, even if I went out in the evening. And this was pretty devastating to my self-esteem and emerging femininity. Also, the paralysing threats went on and on. 'If you do that again – if you're not top of your form – if you don't get over 90% … I shall put you in the gutter where you belong. Everyone wonders why I took you in the first place because they knew I hated your mother. And don't think your father wants you, because he wishes you'd never been born.'

Unfortunately, I knew the latter statement was true. I used to try to make my father love me in various ways, but it was patently obvious that he didn't. Sometimes, he would actually push me physically out of his way. I absolutely adored him, as little girls do with their fathers – and one Sunday morning when he was home for the weekend, I decided to get up early and take him a cup of tea in bed. We had quite a big house with outbuildings containing an outside lavatory. Whilst waiting for the kettle to boil, and not wanting to wake him by using the bathroom, I went outside to this loo singing. He flung open his bedroom window and roared, "For God's sake, stop that bloody row!" I literally froze in my tracks and dared not take the cup of tea to him. I didn't know what he would do when he came downstairs and my stomach tied itself into a thousand knots. All my life, stress and my stomach have had a very close relationship.

It is sad when parental relationships go awry; the effects go deep. But I realise now how difficult it must have been for my father to relate to me. He probably thought it was my fault my mother had died; there was always an implication that my conception had precipitated the marriage and he probably felt a certain amount of unacknowledged guilt at signing me away legally to a sister whom he privately considered to be potty. Their relationship was never good: she had always made a point of belittling him, and making fun of him, and there was an apocryphal story of him being goaded until he hurled a pot of marmalade at her head because he could not stand it any longer (the pot went through a window and smashed it).

There were plateaux of happiness and security however, as whenever my aunt and her family went off on some exotic and sophisticated holiday, unsuitable for a child, I was despatched to Cropston, and oh, what excitement ensued. I felt like a prisoner released from jail but alas! I was only out on parole, and as the day drew nearer for my return, I experienced an ever-deepening feeling of utter despair. On the day fixed for my return, my stomach would perform its usual gyrations – quite often resulting in such pain and bouts of vomiting that I was prostrate in bed, so attaining my goal of being unable to return to my house of horror. Here we have the pattern of illness as an escape reinforcing itself yet again, and targeting my stomach as its main area of expression.

I often speculate about what life would have been like had I had my own way and stayed at Cropston. This would have meant leaving a village school at 14 at the latest, because with the best will in the world, even if I had won a scholarship, there wouldn't have been the money to maintain it. Auntie Edie and Uncle Tom could not have provided for this financially. There was also the belief that education was wasted on girls, as women had to leave most jobs when they married, and became the responsibility of their husbands. At most, I would have become a typist but would more than likely have ended up in a factory.

I learned a great deal from this apparently harrowing childhood by recognising and working through the problems it created. It is interesting to note that it gave me a desperate desire to be liked, and at the same time a total disbelief in any overtures of affection or regard, a lack of belief in myself and my accomplishments, a tendency to toady to anyone apparently in authority, and a need to balance self-esteem and self-assertion so that it does not tip over into selfish egotism.

Thinking back to this time, I realise that I began to learn about love, which is the most effective balm to soothe and heal the pains and hurts of life. Unfortunately, most people equate love with sex, eroticism or sentimentality. So I would choose the Greek word Agape, which is only one of nine different words the Greeks have for different kinds of love. This word Agape fits the feelings of gentleness, mercy, kindness, compassion, peace, joy, non-judgement, and a genuine concern for other people – which effectively describes love as a strength and not a weakness. You can't perceive this love through any of your physical senses; it is recognised by intuition. It is an energy which you can feel in a room, in a person, and most importantly within. We all have this love but in most it is hidden, buried beneath guilt and loneliness, fear and self-doubt. We are afraid to love because we are afraid we will get hurt. I have learnt that it is well worth taking the risk.

It is interesting to note at this point how an automatic dislike, or liking, arises during our lives with people who physically resemble the bad characters in our childhood. For instance, a woman who looks like Aunt Alice, or a man who resembles my father, will trigger an automatic repulsion until I stop and realise what is going on. Incidentally, I am quite horrified these days by a sudden reflection of myself in a shop window – an image which closely resembles my paternal grandmother. Horror! This also works the other way, of course: Uncle Tom, whom I absolutely adored, was the spitting image of Joseph Stalin. So it is best not to be too impressed by appearances.

I was so desperate for understanding and affection that I would go completely overboard if someone appeared to be the answer to my problems, only to be disappointed by the inevitable weaknesses of human nature. But, to quote the Desiderata, 'Let this not blind you to what virtue there is. Many people strive for high ideals and everywhere life is full of heroism.' The ideal is to find the answers to problems within yourself, and this almost always needs help of some kind. My early childhood was a roller coaster of ecstatic visits to Cropston alternating with the inevitable bleak desolation of my return. I still recall the feelings of utter hopelessness as I sat with Auntie Edie and her family, waiting to return to Leicester. None of us spoke – our feelings of pain and desolation were too deep for words.

This sad and dreary childhood had the positive effect of making me determined to get away – from Aunt Alice, Auntie Annie, my grandmother and the whole nightmarish situation. These feelings of pain, sadness and desolation have swept over me from time to time all my life, and I count myself fortunate indeed to have been led to various sources which have helped me to understand and to manage them. Understand and manage – not completely dispel or cure. Life is managed, it is not cured. As I have mentioned, it seems that a constantly repeated thought or feeling makes a deeper and deeper groove in the brain like a new pathway: the more feet that have walked over it, the smoother and easier it becomes, and the more difficult it is to erase.

Chapter 3

My education was to be terminated after School Certificate and I was to go to secretarial college, get a job as a secretary and stay at home as an unpaid domestic for the foreseeable future. Marriage was not even to be thought of. Bizarre though it may now seem, I understood that I had been paid for in order to look after my aunts as they became old, and then to inherit a considerable fortune on their death. The constant refrain of 'money, money, money' nearly drove me demented. My father continued to make the occasional duty visit and sang from the same hymn sheet: what a lot my education was costing – it was all a waste of time anyway because I would get married and everyone knew that education was wasted on girls.

My headmistress wanted me to take a degree in English. I was very interested in medicine, but I knew I wouldn't get the maintenance even if I gained a scholarship. But all was not lost: a scholarship was advertised for a teacher training course at the local domestic science college, which also offered a maintenance grant. So without saying anything to anyone, when I was 17 years old and in my last year at school, I applied for it and it was awarded to me.

This brought a load of calumny on my head from Aunt Alice, who was absolutely furious. She couldn't deny my taking it because, being a teacher herself, it would have looked bad if she had prevented her own niece from getting a training to be one. Her anger over my scholarship grew; she kept up a continual threat of suicide, rushing from the house late at night, declaring that she was going to throw herself into the canal, and that it was all my fault. I used to sit at the top of the stairs shaking with guilt and fear until she returned in the early hours. I had very little sleep and a great deal of studying to do. However, the thought of my eventual escape from such a hell hole enabled me to survive and persist in my endeavour. I was 'cunning, ungrateful, scheming and deceitful'. My living situation was made worse: because I was a day student, and had to live at home, there was no escaping my aunt's expectations. In addition to all my college work, I still had most of the domestic chores to do when I returned home.

My other aunt – Auntie Annie – was a pale shadow of Alice because Alice held the purse-strings and Annie was a poor relation. I tried so hard with this family to make them love me but of course you can't force anyone to love you. I was always aware of a terrible emptiness which seemed to be located in the region of my solar plexus and gave rise to frequent bouts of heartburn, indigestion and vomiting, and a feeling of having been punched in my middle, and struggling for breath. My primary emotion was deep, annihilating fear and a truly desperate need for someone to take some notice of me, however superficial. In order to be noticed, I would tell lies about my father and how much he loved me, about my home life and, most of all, about the hordes of young men who were all hopelessly in love with me.

Whilst at college, I submitted some embroidered handkerchiefs for my coursework in needlework which I had not done myself, and to my horror, was summoned to the Principal's study to be confronted by my deception. I was given an opportunity to confess and to do the embroidery all over again myself. I still remember the overwhelming terror of that situation – on the one hand, my self-hatred as I heard myself lying and lying and lying; and on the other, the paralysing fear of admitting the truth and having to actually do the work which I knew I just didn't have time for. Already I was covering the crack under the door with a blanket to stop the light showing whilst I studied late into the night. Shortly afterwards, there was an announcement in the local paper, saying that the scholarship was being withdrawn in future as recent recipients had proved to be unsuitable. This did enormous damage to my self-esteem, but at that time there was no one to whom you could go and ask for help – authority was unapproachable and gave no quarter. My cousins were all full of ridicule for me, wagging their heads and looking very disgusted.

I'm still amazed at the way I maintained my deception and at the time was quite frightened by what I was doing. I suppose I saw my diploma as my passport to freedom and was willing to do anything to obtain it. It's been a valuable experience as far as teaching is concerned; it taught me to understand the children who lied, and whom I knew were lying. I used to tell them this story and say how much better it would have been if I had been able to tell the truth and get some understanding and some help. 'I'm here to give you the understanding and help you need to tell the truth,' I would say – and more often than not, it worked! There's always the pathological liar, of course, whom no one can help, but most people tell lies for a reason.

The constant denigration of the almost superhuman effort I was making to do well was like cycling uphill with the brakes on, and I felt I could have done so much better had I been loved and encouraged. I felt very dissatisfied with my performance at college at the end of the three years; I had started so well, first with the scholarship and then with my work, particularly of the creative kind involving the use of colour, texture and design. Then I gradually became more and more overwhelmed with all that I had to do at home to fulfil their expectations, so that I felt as if I was running helplessly on a treadmill at increasing speed. So the nervous breakdown I had in my third year at college was inevitable, and was seized upon as proof that it was all too much for me. I'd 'never been strong, and should give it up, and get an easier job and stay at home.' However, with a very great effort, I finished the course and was awarded my diploma. I was so relieved to have made it through, it was my ticket out, and I knew I had to leave Leicester.

There were lighter moments throughout the three years; there were fellow-students who really knew how to have a good time, and with the help of their parents and a few lies, I was sometimes included in their activities. There was a war on and no shortage of young men looking absolutely fantastic in uniform, all eager to make the most of their off-duty time. It was a hothouse atmosphere in which romance blossomed easily, and one was constantly in love with someone or other who had just gone back to Europe or Africa or to an airfield from which they were very unlikely to return.

I belonged to the local church, mainly attracted by the extreme good looks of a member of the choir, at whom I would gaze steadily throughout Evensong, but never ever spoke to. And there I met other young people with whom I played tennis, danced and went for walks, and generally larked about in an incredibly – by today's standards – innocent way. I was allowed to pursue these activities because it was 'a church'. I became friendly with three young men who called themselves 'the three stooges', and with one of them in particular called Bill Burton. I used to invent a tissue of lies in order to get out to meet him, and was inevitably found out. One nightmarish evening we'd been to a fancy dress dance at the church youth club. Bill was dressed as Captain Hook and wore a moustache and beard made from burnt cork. I had to be in by 9.30 pm and after a few kisses on the corner of the street, I rushed in, to be greeted by a face of doom articulating, "Who has been kissing you?" Not having seen myself in a mirror, I assumed an expression of righteous indignation and replied, "Why, no one. You know I don't do that sort of thing." To which she replied, "Look in the mirror!" I was not allowed out in the evening again for the rest of term, and life in the house became even more unpleasant.

In my third year at college, Bill Burton went to Corpus Christi at Oxford and invited me to the May Ball. To my great surprise, I was allowed to go. I suppose the cachet of being able to say, 'My niece has been invited to the May Ball' was too tempting to forgo! And I had a great weekend. It was all very innocent. I stayed in a small hotel; we walked, talked and did a very little experimental fumbling with one another, and were completely captivated by the Ball itself.

I returned home in a romantic haze and was totally stunned when, returning one evening from college shortly afterwards, my aunt hurled a letter from Bill across acres of refectory dining table which I had polished to such an easy slide, saying, "What has he done to you?" She opened all my letters, although I was 20, and in this one he had said, "I enjoy doing things with you much more than with anyone else" – which was immediately interpreted as sexual activity of great depravity. I honestly didn't understand what she was talking about, and I was very frightened. I wished that the ground would open and swallow me up. A fatal heart attack would have been equally acceptable! It was a feeling of total disintegration, of sinking helplessly into complete annihilation, of terrifying emptiness. There is a phrase which says: 'My bowels turned to water,' and that was exactly how I felt, and of course how my bowels literally reacted! I felt sick, bathed in perspiration, and just wanted to run away from it all.

Whilst at college, we had to spend three weeks in a practice house where three of us took a week each as cook, parlour maid and housemaid/hostess. This was great fun, from getting up at 6.00 am to scrub and whiten the front steps as housemaid, to coaxing a disgruntled Aga into producing meals on time as cook, to wearing a frilly cap and apron as parlour maid, and inviting nine guests to dinner as hostess. We also had the opportunity to go out two or three evenings a week until 11.00 pm and cut a swathe through the hundreds of soldiers, sailors and airmen in the local pubs and at the local Palais de Danse. After having to be in by 9.30 pm at home, I was drunk on freedom! How innocent it all was then; we were always called for, treated like a fragile ornament, returned home safely with perhaps a few goodnight kisses on the doorstep. Men seemed to have an innate ability to assess the sexual situation and the pace was always set by the woman. There was the occasional over-enthusiastic aspirant of course, but they were fairly easily controlled – at most, mumbling a few criticisms of one's inability to deliver. Maybe all their sexual energy was channelled into the war.

Towards the end of my college course, my aunt went to see the Director of Education in Leicester, and begged him to give me a job locally, saying that she and her sister were getting older and needed me at home to look after them (she was 55 at a time when life expectancy was much shorter). There was no Home Economics post and I was offered one in General Subjects, which I refused, as I was then almost 21 and legally able to make my own choices. There were more threats of suicide, trips to the canal, and shiverings at the top of the stairs. But I just knew I had to get away – not only for my own sake but also for hers – I found myself constantly entertaining thoughts of murder.

So, in July 1942, I found myself looking for a job. In those days, of course, it was just a question of perusing The Times Educational Supplement and more or less shopping around. So far as I was concerned, the chief criterion was putting as many miles as possible between me and the dreaded house in Leicester. I found my first job in Shipley in Yorkshire, which was in fact a very smart move, as it was here that I was to meet the most important person in my life – my love, my alter ego, my twin soul, literally my other half. But this was not to happen for another eighteen months.

Chapter 4

Saltaire Road Girls' School was a grim-looking place with a definite flavour of 'dark satanic mills' about it. The staff were dedicated but waspish spinsters while the pupils were wonderful Yorkshire kids, all eager to learn, and grounded in awe and respect for 'baking'. I made quite a few mistakes in my first year, the worst of which was ruining a precious collection of fats, eggs and sugar – all on ration at the time – which had been donated to make refreshments for a Christmas party. I had no training in catering at college, and I just didn't know where to start. The result was a mountain of literal rock cakes – and still harder biscuits, which would have made suitable ammunition for the guns protecting our coastline. I was utterly devastated by my performance, and the situation was not improved by the pursed lips and self-satisfied smirks of the assembled spinsters, all of whom – being Yorkshire lasses – could cook a great deal better than I could. There was much nodding of heads, gossiping in corners and sudden halts to conversation when I appeared in the staff room, causing even more damage to my fragile self-esteem.

In spite of the 100 miles between us, my aunts still kept a tenacious grip on me. I was expected to go home every holiday and half-term where all the major cleaning jobs were saved up for me to do – like taking down and washing curtains, shampooing carpets and cleaning paint, although there was a servant and a daily help to do these things. The domestic tasks at the weekend bungalow in Cropston were also saved up for me to do, so that it was no holiday as such – certainly no rest, no recuperation from the obvious accumulation of stress which I was feeling in my first teaching post. I had been programmed so well in my childhood that I actually paid my aunts thirty shillings a week, which was a princely sum in 1943, for the doubtful privilege of living there and for my food, heat, light and shelter – also for a constant atmosphere of hurt and vituperative recrimination.

As I look back at that 21-year-old self, I wonder why on earth I voluntarily returned over and over again, to indulge such masochism. But of course I had been thoroughly programmed, and it has taken more than 50 years of work with increasing self-understanding, to alter such Pavlovian responses. I now recognise the old mindset when it arises – it still does – and say, 'Stop! Sit down, see the situation as it really is and do something about it.' Life is a learning experience – it's tough – but the only thing to do is get on and learn, because in the end it's far less painful that way.

In Shipley, I lived as a paying guest with two women in their fifties called Gert and Sylvia. One worked as a shop assistant, the other – who was quite delicate – did the housekeeping. All went quite well there until the prune-stealing episode, after which I felt like a prisoner on remand. It was Gert's practice to have a bowl of prunes soaking on the draining board ready for stewing the next day, and it was my practice to pinch and eat one from time to time. This was discovered and I was regarded with suspicious disapproval and told that if I wanted a prune, I should say so and pay for it.

I didn't go out much – I had very little opportunity to meet young people, and my chief joy was window-shopping for clothes. This was the beginning of my love affair with colour and designs, make-up and hairstyles, which of course was labelled 'Vanity' by Gert and Sylvia, and by my aunts who still appeared on the scene from time to time to check up on me. Vanity or not, I have found looking as pleasant as possible incredibly therapeutic. If you know you look good on the outside, it helps the sad, empty, desolate feeling on the inside no end. And after all, it's other people that have to look at you!

I met a very beautiful girl called Barbara Appleby who was the daughter of the Police Superintendent at Bingley, and with her I went to various dances in the district. This, however, did absolutely nothing for my self-esteem as I was completely ignored by all the young men who were clustered around the truly beautiful Barbara. One time, we were invited by two Tank Corps officers to go to a Mess dance; they were obviously attracted by Barbara in the first place, but willing to put up with me. They called for us at the police house in Bingley and I was so busy looking back at the one that was 'mine' for the evening, I hurtled down nine stone steps (there was a blackout at that time) – I was so busy gazing at this fabulously romantic creature! I was carried inside and given brandy but insisted on going to the dance. There I sat, green with nauseating pain, unable to dance and with a rapidly swelling ankle, wrist and shoulder – and increasing waves of blackness which threatened to engulf me. I had in fact broken several bones. Poor young man – how he must have hated the whole evening! Certainly, I never saw him again. Such is the desperation of youth to end its loneliness and of course to satisfy its sexual desire. I don't really think I want to be young again, contrary to many people my age, as I am more contented now than I have ever been in my life.

This desperation occurred again a little later when, during a visit to Leicestershire, I ran into a man called Peter Ireland with whom I had shared a desk way back in junior school. I didn't recognise him as he was now six feet tall and wearing the uniform of an Air Force officer, complete with the wings which always triggered a certain reaction in me – as in so many young women. He became quite friendly and came to Shipley to see me every time he was on leave, and eventually he proposed. I was 22 and in those days, if you were not engaged by that age, you'd almost attained the dreaded spinsterhood! Beset as I was by the aunts, my colleagues and my landladies, the prospect appalled me so much that in a half-hearted way, I agreed that I would marry him. It seemed to me then that all the romantic messages from films, popular songs, poems and literature were so much nonsense. I certainly had not seen any evidence of true romance in my lifetime!

I have always felt very sorry about the way I treated Peter; I used him, as many girls did in those days, as insurance. I must have hurt him deeply and I hope, in finding happiness with someone else, he was able to forgive me. In the meantime, he continued to visit me in Yorkshire. I had moved by this time – I couldn't any longer stand being regarded as a purloiner of prunes – into a very elegant house at Frizinghall, near Bradford, owned by a solicitor, and his wife who was a medical secretary. They no longer had servants so they let the two attic rooms to me. These were cold and claustrophobic with only a small skylight in each. It was also very difficult for me to adjust to being alone for the first time, and to being responsible for feeding myself. Today I would recognise the frightening feelings this situation triggered in me and take appropriate action, but at the time I felt quite paralysed with fear. I felt totally alone – isolated and desolate – and quite unable, even physically, to plan what I would eat. Obviously, I made myself do these things and the negative feelings manifested themselves as constant viral infections, perpetual tiredness, nausea and diarrhoea, and the feeling that a hand was clutching my solar plexus so tightly that I could hardly breathe. I also found that my muscles were in a state of constant tension and I just couldn't relax.

In those days, such symptoms were labelled 'nerves' and regarded as weak, contemptible and despicable. You were advised to snap out of it, to forget it – if only you could – or that it 'would all be the same in a hundred years' time. 'Go on like this and you'll end up in the loony-bin.' If you broke your leg, or had pneumonia, or an appendectomy, you were cosseted and visited by people bearing flowers and fruit, but if your illness was labelled 'nerves', you had no help at all. In fact, your condition was worsened by the derision of the people around you.

In the Frizinghall house, there was another tenant, a most elegant woman called Sheila – and she, Mrs W and I all shared the kitchen. What a mistake! Three women to one kitchen? I don't think so! We shared the larder and store cupboards – there were no refrigerators in 1943 – and kept our food in containers labelled with our names.

Time passed fairly smoothly; I went to several local dances and helped out at the local Forces' canteen so that I met several young men with whom I walked, talked and drank at the local. But there was no more magic in it than there was with Peter. So I continued to see him every time he came on leave. Life is like this though, isn't it? We plod along, with one day seeming very much like another when suddenly the whole thing changes and a series of earth-shattering events take place.

The first event occurred in the Frizinghall kitchen, where I was accused of stealing cakes and biscuits from Mrs W's tins. I was told that if this continued, I would have to leave. This accusation was totally unfounded, as after the prune-stealing episode, I was particularly careful to leave things alone. I suggested that it might be Sheila as it certainly wasn't me. But this possibility was totally refuted because Sheila was 'such a lady'. After several more weeks of things being stolen from the larder, I was accused again and given a month's notice to quit. One of the girls I taught had a great-aunt who did some dressmaking for me and was housekeeper to one of the mill owners in Bradford, a Mr and Mrs Ratcliffe who lived in a very grand house on the outskirts of Shipley. She and I got along extremely well; I used to sit in this lovely, warm, spacious kitchen and tell her all my troubles. When I told her about my notice to quit, she was incensed and said, "Go back and pack your things; you're coming here now." So I moved to this beautifully appointed house, into an elegant comfortable room, and had the most sumptuous meals prepared and put in front of me. What heaven! It was in that house that I discovered I was able to put on weight. My previous life had been so stressful that I was permanently thin.

Incidentally, the food continued to disappear from the Frizinghall kitchen after my departure. Sheila was requested to leave and I was begged to return – I really enjoyed turning down the invitation! I was so happy at the Ratcliffes'; they were a family like the one for which I had always yearned. They lived as well and as elegantly as wartime conditions would allow. And I learned a great deal about the social niceties of life which has stood me in good stead. It's a very good feeling to be at ease in any social situation in which one finds oneself. I also had this amazing surrogate mother who pampered and spoiled me. However, I knew that, welcome as I was, it was not a permanent arrangement. I was in the guest room, and one day, when the war was over and life returned to normal, they would need it again.

I also realised that I wanted to move on career-wise and I applied for a more responsible post in Chester. I went for an interview in November and was asked to start teaching there in January 1945. So it was a time of mixed feelings until December 13th when my whole world turned upside down and I have never felt the same since.

Peter had been on leave for nine days, staying at an hotel in Bradford and taking me out every night. We had danced, walked, visited pubs and stayed out until one and two in the morning – just for the hell of it. After such a restricted life with Aunt Alice, I had this uncontrollable urge to stay out late. Not that it was very exciting, being wartime and everything closing early – also there was a blackout and there was little to do but stumble about in the fog and frost, as it was November. We stopped occasionally for a fairly sexless embrace, bundled up as we were with greatcoats, scarves, gloves, etc.. By the time Peter went back to camp, I was like a zombie, as I had been teaching every day and taking adult education classes in cookery on two evenings a week as well. But the destiny that shaped our ends was busy hewing out a plan which would cancel out all my fatigue.

As I staggered through the front door after one of my evening classes, with no thought in my mind but sleep, sleep and more sleep, the telephone rang and it was the beautiful Barbara, saying that she and two Detective Sergeants were coming to collect me to go to a police dance, and I must go as if I didn't, she couldn't; her father wouldn't allow her to go. One girl out with two men was considered to be highly improper in those days. I protested and protested but she won.

Most of my clothes were already packed to go to Chester, including the only evening dress I possessed, so with very bad grace, I dragged out the crumpled taffeta, dressed myself in it, and dragged a comb through my hair which was a real mess. In those days, you only washed your hair once a week, after which it was set into waves and curls which rapidly deteriorated as the week progressed. But I was so dead on my feet that I didn't care. We duly arrived at the dance – I fell over in the snow as we walked in, which did nothing at all to improve my sleazy appearance – then we sat on the sidelines whilst Barbara danced with one Detective Sergeant and I was more or less held up by the other one as we shuffled around the floor. I must have looked as if I were in custody! But destiny was silently working away in the background. Just before the interval, when the band had a rest and the dancers had refreshments, these two policemen were called back to the station. Through the haze of my somnolence, I was conscious of a really attractive man walking in on his own. Reacting to the Air Force uniform, I actually woke from sleep. However, I just as quickly decided to drop off again: with the combination of the beautiful Barbara and my jumble-sale appearance, I didn't have a hope of attracting this gorgeous creature, though I felt even then that, in some strange way, I knew him. Some enchanted evening indeed!

I watched through half-closed eyelids as he started to cross the room to us, just waiting for him and Barbara to glide off together – when I heard a voice saying, "Don't you want to dance?" And realised that he was actually addressing me! Me, with the tacky hair and crumpled dress, and an equally crumpled sleepless face, actually being asked to dance by this godlike creature straight from my dreams! We floated off, and exchanged the usual, 'Do you come here often?' banalities, but very quickly moved into a much more meaningful conversation. When the dance was over, he actually sat down beside me and offered me a cigarette. Even when I introduced the devastating

Barbara, the reaction was only normal politeness. And when he walked me home through the snow, I felt like all the movie heroines rolled into one.

I told him the story of my reluctance to go to the dance, and he said he'd had a similar experience. He was home on leave; all his friends were away, so he'd gone into a local pub for a drink. A man had offered him a ticket to this police dance, and he had actually spun a coin to decide whether he would go or not. I think an experience of this kind is absolute proof of some predestination in one's life. He was, and still is, the most significant person in my existence, and yet our first meeting was such an incredible combination of apparent coincidences. We knew we were twin souls and deeply in love right from that very first night, trudging arm in arm through the moonlit snow, singing, *I'm going to dance with the dolly with a hole in her stocking* as we went.

Chapter 5

When we reached my door, Ron shook my hand and arranged a meeting for the following evening. He shook my hand, for heaven's sake! I always felt that my feet were off the ground when I was with Ron, and this feeling started that night. Our relationship was quite out of the ordinary; therefore I do not think we experience this extraordinary bonding in every incarnation; if we did, we would remain so joyfully content that we would not have any cause to grow.

He had seven days' leave, so once again I was teaching all day and out every night. But this time it was quite different: I was full of energy and sparkle and well able to get by on four hours of sleep. I loved everybody, felt kind and understanding towards the spinsters on the staff at school, and saw good in everything. Such is the profound influence of the emotions on mind and body.

His name was Ronald Swan, and when I asked him why he had asked me to dance, and not Barbara, he said he didn't notice her, so some power greater than the usual sexual attraction must have been at work. The feeling that somewhere, somehow we had been together before strengthened as the week progressed. But although we explored our lives right back to birth, we couldn't find any single place where we had been. The nearest was 100 miles apart.

I was reminded of Kalil Gibran's observation in *The Voice of the Master*, "I knew at our first meeting that I had known you for ages," but luckily didn't recall the rest of the quotation, which goes on, "And I knew at the time of parting that nothing was strong enough to keep us apart."

One of the classic myths about the ancient gods is their fear that human beings will become as powerful as they themselves. So the gods split human being into halves, male and female, who were no longer capable of competition with the gods. But as half-beings, we were left yearning – incomplete, and for ever searching, hoping that in sexual union with that other half, we might find our god-like bliss. To me, this is a comforting and believable myth, as it implies that our sexual feelings of being incomplete arise out of a need for wholeness, which can lead to the search for spirituality. Not that sex and spirituality are the same thing, but they can spring from the same source, both in myth and in human experience. So this is how we felt – that we had been truly blessed in finding, quite literally, our 'other half'.

We certainly generated our own warmth. The weather was very cold and wintry, but we would stand for an hour or two in a blizzard, just holding one another. Every time it snows, I recall the feeling of the soft and gentle flakes mingling with his kisses on my face.

I went to Cropston for Christmas as the two aunts were off to stay at The Dorchester, and I haunted the letterbox, waiting for him to write. The letter duly arrived, the first of many I was to receive over the next ten years, when his neat, small but masculine handwriting became as familiar to me as my own. Twenty years ago, when I was 65, I decided to burn them all – certainly not because of their erotic content: they were more lyrical than sexual – but because to me they were an intimate part of him that I did not want to share with my executors. I still miss those letters, but have such a strong sense of his spiritual presence that the need for tangible comfort grows less all the time.

I wrote to Peter Ireland to tell him I had met someone else, and to my everlasting shame suggested that if he had bought the handbag he had promised me for Christmas, I would still like to have it. How very cruel we are when we are young! I have no doubt whose photograph was pinned up on the Mess dartboard that night!

Ron was no longer flying, as he experienced extreme giddiness at over 5,000 feet due to a malfunctioning of the semi-circular canals in his ears. How grateful I was for this as five airmen I had previously dated had been killed in action or horrifically burned. After Christmas, I moved to Chester, where I lived with a dentist's widow, very aptly called Mrs Cocaine. Ron came to see me every weekend he had leave – if not, I would go down to Kenilworth to see him even if he only had a few hours off-duty. The sense of unreality continued; there was no need of growth in the relationship. We were already where we wanted to be and had been from the moment he walked into the dance, or indeed, from the beginning of time itself. We had such a oneness, there was no need for disagreement. You don't have to argue with yourself and we were one person. Psychiatrists will tell you that such interdependence is not healthy, that two people in such a relationship cannot grow, but the way I felt after my particular childhood, it was absolute bliss. I echoed Anne Bradstreet who wrote to her husband, 'If ever two were one, then we were.'

I had been, and still was, terrified by my own aloneness – the frightening inner feeling of emptiness caused by the adults in my childhood failing to fulfil my need for affection, attention and true caring. Children who grow up in a house where love and care are lacking, or given with painful inconsistency, can enter adulthood with a feeling that the world is dangerous, unpredictable and mean, and this inculcates a terrible feeling of total insecurity.

One weekend, I met Ron in Birmingham as he was free from six in the evening until eight o'clock the following morning. We stayed at a small hotel (long since demolished) in the Bullring in two single rooms – only occupying one, of course! All night we lay together in one of them, talking and making love as far as possible without actual intercourse. During that night, we agreed that we wanted to spend the rest of our lives together. I will always remember a crowd of drunken revellers in the street bawling out McNamara's Band as we plighted our troth.

The actual proposal of marriage was made while walking up Hoole Road in Chester, and consisted of, "Well, I suppose we might as well get married then." But I still heard the violins and smelt the roses. Of course, there was still the dragon to be slain in the shape of Aunt Alice whose sole reason for adopting me was, as I have said, as insurance for her old age. She even had a book with every penny and halfpenny recorded in it that she had spent on me during my lifetime; the total amount came to £1,000. Not having met her, Ron could not understand all the flight and fright symptoms I was increasingly exhibiting. He just saw her as a silly misguided old woman who needed to be put straight! He was still willing to talk reasonably to her and even to ask for her blessing.

We arranged to go to Leicester for a weekend to discuss the matter, and arrived on the doorstep one Saturday afternoon in January 1946. We rang and rang the doorbell, but no one answered. Apparently, she had gone out into the garden and refused to come in, saying, "I will never speak to that man." Eventually, Auntie Annie let us in and we waited in an uncomfortable silence until Alice appeared, shooting sparks of total hatred towards Ron and totally ignoring me. She finally started to scream and shout that he owed her £1,000 for my upbringing – that I belonged to her – and finally that she would commit suicide if we married, and how could we live with that?

In a calm and reasonable tone, Ron said, "Very easily, actually. And, by the way, if you are going to commit suicide, do make sure you make a good job of it, because you know – don't you – that it's a criminal offence?" Which it was, in 1946. I have never seen such a proverbial pricked balloon. She just sat there with her mouth open until it began to tremble and she cried. "And as for the £1,000, Miss King," said Sir Galahad, "how absurd! Don't you know you can't buy a child, much less its love?" My mouth was open too, in utter adoration and amazement. So it was a fairy story I had got myself into after all!

We fixed the wedding day for the 13th April, agreeing reluctantly to get married from my aunt's house. Without rations, and so soon after the war, there was no possibility of a white wedding, so using precious clothing coupons, I had a suit made and bought a pretty blouse and a hat which I decorated with flowers. Auntie Edie and her daughter had made me a present of some very snazzy underwear, which excited me far more than any of my outer garments.

The day itself was a bit of a nightmare. Ron's mother had arrived the day before: she was discussed audibly by the aunts in the most unkind way, and my father was throwing his weight about in his usual bombastic and insensitive manner. Eventually, I found myself walking up the aisle to meet my beloved, and all the sad and painful events of the previous 24 years seemed to dissipate in the healing lights of the boundless love which overwhelmed me. Even the sun came out and bathed us in warmth as we made our vows. The ceremony took place at Holy Apostles Church, on the Fosse Road in Leicester.

What tender and beautiful vows they are! How difficult to keep – and how fortunate I was to marry a man who took them so seriously!

It's sentimental to think that all divorced or separated people have to do is to have courage and goodwill in order to start all over again. But there is a certain dignity in trying. Why is it such a great virtue these days to give up? I don't have many years left or much money, but one thing I have learned over the years is a sense of values. I used to think brains and beauty were all-important. In my youth, social position meant something too. What I thought of as good taste was a kind of god to me, and I suppose – although I never admitted it – I loved money too. Now I have different ideas: I value the ability to accept responsibility and I value courage in the face of defeat. I think I value that most of all, because every one of us, in one way or another, is defeated so much – degraded, disgraced, humiliated. Which of us hasn't been all those things at one time or another? Look at the people walking past you in the street: what do most of them have to look forward to? Or back to, for that matter? They go on, hurrying to their jobs, supporting their families, doing the best they can. There's a lot of courage in the world, and a sense of values is nothing if there isn't enough courage to back it up.

Ron and I were totally exhausted by the time the taxi finally arrived to take us to the station. Sinking into the back seat, we exclaimed simultaneously, 'Thank God that's over!' and just held hands in mutual gratitude and support. In that moment, I really felt that all my troubles were ended, my dragons slain, and the future stretched before me like the road to Paradise. I did not realise then that, if we want moments of supreme happiness, it follows we must have moments of extreme misery. As CS Lewis wrote in his agonising grief, 'The pain now is part of the happiness. That's the deal.'

We went to Hoylake on the Wirral for a fortnight of total, unadulterated bliss. The sun shone literally every day, the golden sands stretched for ever, and we became the androgynous whole of the Greek myth. When the day came for us to part – he back to camp and me to my teaching post in Chester – I felt as if everything inside was raw, that it had been ripped apart, and as if that feeling would not go away until we were reunited. I was in a state of total physical tension in my muscles and in my stomach, in case I fell apart in agony.

We wrote to one another every day, and met almost every weekend. We used to stay at The Queen's Hotel in Chester and produced our marriage certificate with smug pride when booking a double room. In those days, hotels were not keen to condone promiscuity, and a handsome man in Air Force uniform was automatically suspected of corrupting his female companion. I am not writing an erotic novel here, but I must say that what went on in those double rooms was pretty mind-blowing – certainly, the earth moved on several occasions!

Ron was being demobbed the following August so I gave in my notice at Chester and we arranged to move to London where he had a job at Shell Mex House. Accommodation was extremely difficult as all the men were returning from the forces, and there was an average of three applications for every property. London was more overpopulated than anywhere else.

After an exhaustive search, we took the empty servants' rooms in a very grand house in Dulwich, which was owned by the aunt and uncle of a previous college friend of mine. Furniture was rationed and utilitarian, so the place was pretty Spartan. We moved in with only a mattress, three sets of bed linen, two plates, cups and saucers, and a few oddments of cutlery, a cooker and a sink. While I was deliriously happy to be reunited with Ron, I began to experience again the frightening symptoms of inadequacy and fear that I had felt on my own in the Frizinghall flat. It seems that if one has never had the experience of mothering as a child, one is left with all the inadequacy and terror that a child feels if it is abandoned with no hope of eventual rescue.

I began to experience all the symptoms of fear – tachycardia, sweating, sickness and diarrhoea, insomnia, the elephant's foot on the chest, the difficult breathing, and – most devastating of all – the weakening of immunity to disease. So I spent a large proportion of my time ill with various respiratory infections, worsened by the frequent dense fogs, the 'pea-soupers' which occurred frequently in London in those days.

Chapter 6

These illnesses made me even more frightened of dying, of looking so awful that Ron would eventually leave me, or of just coping with day-to-day existence. I see now that I was like a child of five, suddenly asked to cope with the responsibilities of an adult. Ron was amazingly kind and forbearing during all my real and imagined illnesses, caring for me like a mother – and this of course intensified my hypochondria. I was reinforcing the pattern of gaining attention by being ill.

In reality, it was a most unsatisfactory situation for us both. He was being forced into meeting unreasonable demands and I was in a constant state of feeling ill, looking unattractive and being terribly worried about his leaving me. It certainly was a test of real love, and he came through it with flying colours. There were some extremely good times, of course: being a true Yorkshireman and a cricket fan, Lords and the Oval drew him like magnets, and we would go to matches together on a Saturday afternoon. As a reward for sitting for hours on a few torturous wooden slats, we would go home in the early evening, change into evening dress and go to The Civil Service Club in Whitehall for dinner and then into dress circle seats in one of the West End theatres. These evenings were magical, and I look back on them with gratitude and joy. There were special occasions too – not just the usual anniversaries like marriage and birthdays, but also celebrations of the day we met, the day we exchanged our first kiss, the day we decided to get married … while on every wedding anniversary he would say, 'You know, this time last year, I didn't think it was possible to love you more than I did then, but here it is a year later, and I do!'

In a way, these all-too-brief years together went by in a kind of dream. I felt strongly that it was all too good to be true, that such tremendous love and happiness were not for me, because here I had not just a husband, a lover and a friend but a whole loving family, the like of which I had not known before. So the years passed, punctuated by my frequent bouts of respiratory infections, but balanced by our romantic outings and some fantastic holidays, where we were always perceived by our fellow holidaymakers to be on our honeymoon!

I had a miscarriage in 1952 which saddened me considerably, but which Ron shrugged off very easily. I don't think he really wanted children: we were such an entity, we never discussed seriously the possibility of a family. I didn't regret not having children of my own; it left me free to relate to the many children whom I subsequently taught. Now I am old, I have a wall of photographs of surrogate children and grandchildren, one of whom calls me 'Supergran' because until very recently, I used to do the yoga headstand, and I am still working part-time in my old age. I also admit to a sneaking feeling of relief that I was never called upon to undertake the enormous and frightening responsibility of parenting, when I hear from patients about the terrible consequences they see as resulting from the smallest parental action.

I am afraid my present reaction to a patient's declaration of, 'I had the most awful childhood,' is, 'So, what's new?' – followed of course by an attempt to unravel the situation, understand and subsequently develop various coping skills along the way. So children were out, it seemed, and devotion to one another was in, which became deeper and stronger as the years passed by. In February 1954, after a particularly virulent bout of pneumonia, my doctor told Ron that if he didn't get me out of London to the coast, he would lose me. He of course nearly went out of his mind, and eventually obtained a transfer to Worthing. We found a maisonette in Hove, with a sitting tenant occupying the upper floor – but we accepted this, as accommodation on the South Coast was so expensive and scarce. A mortgage was out of the question as, in those days, a very large deposit was essential.

We moved in, and were delighted and amazed by the backdrop of the Sussex Downs and the beautiful seaside with its incredible fresh air. Our joy was soon marred, however, when we discovered that the couple in the basement below us had a baby who cried all night and a dog which barked all day, and that the old lady who lived upstairs was not only a drunkard but also a kleptomaniac! The doors to our rooms had no locks, and it took us some time to realise that not only were small things missing from time to time, but the contents of our cupboards and drawers had been disturbed. She even took the odd tin of cat food, as we had taken over a beautiful blue Persian from a friend who was going abroad. Maybe she ate it – there certainly wasn't much evidence of other nourishment, apart from empty whisky bottles. Of course, we fixed locks to our doors but it was both irritating and time-consuming to live in what seemed to be a replica of Fort Knox! She also took to hurling abuse over the banisters and singing Scottish songs in a loud tremolo. As a situation comedy, it would have been very funny, but as a constant accompaniment to the dog and the baby, it was totally nerve-racking.

I had taken a part-time teaching job and spent the rest of my time pounding the pavements of Brighton, Hove and Worthing in a vain attempt to find somewhere else to live. Meanwhile, our blissful time together on earth was ticking relentlessly away. I, who had always been the sick one in the partnership, had never in my wildest dreams envisaged the possibility of Ron becoming ill. He had never even had colds or flu, and always seemed to have boundless energy. I went up to Leicestershire, as Auntie Edie had been very ill and wanted to see me. I think she thought she was nearing her end. Ron saw me off at Hove station, and I remember saying, "Don't go off with someone else whilst I am away, will you?" And his unforgettable reply, "Don't be silly. Other women are a different species to me." As the train drew out, he looked so handsome standing there, tanned by the sea air and sun, with such an expression of loving-kindness, my heart melted towards him – as it still melts at the memory now, even 55 years distant.

Auntie Edie was well on the way to recovery when I returned a few days later and I felt happy and relaxed, and delighted as always at the prospect of reunion. When Ron came to the door, I was suddenly shocked by his appearance; his skin seemed to have yellowed, and the bones of his face seemed almost fleshless, so sharply did they protrude through his skin. I had a sudden devastating picture of Leonard, my uncle, when he had cancer of the pancreas. I suppose it is only after absence that we really see people with whom we spend most of our time. He said he was OK when I asked, and although still troubled, I decided that it was a trick of the light or that he was tired. I'd noticed since we'd moved to Hove that our sex life was diminishing. But as there was always a great deal of demonstrative affection, I put it down to the stress of moving and the new job as an accountant at the tax office in Worthing.

Ron became progressively more tired and listless, and we had a very quiet Christmas that year, just the two of us, instead of going to Cropston. It was at this time that vague intimations of tragedy loomed, and I experienced a terrible fear. One evening, early in 1955, he came home looking particularly ill, and I insisted on taking his temperature which was 101 (Fahrenheit, in those days). He was only too willing to stay in bed the following day, and I called the doctor who was extremely dismissive and said it was gastric flu – not to worry, there's a lot of it about, etc. This was the start of the worst personal hell I have ever experienced. He became so weak he couldn't go to the bathroom without support, could barely eat and worst of all was my feeling of total inability to do anything at all to make him better.

It was one of the worst Januarys on record weather-wise. There was a total covering of ice and snow; we had no central heating – only a fireplace in each room. The coal was bunkered down a flight of very steep stone steps outside and it was necessary to keep a fire going all night, as Ron was so ill. I think it was at this time that I began to believe in my personal angel; certainly, I was begging for some help from somewhere, as I slipped and slid down those icy steps to fill and refill the coal bucket. I also did some begging every time I went shopping, to try to find something he would eat or drink. I remember one evening going out six times, only to have him take one sip of a drink and refuse more. I ran through the whole spectrum from soda water to champagne, but none of them were acceptable. The doctor called, at widely-spaced intervals, still laughingly dismissing what by now was obviously a serious condition, as gastric flu. I finally insisted on an X-ray, but before the results were through, he had a terrible lung haemorrhage which covered the bed with bright red blood and lumps of tissue. As soon as he was calm, I ran to call the doctor, only to be answered extremely rudely by his wife. I said, "Will you tell Doctor X to come and see Mr Swan? I think he's dying." To which, she replied, "We don't tell the doctor anything, but I will give him your message as you gave it to me, and it's up to him whether he will come." I don't think she ever gave him the message: no one called all morning. In the meantime, I cleared up the mess, and did what I could to make Ron comfortable. We were both very frightened. Angels on the job again however – this time in the shape of the greengrocer who called at lunchtime with an order I had given to him. At the door, I burst into tears, and he rushed into the bedroom, took one look at Ron, raced out, jumped into his van and stormed to the doctor's house. The partner came at once, and within ten minutes, there was an ambulance at the door and, with bells ringing, we were off to the Royal Sussex County Hospital. Ron was put to bed, and I went home, feeling more desolate than I had ever felt in my life.

It does not do to assume one has plumbed the ultimate depths of despair until the very end of life, when we may know what we are talking about. Certainly, the higher we fly, the further we have to fall. If we want moments of supreme happiness, I think by the very relative nature of things, we must have moments of extreme misery. As Nietzsche says, 'That which does not kill us, makes us stronger.' Tough words for an exceedingly tough world!

So began an even bleaker phase of my life. I felt suicidally lonely in the maisonette with the maddening uproar continuing upstairs, only relieved by my visits to the hospital where the doctors were making a test on Ron's lungs and liver. About a week later, he was moved to New Cross Hospital in London, given a bronchoscopy and a liver biopsy, and started on chemotherapy which was a particularly nauseous and vile form of nitrogen mustard. By this time, his sick pay had halved, and I had to take on more teaching. Poor kids – they must have thought they were in the charge of a zombie! In those days, discipline was automatic, no matter how inadequate the teacher. Thank heaven for that! Visiting times at the London Hospital were strict – only two hours in the afternoon, and one in the evening. But I managed to get there every day, and it was in this ward that I discovered how stressful nursing can be behind the calm and unruffled façade that nurses wear as part of their uniform. There was a pretty, young nurse whom I noticed during the rare moments I could tear my eyes from Ron. This nurse was always watching us with an expression of agonised concern, and a couple of weeks later, she was no longer on the ward. When I asked Sister where she was, I was told that she could no longer bear to see the two of us together, knowing the ultimate prognosis. I have never forgotten that nurse, and how strangely comforted I was by her true compassion.

While Ron was in New Cross Hospital, the lease expired on the maisonette, and we were required either to renew or quit. We had intended to take out a mortgage on a bungalow at Durrington but, with things as they were, it seemed extremely unwise to do so. I still had to get out though, and finally in desperation, moved into a decidedly downmarket hotel in Brighton, very different from the upmarket establishments we had frequented on our numerous honeymoons! The day I moved our furniture into store, and myself into the hotel, was a nightmare of despair, still accompanied by the shrill, maniacal taunts and sneers from the old crone upstairs. One of the symptoms of severe nervous exhaustion is blurred vision, and when I visited Ron that evening, I was alarmed to see two of him lying on the bed, and both so real that I didn't know which one to embrace. Luckily, I picked the right one! Because now, I had to be strong, I was the one in charge of everything, and he was the frightened child, totally bewildered by the uncontrollable world around him. It is interesting to note that, during this incredibly difficult and threatening year, I didn't even have a cold!

One day in April, I received a letter from the consultant at New Cross, asking me to take some clothes to the hospital as Ron was getting better and being discharged. Knowing instinctively that this was an understandable cop-out, I replied immediately, stating my need to know the facts in order to make suitable plans for the future, and my own disbelief in the 'getting better' theory. I received a phone call from the consultant's secretary immediately, asking me to meet him, as he was operating at Bevendean Hospital in Brighton, the next day. A couple of weeks earlier, I had had a deeply disturbing dream in which I had walked into a room in a hospital, with a table and chair in the centre, two doors opposite one another, and a window facing one chair. A surgeon dressed in green operating clothes, complete with boots and mask, came through the far door, went over to the window and, looking out, said, "Your husband has only three months to live. I am sorry." I had woken up with my eyes full of tears, thinking, 'Thank God, it was only a dream!' Now I thank God for the dream, as it gave me strength for what was to come.

I went to Bevendean Hospital and was shown into a replica of the room in my dream, and like the dream, in came the surgeon gowned in green, who went to the window to utter the same awful words. This a remarkable instance of a dream being given from the unconscious as a loving warning, and amazingly the surgeon was dressed in green, which was only just starting to be used instead of white, a fact that was not known by the general public at that time. It must always be a dreadful task – to have to tell someone of a loved one's imminent death, particularly when the patient is so young. Even prepared by the dream, I sat stunned until he turned from the window and said, "Are you all right?" "Yes," I said, "I knew." He left, and I staggered to my feet, down endless stone stairs and endless bleak corridors to wait for a bus back to my even bleaker room in the hotel.

I decided that (a) I could not go through three months of watching Ron deteriorate in slow agony, and (b) there was no way I could live after his death without him. It was just not even possible to think about. So that night I sat up in bed with a full bottle of sodium amytal, which I had been given to help me sleep, and proceeded to take them. I had swallowed three when a picture flashed into my mind, of the two of us reading in bed one night about five years previously. A young woman who lived opposite had just died of polio, leaving John, her husband, totally distraught. And Ron said, "You know, I can't help thinking about John. If you had died, I'd be dead myself by now. There's no way I could go on without you." To which I replied, "Yes, I'd do the same. But don't even talk about it. Read your book!" There was a short silence; then he laid down his book, turned to me and said, "I've been thinking and I want you to promise me, that if I die before you, you won't commit suicide, because I am sure our souls would find it very difficult to meet again." This was getting a bit too much for me in the egotistical state in which I lived at that time. So I laughed it off and said, "For goodness sake, shut up about it – it's too awful to think about." But he took my book from me, and with a seriousness too great to be ignored, made me promise that, however bad things were, I would not take my own life.

He said with great solemnity, "When our bodies die, we shall be reunited immediately." I couldn't possibly ignore the intensity of the request, and said, "Oh, all right then." But he took me by the shoulders and said, "No, that won't do! Promise!" So I did, and this promise was what I now heard, loud and clear, dominating my thoughts completely as I reached for the fourth capsule with a sense of ultimate despair, and put it back in the bottle. At least, I had a reasonable night's sleep!

I went to Victoria on the train to collect him from hospital, and remember so clearly the heartbreaking beauty of the primroses covering the embankments by the side of the railway. We came back to the hotel and had a week together, which in its way was as blissful as our honeymoon, although shadowed, for me, by the awareness of its appalling brevity. Ron had not been told that his illness was terminal and I kept waiting for what I felt was the right moment. It seemed wrong to mar the bitter-sweet joy of our being together for the last time. I often wonder whether I did the right thing; his doctor had advised against telling him, but with hindsight, I think I was possibly unable to face up to the situation myself, and perhaps hoped in a childish way that, if it were not spoken of, it wouldn't happen.

In the meantime, we were able to eat and sleep together, go for ever-shortening walks on the seafront, read and talk, with all activity sharpened by an agonising feeling of imminent doom. I remember so many things about that week: the sharpening bones of his face filling my heart with almost unbearable love, holding his hand while watching the sunset over the sea, trying to find words to describe the colours of a seagull's wing, and declaring our ever-growing love for one another over and over again. As Shakespeare says:

> Love is not love
> Which alters when it alteration finds.

And:

> Love's not Time's fool, though rosy lips and cheeks
> Within his bending sickle's compass come;
> Love alters not with his brief hours and weeks,
> But bears it out even to the edge of doom.

The physical changes were occurring rapidly now; his bones were very close to the surface of his skin which had yellowed and dried like old parchment. There were no more walks, and he had difficulty breathing. One day when I returned from school, I saw the doctor's car outside and terrible screams were coming from our room. The proprietress of the hotel caught my arm and said, "You must get him out of here. He can't die here – I have got my business to consider. People don't like deaths when they are on holiday" – a comment I have never forgotten. I only hope that when her own time came to die, she found somewhere to do it!

The doctor suggested that Ron be moved to a hospice and called an ambulance. Another journey I shall never forget, but at least there was some peace for him at the end of it: a lovely clean, comfortable room and frequent pethidine injections to relieve his pain; also a couple of saints in charge in the shape of a kind and motherly Matron and a sympathetic Sister, who at the same time exuded wonderful efficiency.

Once again, I left him and tottered back to the hotel. Once again, to fondle the bottle of sleeping pills, and do battle with an overwhelming desire to leave it all behind. And once again, I was stopped by hearing him say, "You promised me" – and I put the bottle down. They say people who commit suicide are very brave, in that it takes supreme courage. This may be true in some cases, but if life is really unbearable, it takes much more courage to stick with it.

I continued to teach part-time and spent the rest of my days at the hospice, watching all that I cared about gradually fall apart until there was nothing but a bag of bones, in some places protruding through suppurating skin in which there was no place any more to stick the merciful needle, and bring relief from the pain.

One day, I was sitting on a bus travelling over the Downs to the school at which I was teaching. It was a beautiful day – warm and sunny, green and colourful with the growth of early summer, and the beauty of it all intensified my grief to such an extent that I felt I had to literally run away – get off the bus and run and run over the Downs until I reached the cliffs and could throw myself into the sea. I actually got up from my seat when I had a sudden overwhelming sense of my mother sitting beside me, and saying, "It's all right; I'm here and I'll help you. You'll get through this because you are not alone." This was an amazing experience because I did not have the faintest spiritual awareness of any kind at that time, and looked on spiritualism with total derision.

This proved to be a turning-point for me, and I became much calmer as a result. I have no doubt that my mother was indeed there and has helped me from that time onwards. I gave a talk on Do I really love my neighbour? to an audience of the 'Unity School of Christianity' in Brighton in 1986, at the end of which a woman came up to me and said, "I saw two people on either side of you on the platform: a handsome young man in Air Force uniform, and a young woman very like you in appearance, whom I am told is your mother, but she can't be because she's too young." And of course my mother had died at 21. The woman went on to say that these two people were always with me, helping and caring for me. I am not a spiritualist but have been profoundly impressed by these experiences. There are indeed more things in heaven and on earth than our philosophy dreams of.

The day I felt my mother's presence on the bus I had a telephone call from the wife of the pharmacist who had supplied Ron's drugs when he was at home. She asked how I was, and at this first kind word from someone who actually cared, I burst into tears. Being both practical and generous, she immediately took over, being particularly incensed by the comment of the proprietress, that Ron couldn't die in her hotel. "You're coming to me," she said. "We've plenty of room. You can't be alone with all this going on. Pack your bags and I will call for you after school." I was very ready to be taken over at that stage, so by the evening I was ensconced in a beautiful room in a large house near the sea and eating the first decent meal I had had in weeks. My weight had dropped by a stone in four months. It was so good to be with people who were kind and caring; it's amazing how many people treated both Ron and myself like lepers, once the cancer had been diagnosed.

There was only one fly in the ointment – in the shape of the couple's daughter, a very spoiled young woman of 15 who had up till then been the cynosure of her parents' attention. Obviously, she resented bitterly the sudden introduction of an alternative focus, and took it out on me in a thousand little ways, like deliberately serving a cup of tea or coffee for everyone but me. Fortunately, I was in such an agonised state of mind that this deliberate contempt more or less washed over me: it seemed a mere pinprick, but became more significant later.

I continued to teach in the mornings, and to be at the hospice all my remaining time. There was a very steep hill I had to climb to get there, and I remember thinking, 'It was all very well for you, Jesus – you only had to climb up Calvary once.' For Calvary is what it felt like to me, burdened as I was with school paraphernalia, as well as clean clothes, flowers and endless items of food and drink that I thought might tempt my husband.

On Sunday 3rd July, the day he died, I went to see him, carrying some flowers, and on the way was chatted up by some young male holidaymakers who invited me to go and have a drink with them. "Sorry," I said, "I'm going to see my husband; he's in hospital." "Don't take the flowers then," joked one of them. "He'll think he's dying." Irony indeed!

When I entered his room at the hospice, the smell of putrefaction, and I suppose death, was so overpowering that I had to rush out and vomit. Matron found me and took me out to a seat on the porch. Sister came out too and they made me put my head between my knees as I appeared to be fainting. Thinking I couldn't hear, Matron said, "This has gone on long enough. If we're not careful, we're going to lose this one too." To which, Sister replied, "Yes." As I raised my head, I saw a look of complicity pass between them. I went back and sat with Ron, and was told I might as well go home and rest, as he appeared to be deeply unconscious. But every time I decided to leave, he would make a frantic effort to raise his head from the pillow, even though his eyes were tightly closed. When I left at nine o'clock in the evening, I put my lips close to his ear and said, "I love you so much and I always will."

Sitting in my bedroom at 11.40 pm, I felt suddenly as if all the life had left my body, as if a bird had flown from my heart through my mouth, leaving me completely lifeless and totally empty. At 11.45, the phone rang and shortly afterwards, Ruth – the person I was living with – came and sat down beside me. She took my hand and said, "You're going to have to be very brave." And I replied, "It's all right. I know."

At first, there was a feeling of great peace and tremendous relief. I felt happy for him, as he had finally escaped from the terrible decaying prison of his body and was free at last, after nine unbearable months. I felt, literally, as if a great weight had dropped from my shoulders. But of course the feeling didn't last.

Next morning, there were all the ghastly procedures of death to go through, which I felt were my responsibility as we were both 'only' children, and there was no one else to turn to. There are few experiences worse than arranging the funeral of the person who has been much dearer to us than life itself, or anything it has to offer. Ron hadn't made a will, which meant that by the time I had paid for the funeral, I had five pounds in the bank.

The actual funeral was almost unbearable. My father came to Hove the night before as a matter of duty, and departed immediately afterwards. His presence actually intensified my pain, because there was such a chasm of separation between us. Years earlier, he had given up on me, and we'd lived literally miles apart, although, of course, from time to time throughout my entire life, I had so desperately wanted to be close to him, but it had not been possible Were we both emotionally autistic? I shall never forget my feelings in the crematorium when the coffin disappeared and the curtains closed. I felt a tearing, ripping, searing agony in my stomach which felt as if it were spreading all the way through me like acid, consuming my very heart and mind.

Chapter 7

I had spent all our joint money, including my superannuation, on Ron's illness. The hotel in Brighton had cost a great deal and of course I was paying my way where I was staying. School had broken up for the summer holidays, and I wasn't due to start teaching again full-time until September, which was two months away, so I took a job as a waitress in a café in Hove, where I worked from six o'clock in the evening until one in the morning. At least, it numbed some of the pain as I was forced to think about orders and money and change, etc. But I felt as if I'd slipped into some ghastly limbo peopled by creatures of nightmare who gibbered and howled around me in a totally incomprehensible way. Strangely enough, my main link with sanity was my watch. I felt that, if I could survive for just one minute without going mad, running away, sitting down and howling like an animal or killing myself, then perhaps I could manage one more, then another, and so on. So I kept looking at my watch to confirm that time was actually passing, and that I was still here. Also, I was always acutely aware of my long-ago promise to Ron that I would not commit suicide.

What a blessing that promise has turned out to be in terms of spiritual growth, as I have learned how to experience legitimate suffering. For avoiding problems, ignoring or pretending they do not exist, can result in even more pain and a total inability to grow mentally and spiritually.

As Robert Frost says:

> I shall be telling all this with a sigh
> Somewhere ages and ages hence:
> Two roads diverged in a wood, and I –
> I took the road less traveled by,
> And that has made all the difference.

In the meantime, through that interminable hot summer holiday, I slaved away in the restaurant, ogled by men, treated like a machine by women, ordered about by the proprietor, wearily putting chairs on tables and sweeping the floor before dragging myself home at one o'clock in the morning. I still have a deep respect and admiration for waitresses, and am a generous tipper. We really don't have the right to criticise anyone until we have walked a mile in their shoes.

I felt Ron's presence dimly, and with it, a desperate need for some kind of belief to sustain me for the rest of my life. The minutes of survival had increased to five-minute intervals, but the pain was still excruciating and I still doubted my ultimate survival. I wanted to find a beliefwhich would help and guide me through this wilderness, but after what had happened, I didn't see how. However, I thought I would give God a chance, and started to go to Communion at a church at the end of the road. I had been confirmed at 14 into the Church of England, but it hadn't really made any impact. I was much more interested in the bridal effect of the white dress and veil.

I got some comfort from Communion and started to go to Evensong as well, but eventually stopped because, when I shook hands with the Vicar at the door after the service, he never really looked at me. I was so desperate at that time for him to notice how I looked and for him to ask how I was and to offer me some comfort. But there was nothing but a limp handshake, a bland smile, a total avoidance of eye-contact, and a quick turning-away to the next parishioner on the evangelical assembly line. Maybe religion is for people who don't want to go to hell, and spirituality is for those who've been there. I now believe that it is what you bring forth from within you that saves you, and that what you don't bring forth from within you will destroy you. So I was adrift in a menacing sea of atheism, cynicism and bitterness, on a meaningless journey to nowhere, denied even the possibility of ending it, because of a stupid promise! Ever since the funeral, I had been unable to cry, to find relief in tears. I felt that if I cried, I would disintegrate into a heap of broken, jagged pieces and nothing and nobody would ever be able to put me together again – what I now refer to as the 'Humpty Dumpty syndrome'.

The school year started in September, and I began to teach in what was then a secondary modern girls' school in Brighton. I was Head of the Home Economics Department in a building detached from the main school, and had an assistant who needed a great deal of help with discipline, so her needs helped to take my mind off my own. I remember one afternoon when she literally threw two girls into my room and screamed, "I don't want these girls in my room again ever – do something!" After which, she fled. Repressing their giggles with difficulty and with bright red faces, they told me that during the bread-making lesson, they had thrown lumps of dough up to the ceiling where they stuck and expanded tremendously with the heat. The group had collapsed into hysterics and control was lost. I found this very funny myself, and was delighted to realise that I was beginning to laugh again. This is how grief goes of course; one is not aware that the tide is turning, but imperceptibly one begins to float back, to at least a semblance of normality. Losing such an integral part of oneself as I had is like becoming an emotional paraplegic; one can never be the same, but there are amazingly helpful prostheses if one is willing to do the hard work of re-education oneself. Whilst I was at this school, I passed another milestone on the spiritual path.

In the meantime, my relationship with the daughter of the house where I was staying was steadily deteriorating. She was so incredibly jealous that she no longer even spoke to me, and this made life very difficult for her parents as well as for myself. So, through an advertisement, I rented half a bungalow in Rottingdean, and shared the bathroom and kitchen. This did not work out as the couple who owned the house had very vicious arguments all the time, and after a day's teaching, it became unbearable. Having spent my childhood in an atmosphere of constant petty disagreement and vicious accusations which only served to worsen relationships, I had made a promise to myself that never, absolutely ever, would I live in such an atmosphere again. I also learned a valuable lesson, that never, absolutely ever, would I share a kitchen! I received much verbal sniping from the woman in Rottingdean: I took far too many baths, I always wanted to be in the kitchen when she did, and since she was at home all the time, there were few moments when the kitchen was empty.

Maybe I should have been firmer and made a stand occasionally but I was too tired and too well programmed by my early conditioning to even think about it. When I found furniture rearranged in my sitting room, and letters obviously read, even I became angry and accused her of interfering. She went totally mad, screamed at me to get out at once, and locked the bathroom and the kitchen. So I was unable to wash or make a hot drink. Luckily, I was friendly with the owner of a nearby café, and was able to at least have a wash, clean my teeth, and eat and drink. However, there has always been an angel working for me, even when I was unaware of its presence, and help came in the unlikely appearance of a TV engineer who arrived to repair my set. I explained why I couldn't make a cup of tea for him and he was incensed. It was the height of the holiday season and there was not a room to be had in the whole area. I also had furniture to consider.

The TV man just took over the whole situation and two hours and a few phone calls later, I was sitting in his van surrounded by my worldly goods on the way to his daughter's flat in Hove. She proved to be another angel – a single mum, on her own, in a tiny basement, who gave up her bedroom to me without question. I find it a constant joy to observe that in this world, for every cruel and malignant person, there is always a kind, loving and generous one who more than tips the scales on the side of benevolence. Obviously, the basement flat could not be a permanent arrangement so I started my search yet again. My angel was really on the ball by now, and through an estate agent, I was led to a large attractive house near the sea where there was a small flat to let. A woman of about 40, with an obvious disability, answered the door and said, "Yes?" in the most abrupt and unsmiling way. This was the owner of the flatlet, which she took me to see. It was high-ceilinged, fresh and bright, with a sea view which immediately clinched the deal for me. After chatting briefly, I arranged to move in the following Saturday. I also learned later how very scared she was of people and of life in general – and the forbidding attitude was her defence. That Saturday proved to be a turning-point in my life, for I was to stay in that house for nearly 25 years.

On moving day, I was standing in the middle of the flat, surrounded by the usual chaos of moving house, when a living piece of Dresden china appeared at the door and asked if I would like to have lunch with them. She told me later that I had looked so young and thin and forlorn, I had brought tears to her eyes. These were certainly not apparent at the time as she spoke beautifully in distinctly upper-class tones, was dressed and coiffed exquisitely, and seemed to have the superiority and self-assurance which is only brought about by good breeding and the very best of schools. Again, I was misled to a certain extent; the breeding and the Swiss finishing school were facts but, apart from one or two ingrained opinions – like men being superior to women, foreigners inferior to the English, mixed marriages unthinkable, and always wearing a hat and gloves to go out to luncheon – she was the most loving, loyal and gracious lady, who eventually became the mother I had missed all my life.

I had lunch with them – not wearing a hat or gloves, just some rather grubby jeans and a T-shirt – and so I was introduced to them all: the owner of the house who had answered the door in the first place, Mrs Guidoux, who later became Jane; her mother, Mrs Crawford, who was over 80; and the 'Dresden lady', Mrs Sawell, their companion, who later became Frida. I, of course, was Mrs Swan – we didn't go in for Christian names then on so short an acquaintance. First names were not used in 1956 unless one had been friends for some time and had been invited to use them. It may sound stuffy now, but to me it had a certain integrity in that when someone asked you to use their first name, you knew they genuinely wanted your friendship.

They were an amazing trio. Jane had married a Swiss opportunist who scented money in the South of France, where she and her mother were on one of the Mediterranean jaunts so beloved of the English upper classes before the war. Once he had control of her money, he had treated Jane like a servant and it was only the presence of her mother that kept him from beating her. The three of them had gone to live in Switzerland where things were so bad that Jane and her mother fled back to Cannes, leaving a great deal of their money behind. Shortly after they arrived there, war broke out and eventually the Germans invaded France. To save herself from internment, being British of course, Mrs Crawford had to pretend to be bed-ridden and lived permanently by her bed, ready to jump in should German soldiers pay them an unannounced visit. Food was very scarce, and they both became quite ill from malnutrition. Jane had been born with cerebral palsy, and had very poor control of her muscles. She had to have all her food cut up and drink all liquids through a straw. She also wore a vicious iron contraption on her right leg in order to walk, and it was heartbreaking to watch her shaking arms, hands and legs attempting to don this prosthesis on her own. Someone always had to do up the buckles. When I met them, Jane's mother, Mrs Crawford, was an exact copy of the old Queen Mary: aged 88, upright in a chair that allowed for no slumping, blind, unable to walk, dressed in black bombazine, with a high pompadour of beautiful white hair, impeccably coiffed every morning by Frida. Mrs Crawford also ruled the household with the aid of a Braille clock, clocking poor Jane in and out and banging loudly on the floor with a stick to demand reasons why she was sometimes late.

And as for Frida, well her story was interesting, too. At 18, she had fallen hopelessly in love with a man who was already married – in fact, her brother-in-law. In order to 'cure' this infatuation, her family married her off to the first suitable man who came along: they did that sort of thing in those days. Unfortunately, her husband died of TB quite soon after the marriage.

This brother-in-law, Jack, had a somewhat rakish career. In those days I think he would have been described as 'a bit of a bounder, doncherknow?' He had been a major in the army during the First World War, then a district commissioner in Africa, and was the manager of a cork farm in Portugal when he married Frida's older sister. Frida's father was in the diplomatic corps in Lisbon. As Frida grew from 10 to 18, I think Jack realised he had married the wrong sister! Eventually Jack and his wife Evelyn bought a guest house in Devon and took Frida with them, to help run it.

Jane and her mother had seen an advertisement for the guest house after their flight from France at the end of the war, and by the time I myself became a pawn in this particular game when I arrived in their house in 1956, Jane and Jack had pooled their resources to buy the apartment house in Hove, as the guesthouse in Devon had failed financially. I felt I had walked into the middle of a fascinating and absorbing story, so that my preoccupation with my own painful history began to pale and a little concern for the well-being of others was born.

During the first month I was with these three in Walsingham Road, a strange thing happened and I encountered further light on my spiritual path. I taught a girl whose father had been killed in the war and whose mother, Evie, worked as a waitress at a Brighton restaurant, where I had lunch on Fridays with a colleague to celebrate the end of the school week. Evie would give us very special attention, because teachers were automatically given respect in those days! And I learned that not only was she bringing up a child on her own, but she also had a mother dying of cancer, and they all lived together in a cramped and crumbling flat in Brighton.

In spite of all her problems, Evie radiated an aura of calm and an unfailing strength of spirit. I was so impressed with her that I invited her to come to have a meal with me, so that she could be waited on for a change. On the way home from school that evening, I did some shopping, and used Ron's wallet. When I got in, I laid it down on a coffee table while I unpacked the bags of food. Evie arrived early, and I poured her a drink which I set down on the table next to the wallet. On putting the glass down, she touched the wallet and went off into what I was to realise later was a mediumistic trance. I had been to the Spiritualist Church in Brighton immediately after Ron's death in a desperate attempt to find comfort but came away disheartened and disillusioned by messages about Uncle Albert's false teeth and Auntie Lilly's hat. I am not being critical of such messages but they weren't helping me.

Now Evie began speaking in a Native American accent, and I thought at first she was having some kind of fit, but eventually I heard the name Ron and realised what was happening. She said, "Your husband is desperate to talk to you, as he wants to tell you that you are not going to die for a very long time yet, although you want to. He says you have a great deal of work to do in the world, and you must stop just going to work and coming home to do nothing but sit in front of the television and sigh. He says you keep doing this – ." Here she took a deep sobbing breath and let it out slowly in a heartbreaking sigh, and I recognised myself immediately. She went on to say, "He wants to prove his identity by telling you that he used to call you Wicky," and at that the hairs really rose up at the back of my neck. No one, but no one at all, knew of this personal pet name he had for me. Then Evie said, "He's laughing because he says he's finally got his desk." This really threw me because when we lived in London, we used to go shopping in Peckham Rye on Saturdays, and he would drag me over to every desk he saw, and say, "Look! There's my desk," because he used to write freelance articles on politics and cricket, and would always pretend to moan because he had to write at our utility post-war table. The combination of this and the pet name was overwhelming. She also described in detail the man with whom I was to have an affair two years later, whom I didn't even know at that time. A little later, she resumed her normal voice, picked up her drink and went on with normal conversation. When she saw me white and shaking, with my lower jaw practically off its hinge, she said, "Oh! Have I been in a trance?" and told me that she was indeed a medium and used by the spirit world to convey vital messages to loved ones left behind.

Although I am not, and never have been, a spiritualist, I will always have a deep respect for genuine communicators like Evie, whose visit was such a turning-point in my life. For, from that moment, I've had no doubt that somewhere, somehow, in some form, Ron still exists and is able to communicate with me, as he did when I bought the desk at which I am writing now. I was walking past an antique shop in Malvern on the opposite side of the road from the shop when I heard in my mind, quite clearly, "Look! Over there, there's my desk." I turned my head and saw a most beautiful one, decorated with cut-out hearts, no less, standing outside the antique shop. I bought it, had it reconditioned and it is a source of tremendous joy.

At the time of Evie's visit, I was really frightened by what she had said, and even with the light on, I hardly slept all night. She said that Ron and I were two halves of a spiritual whole and all my life I would feel bereft, isolated and incomplete – but because of this experience, I would become very strong psychically and be of help to other people. I was desperately disappointed to hear this at the time because my great wish then was to die and join Ron wherever he was. I looked all the time for signs of terminal illness and must have been a real OGNHA (Oh God! Not Her Again) to all the many doctors I visited, hoping for the final fatal prognosis. I felt excruciatingly lonely; my whole body cried out for some kind of physical contact. I missed the feeling of being constantly, literally, in touch with Ron – we were always holding hands, walking about with our arms round one another, and although the sex hadn't been great, the affection was like being wrapped constantly in a warm, protective security blanket. Arms around you are rather like the iron bands which contain the wooden slats of a barrel; take those hoops away and the wood collapses on the floor, allowing the contents of the barrel to run away. Although there have been no physical arms around me for forty-odd years now, I feel the iron bands of spiritual awareness holding me even more firmly. But it's been a long, hard road.

Chapter 8

In September 1956, Auntie Edie died and Uncle Tom was inconsolable, not allowing anyone into her room, not eating or sleeping, and crying all the time. His daughter begged me to go and see him, as we had always been tremendous friends, so I took the train to Leicester one Friday after school and found him in a dreadful state. We talked all night, and in the morning, he allowed me to tidy up Auntie Edie's bedroom from which she had been hurriedly taken to hospital in a diabetic coma. I also managed to remove two bottles of whisky and the rope hanging from a beam in the garage from which he said he was going to hang himself.

It had been a terribly exhausting weekend and when I alighted from the train in Brighton on the Sunday evening, I suddenly realised that I couldn't remember who I was or where I lived. A very kind policewoman took me home (finding this from the address in my bag) where I collapsed across my bed in a paroxysm of grief and cried uncontrollably until the next morning. Obviously, I couldn't go to school and whilst I was in the hall telephoning them, Frida came down the stairs and asked what was wrong. I burst into tears again, and she just took me over. So began a wonderful period of loving, satisfying mothering which I had never known before. The long-held-back tears had arrived and manifested themselves physically in a severe attack of sinusitis. As I have said before, I have suffered intermittently from sinusitis all my life, which I see now is directly related to unshed tears. Naturally, if you don't shed them, the whole sinus and eye area may congest and swell, and appear as sinusitis and conjunctivitis. It is so important to cry when we are very unhappy, because it brings us such relief, not just physically but emotionally and psychologically as well. It has been proved scientifically that there are fourteen stress hormones in tears. The stiff upper lip is responsible for much unnecessary pain.

Thinking of this 'culture of controlled emotions', I would say that of course, we need to practise self-discipline, but more than that, we need to find a balance between the two. Mature mental health means that we must constantly maintain the delicate balance between conflicting emotions, our needs, responsibilities and our duties to other people. I was ill for six weeks with sinusitis, in great pain and constantly in tears, but treated with such loving care by my two new landladies that the terrible hole left by Ron's death began to fill and heal. By the time I was well again, Frida and I had forged a strong mother-daughter relationship, and we began to do all the lovely things that mothers and daughters do: shop for clothes, go to concerts, films and the theatre, and gossip together. She also took to cooking meals for me, which was most acceptable after spending all day teaching cookery at school. And what joy it was to have someone waiting eagerly for my return at the end of the day!

Eighteen months passed in this pleasant convalescent atmosphere. I was now 35 and able to envisage some kind of future at last. The job at Margaret Hardy School was not really what I wanted to do for ever, so I cast around and put in an application for a teaching post at the Naval Officers School in Malta. I had such dreadfully unhappy memories in Brighton and Hove, I felt I just wanted to get away. But after I had been interviewed and accepted, my fourth-year GCSE girls told me that, for their fifth year, they were moving to a new co-ed grammar school which was being built on the Sussex Downs outside Brighton. They asked me to go with them, and as the prospect seemed attractive, I decided to apply. Because I was still feeling lost and rootless, when I was called for interview, I had no real inclination towards either job, as life still seemed to some extent difficult and pointless.

There were four other candidates, all with superior qualifications, and I was amazed when I was offered the post. By then, I had become very attached to Frida and Jane, and to my GCSE pupils, so I gave up the idea of glamorous naval officers in a warm climate, and accepted.

This was one of the most important decisions of my life and was to affect me for the next fourteen years – all done almost by the metaphorical tossing of a coin, just as meeting Ron had happened. Immediately, life became much more exciting. I was both gratified by my new status and terrified. There were a thousand things to do, from equipping a whole department from scratch and the working out of lesson plans – more than I had ever undertaken before. I was head of a department, and as such, the responsibility for it was mine totally.

During that last term at Margaret Hardy, preceding the opening of the new grammar school, I met a man whom I will call John, who was to be extremely significant in my life, causing me great joy and also great pain. He was at a dinner party on his own, so I assumed he was either divorced or a widower, as no mention was made of wife or family, either by him or by our mutual friends. He was an extremely intellectual man, having a degree in both arts and science – in fact, an altogether very attractive individual. He was ten years my senior, and seemed to come into the father-figure category, so that any possibility of a sexual attraction between us seemed to be verging on the obscene. He took me home and asked if he could see me again. It all seemed extremely amusing at the time, and of course I was flattered: here was this distinguished person seeking my company, wanting to take me to exotic places, to hang on my every word, and generally to cherish me in a way that I had missed so much for two very long years. He sympathised with my extreme loneliness and understood my despair to such an extent that I inferred he too was alone, and was well and truly caught in his net before I realised I was in there with a bit of a barracuda!

We went out quite a lot together during the last term I was at Margaret Hardy, and I began to feel almost happy again. I was cherished and cosseted by John and Frida, busy equipping my new department in the newly-built grammar school, and enjoying a most satisfactory social life with John. There was still no mention of a wife or children, only the continued understanding of what it was like to be alone.

Chapter 9

Term started in September 1957, with the first staff meeting at Westlain, as the new school was called. We were a young new staff in a beautiful, new building set in a fold of the Downs, well away from the town. The teachers had been well chosen by the new headmaster, and we became a cohesive, supportive group, almost like a family, right from the start. I was quietly amused by the incredible names of the Biology master Mr Skull, the canteen manageress Mrs Proffit, and the caretaker Mr Broomhead – a bit like Happy Families!

The boys and girls aged 11-16 (we had no Sixth Form that year) were a delightful crowd, in neat, clean uniforms, respectful and disciplined, and actually eager to learn. There were the usual few dropouts later on, of course, but at the beginning everyone was inspired by the new start implicit in the whole enterprise.

My own department consisted of two attractive, large and airy rooms, one for Dressmaking and one for Home Economics in general, at the end of which was a furnished sitting room and balcony in which meals could be served, staff and pupils entertained, or groups assembled for discussion and counselling. I was drawn towards counselling straightaway and scarcely a day went by without at least one tearful individual finding their way to the sitting room with some real or imagined problem. There was no counselling in schools at that time – most people thought the word 'counsellor' referred to someone on the town council. My heart went out to these kids, quite a few of whom came from homes where the grammar school ethos was quite incomprehensible and where conditions for doing homework were practically non-existent. The school encompassed quite a wide spectrum of society, and looking back, I believe it was an excellent example of genuine all-round education. The staff too used to find their way to the Home Economics Department when they had a grievance, so that it gradually became the social centre of the school. This was balm to my wounded spirit; nurturing the children helped nurture the wounded child within me and being a source of succour to the staff boosted my self-esteem no end.

John continued his pursuit and appeared suddenly late one night, tapping on my ground floor window. I opened the window and he climbed inside. Without a word, he took me in his arms and made love to me. I do not wish to imply that I was anything but a very willing participant, nor do I wish to make excuses. No doubt nowadays very little importance would be attached to it but afterwards I felt exhilarated, while at the same time extremely guilty. After a sexual deprivation of several years, I was crying out for the basic satisfaction of sex, and also to be held – but of course, once a relationship crosses the boundary between platonic friendship and active sex, one loses one's reason entirely and there is no going back. I was in love again, and it was to be another nine years before the stronger emotions of anger and frustration overcame this love that I first thought was a continuation of the very real emotion I had felt for Ron.

Seven weeks after this, I saw John in his car in Brighton with a woman whom I took to be his mother, but found out subsequently was his wife. She had stayed in their London house while he was in Brighton, partly on business and partly to buy a house there. When I confronted him, he told me he was indeed married and had two teenage children for whose sake he and his wife kept up a semblance of secure home life, so no way could he get a divorce. However, when his children were grown-up, he would consider it. This is such an old story, it is a wonder anyone is taken in by it. But love is not only blind, it is very deaf as well, let alone witless.

I was upset by this news, because by now I was deeply involved; he was the only man besides my husband with whom I had had a sexual relationship, and I was very deeply hurt by his deception. I decided I would leave Brighton and seek a job elsewhere, even going so far as to attend interviews – as far apart as St Annes, Shrewsbury and Cambridge, but always failing to accept the proffered posts because I was too weak to leave the loving care of Jane and Frida, the security and satisfaction of a job I loved, and, contradictory though it may seem, an affair which was like the icing on the cake.

I threw myself more and more into the school, arriving early and leaving late; in fact, I woke up one morning and realised I had quietly married the place! It really was husband, children and home to me. My fellow members of staff were a joy; we worked and played together and, most of all, we laughed. There was always someone who lived near me who gave me a lift to school and back home again. The Art master, Clive, was tremendously witty and intelligent; he had a beat-up old Jaguar in which we bowled over the Downs together in the early mornings, frequently in such paroxysms of laughter that he had to stop the car whilst we recovered. He integrated Art with my subject of Home Economics beautifully. I remember once we took the fourth year into some woods on the Downs to find a natural design which was subsequently screen-printed onto material to make curtains and cushions. The two of us also organised a hilarious day out to London, to Carnaby Street and the Design Centre during the Swinging Sixties.

The Languages Department too were involved, by means of relevant national meals – French, German, Russian and, later, Italian. The English Department was connected through Drama and Costume and Comprehension, and RE to charitable enterprises – and of course there were obvious links between Physics, Biology and Chemistry. We took groups of pupils to places of interest locally and to the theatre in London.

As an aside here, I should tell that my worst experience with overwhelming fear took place after one of these visits to see Romeo and Juliet at The Old Vic. We brought the children back to Brighton by coach, and were required to see them all individually to their homes as it was well past midnight. My fellow member of staff had disembarked at his home and I undertook to see the rest of the party safely through their front doors. There were not many frightening episodes in the early sixties, but it was Brighton, after all, and not exactly rural England. The driver finally dropped me near my home at 2 am and I started to walk the quarter mile or so along this very wide and elegant road, lined with large detached houses on either side, each with its own extensive front garden. I was tripping along in fairly high heels and a tight skirt when five youths in studded leather jackets appeared walking towards me. Deciding discretion was the better part of valour, I crossed the road, and so did they. By this time, I was fairly frightened and so I crossed the road again, only to see them do the same. At that moment, I knew exactly what it means when people say, 'My knees turned to water', because – believe me – they really do! How I remained upright and continued to walk, I do not know. We finally came face to face, and as I prepared for the attack, one of them said, "Hello, darling. What are you doing out so late? You shouldn't be out as late as this. Someone might attack you." The relief was almost more weakening than the watery knees, and I nearly collapsed. They had booked into a guest house in Hove and couldn't find it, so I was able to give them directions. They insisted on seeing me home, with many admonitions about being out so late on my own. They were genuinely concerned and insisted on waiting until I was safely indoors. Never judge a parcel by its wrapping!

Although I have not forgotten that episode because I have never been so frightened since, it helped to nurture my growing core of strength and independence and this has stood me in good stead during many years of being by myself.

There were many other attractive facets to the diamond that was Westlain School. Besides the academic side of life there, it was a mixed staff which included several unattached men with whom I flirted from time to time. I was taken out to dinner and the theatre, to concerts and to some splendid balls at the Royal Pavilion. I have always loved clothes and dressing up, and in the late fifties and early sixties in Brighton there were plenty of opportunities. But these occasions had a bitter-sweet taste, wishing as I did, that either Ron or John were with me instead of the hapless young man at my side. I did redress the situation somewhat by introducing at least two of them to the women they would eventually marry and settle down with.

As part of the enjoyable social life at school, we met every Wednesday to play badminton, and then we went to the pub to play snooker, then to the beach to eat fish and chips. We also had a great deal of fun amongst ourselves; there was a time during an A Level lesson when I sent a note to the Biology master to ask exactly how chickens get their eggs fertilised, and the reply came back, "Same as us with feathers on." The same master, on being told the pudding in the canteen was Spotted Dick, retorted, "Sounds more like a disease than a pudding." We laughed at the statement in an RE exam that an Epistle is the wife of an Apostle, and in one Home Economics exam, that the reason for the U-bend trap under a sink is because Germans cannot pass water. This kind of fun could also be shared with the pupils: I remember one afternoon, trying to give a theory lesson, and being drowned out by rock music coming from the sixth form common room next door, whose sole occupant was Philip Kyundu, the son of a Nigerian chief, a very self-possessed and extremely autocratic young man. I banged the table with my fist and shouted, "Look here! Can we have it off?" In answer to which, he drawled, "Any time, Mrs Swan, any time." I managed an expression of supreme disdain long enough to reply, "You should be so lucky!" and rushed back to my class where we all laughed till the tears rolled down our cheeks.

In spite of this easy camaraderie, or perhaps because of it, our O and A Level results were excellent. I still see some of my ex-pupils who are now in their forties and early fifties, and they are loud in their praise of the education for life in general that they received. Some of them arrange a party from time to time for the old staff who taught them. They were particularly grateful when their own children entered senior schools at twelve, and they, as parents, noted the differences from their own school days.

I continued to regress into illness quite frequently, still in the usual form of upper respiratory problems. I had established this pattern of retreat very early in my life and although these illnesses were psychosomatic in origin, I was nonetheless ill, but I had the loving care of Frida at home as she nurtured and cosseted me, and again my subconscious wishes were being gratified.

John was not very sympathetic and usually implied that I was making a fuss about nothing. I see now, with hindsight and understanding, that it was a very selfish relationship on both sides: we were each taking from the other, and giving little in return. We were also very deliberately deceiving innocent people and this can never succeed. And there is no situation more lonely than sharing a bed with a man wearing nothing but a watch, reminding him of his responsibilities elsewhere; they are obviously more important than you are, even though you are the one to whom he has just sworn undying love! There were some positive effects in that I felt temporarily safe and secure, nurtured and loved, after I had seen John, and therefore able to be much kinder and more understanding towards my colleagues and pupils, and to do my job more efficiently. Looking back on that time, I see that there was a mutual sexual satisfaction, but it was a poor, pale shadow of the total love and commitment I had experienced with Ron.

As Frida and Jane were getting quite old and infirm, I was gradually taking over the running of the house. They were the archetypal 'ladies in reduced circumstances', which meant that although they knew all the rules of etiquette, they didn't have a clue about managing money matters or awkward tenants or workmen. For instance, Jane burst into my room in tears one morning because the electricity bill had arrived and was frighteningly high, and on another occasion when I returned at 11 o'clock after a day's teaching in school and the evening teaching yoga, I found her sobbing uncontrollably because, 'the window cleaner didn't call.' While they were running rented accommodation, tenants were ripping them off left, right and centre, doing moonlight flits, wrecking furniture and ending up in rent arrears. It's interesting to note that people like myself, who are weak when it comes to standing up for themselves, can stand up quite well for people whom they see as unfairly exploited.

Frida and Jane had met John, and were charmed by him, so he often came to the house and took them out from time to time in his car. Now, as my relationship with him had become so important to me, school holidays were always desperately unhappy times during this period: John would go off to exotic destinations with his family and I was left, feeling lonely and rejected, subconsciously re-experiencing all the painful times in my childhood when my aunts went off and made it apparent that I was not wanted on voyage. As Auntie Edie had died, I used to go to stay with her daughter May and son-in-law occasionally, but this was never successful as May was the antithesis of her mother, being jealous, mean-spirited and envious to a degree. She spent most of her time putting me down with remarks like, 'I don't know why you are putting all that muck on your face, because no one's going to look at you here,' or 'That skirt's much too short for someone of your age.' The last straw for her was when a man on a bus referred to me as 'your daughter'.

Chapter 10

Eventually, I started to go away on my own, and found that in fact I had a more interesting time. More people will speak to you if you are on your own than if you are obviously attached – not just men, but couples and families who would invite me to go with them on various excursions. I discovered the joy of coach trips when you become a member of a group as soon as you set foot on board. I had several memorable holidays abroad and also went on a very interesting cruise in 1968. I didn't find romance in the conventional sense, just a number of men out for sex of the 'Wham! Bam! Thank you, Ma'am' variety, who could be incredibly persistent in their pursuit. Luckily, I had a huge Irish steward who would appear every time a man knocked at my cabin door, with a menacing "Was you wantin' sump'n'?" and they would rapidly melt away into the night, only to keep telephoning till I took off the receiver. I found this attitude remarkably distasteful and unbelievably crude – yet there were many women aboard who were equally voracious. My romance came with the nights off the coast of Madeira and North Africa with the moon and the stars so close in the dark blue sky you felt you could pluck them down, the lights shimmering romantically on the passengers in evening dress, and the trips ashore to the casbah to ride on a camel or swim in the warm sea. I found that the feelings I had had for Ron were gradually resurfacing and I knew that I was not a candidate for casual sex.

In May 1965, John and I met for dinner at a country pub, and it was one of those evenings when everything conspires to make it memorable: the weather, the food and drink, the atmosphere between us, and the excitement of being apparently in love. The love-making that followed was transcendental; I felt more deeply involved with this man than ever before. We had discussed the possibly of pregnancy many times, because although I was menopausal, there was always an outside chance. His reply was always the same, 'That would be the sign for us to go away together. My children have grown up now, I could get a job in Canada, and we would live there with our own child.' Guess what? I believed every word!

About three months later, I noticed how difficult it was becoming to fasten my badminton skirt, but concluded I was putting on weight at the menopause. I continued to lumber around playing badminton and tennis until two months later when I went for a mandatory test for cervical cancer and TB. A few days later, my doctor telephoned to say that albumen had been found in my urine, and would I go and see him? He did various tests for more sinister reasons which proved negative, and finally he asked if I could be pregnant. At this point, bells started to ring and I finally put two and two together and got the picture. The doctor did a pelvic examination, found a well-formed head, and calculated that I was about six months into gestation.

This all sounds an incredibly naïve situation for a 44-year-old woman to find herself in, but although the sixties were definitely swinging, the swing didn't actually include the middle-aged, and the Pill was not lobbed out indiscriminately to unmarried women. At first, I was deliriously, frantically happy: I walked about with a stupid smile on my face, my head full of dreams of a child and a family of my own at last.

I was overjoyed and couldn't wait to tell John, imagining he would be equally overjoyed, take me in his arms and off we would go into the sunset together. The reality was horrible: I had been expecting a call from him to arrange our next meeting, during which I planned to tell him about the baby. The time went by until I was so frantic I telephoned his secretary, pretending I wanted to make a professional appointment. In a voice choked with emotion, she told me that he had had a heart attack whilst playing squash, and that he was dead. I managed to say how sorry I was, put down the phone and stagger into my bedroom. Luckily, Frida was at home and I was able to pour out all my sorrow and considerable fears for the future to her.

The next few weeks were unbearable and I walked about like a zombie, still able to perform the usual human activities of eating, bathing and dressing and, incredibly it seems, teaching. It is strange indeed how the body goes on functioning when the mind and the emotions are completely shattered. Before long, I realised that, terrifying as it all was, it was not nearly as painful or difficult to bear as the death of my husband and after all, there was a new life in the situation, which would not be denied. In fact, I had never felt so well physically nor looked so radiant.

I was able to tell people that the father of my child had died and everyone was incredibly sympathetic and helpful. The governors of the school proved to be a pretty enlightened bunch and wrote a letter to me, saying they were not about to lose an excellent teacher and that my job would be waiting for me when it was all over.

During the latter part of my pregnancy, Uncle Tom died and I was unable to go to his funeral. This was a source of great sorrow to me and of course I had to pretend to the people in Leicester that I had an illness at the time.

I shall never forget those months from November until the baby's birth on 11th February. I was bereft of all the props that normally supported me: my job, the pupils, my colleagues, and the whole network of raison d'être on which subconsciously I had relied so much. The weather was dark, dank and foggy, and waking up each morning to this total emptiness was the stuff of nightmare. I couldn't go far, and sitting thinking about the apparently hopeless situation I was in, almost drove me to suicide. But of course there was the long-ago promise to Ron. There was also the fact of another life which was not mine to destroy: this bump inside me was getting bigger and bigger, and it seemed incredible that it could ever get out.

There were bright spots: my colleagues on the staff at Westlain were great. They had a rota whereby one of them came every evening to take me out to a meal, thereby ensuring that I ate properly, whilst at the same time keeping in touch with the real world and maintaining some sort of hold on it. Frida too was amazing for a woman of her Victorian principles, and saw to it that I got up in the mornings, ate properly, and exercised.

I couldn't believe that after such a horrendous childhood and the unbearable agony of Ron's illness and death, I was still going to experience the loss of yet another extremely close relationship. For by then, I had made the painful decision to have the child adopted. I had only my teaching salary and a very small flat, no family, and most importantly, I was 44. That meant that by the time the child had finished school, I would be over 60 and if it was a boy, he would grow up without a father, which I thought was not fair either. So I had yet another nightmarish day, at an adoption society making arrangements, and buying a layette ready for the birth.

The adoption society gave me a list of adoptive parents, and I was at least able to choose a couple whom I felt would give him a good family life. They also lived and worked in Kenya, which meant that they would be far enough away for me not to continually agonise over imagining I had seen the baby or would be able to make contact with him.

Although this situation had arisen out of my own foolishness, I felt overwhelmingly cheated by life in general. It seemed to me that, right from my mother's death, I had been given some semblance of security, just long enough to feel safe, and then to have it literally torn away from me, leaving a gaping, bleeding hole which was totally irreparable. Here I was having a child, who was apparently very healthy, when Ron's child had only lived a very short time. I seemed to be confronted on every side by women surrounded by loving husbands and families of their own.

I suffered a great deal of ignominy in various subtle, and not so subtle, ways. People were not as broadminded in 1965 as they are now, and although I have said that the staff were most supportive, there were a number of my female acquaintances who were slyly enjoying the situation and doing their best to prevent my return to my job. I felt like Oliver Twists' mother – disgraced and guilty. There was not the help available with a pregnancy outside marriage that there is today, and I felt like a complete social outcast with no one to turn to. Luckily, Frida and Jane were very sympathetic and at least I had a roof over my head. Now, the scales had literally dropped from my eyes, and I saw the whole sorry situation in a totally different light. Whereas before, it had seemed romantic to a degree, with the snatched meetings, the concentrated avowals of everlasting love, the implied promise of a happy ending, it seemed now to have been both sordid, stupid and extremely distasteful. I realised that, had I been an onlooker, my reaction would have been, 'What a fool the woman's been; for heaven's sake, she's 43 – surely she knows better than to have a baby at her age?' And possibly, 'Well – it takes two, after all.'

Love sure is blind. It seems to me that falling in love is totally concerned with sex, but this truth was not apparent to me then. We do not fall in love with our friends of either sex although we love them in the sense of caring very much for them. Falling in love is temporary because, sooner or later, the ecstasy always passes. This is not to say that we stop loving the person with whom we fell in love; in fact, this is the point where real love as an act of will and choice begins. I like Scott Peck's definition of real love in his book, The Road Less Travelled : 'Love is the will to extend oneself for the purpose of nurturing one's own or another's spiritual growth.' As he comments, 'Love is too large, too deep, ever to be truly understood or measured or limited within the framework of words.' So any definition is likely to be in some way, or ways, inadequate.

A strong physical attraction, caused by a strong sexual need, will totally blind most people to the reality of the situation, and they truly are temporarily insane. In a sense, it's very pleasant to be out of your mind about another human being. The fact remained however, that I had taken something which didn't belong to me – I had stolen by engaging in a sexual act which – au fond – was purely for my own gratification.

Retrospectively, I can see that although I suffered greatly and could never be quite the same again, there were several compensatory factors: my self-confidence had been boosted tremendously by having an extremely eminent man apparently besotted with me in spite of the clandestine nature of the affair. I was much more self-confident at school and much more effective both as a teacher and counsellor and instigator of extra-curricular social activities. I ran a badminton and tennis club for the staff, and was heavily involved in the drama club and the school choir.

The 10th February 1965 dawned at last and with a heavy heart, I took a taxi to the nursing home in Hove where the baby was to be born by Caesarean section the next day. The home was quite splendid as I was then a member of Private Patients Plan, and as it was an abnormal birth, I had a room to myself, but I still felt degraded and guilty; there was no name on my door and everything was very furtive. I had no food for a day and just sat up in bed pretending to read, very anxious about the unknown horrors of the operating room, and anticipating yet another period of grief and loss. I had the Caesarean section the next morning, and was very ill and on the danger list for 48 hours, heavily sedated with morphine. However, an injection only lasts so long and there were many hours of almost unbearable pain in between.

In those days, Caesareans were not the neat, small transverse incision of today, but a vertical slash which had to be held together by metal clips, as well as the more conventional stitches. I had asked not to see my baby, as I knew that if I did, I would not be able to go through with the adoption. But I could hear him crying from time to time in the nursery – a pathetic, hoarse little cry as if he had been smoking too much. And this accentuated the physical pangs which were already tearing me apart. When things were at their very worst, I used to fix my gaze on a large crack in the ceiling and was amazingly strengthened by memories of Douglas Bader. I don't know why he came into my thoughts so much – maybe I had seen the film recently – but he was tremendously helpful. I used to think, 'Well, if he could survive his terrible injuries, and walk again on his tin legs, I can jolly well survive this, and get on with my life somehow.'

I was not allowed visitors, and I remember on the third day hearing Matron on the phone to my surgeon, saying, "We are very worried about Mrs Swan; she seems to be sinking." And my own delighted reaction of, 'Good, maybe I am going to die – splendid!' I floated in some limbo between life and death and it was all very pleasant; there was no pain and nothing whatsoever to worry about. I remember thinking, 'Good, good, good' and just letting go. If death really is like that, then there is absolutely nothing to worry about.

However, I was not going to be let off so easily; my surgeon bustled in and sat on the bed, took my hand, and said, "Now, Mrs Swan, you are not going to let me down, are you, after all the work I've done?" And I wearily replied, "No, I suppose not." Very reluctantly, I returned to consciousness.

I still regret not slipping away at that time, but 'Thy will, not mine' is the rule, and has to be obeyed. I was in the nursing home for a fortnight, and then had to convalesce for six weeks. I was so fortunate to have two wonderful friends, Phil and Mair Smith, who took me in for the whole convalescence, and were unbelievably kind. He taught English at Westlain and she was a loving, generous soul who had two young children of her own. I will never forget my arrival at their house, unable to stand up straight, still in pain physically, but far, far more torn apart emotionally. I was taken to a lovely room, newly decorated in bright yellow and white, with the biggest bowl of primroses I have ever seen on the dressing table.

Staying with Phil and Mair was balm to my wounded spirit indeed. They nurtured and restored me, at least to a semblance of my former self. My son was rushed to hospital when he was six weeks old and I had the painful task of having to sign a consent form for his operation but I dared not go to him; I knew it was better for him to be adopted and have a much better life than I could ever give him. He recovered and was put with foster-parents until he could be legally adopted.

I had to go to court and swear that I would never, ever make any attempt in the future to see the baby or make any enquiries as to where he was. It was a very cold, hard process with people looking at me as if I were a criminal, and addressing me as if I were just not worth their attention. They certainly could be very sure that if I had committed a criminal offence, I was being punished. My heart was absolutely breaking and still does from time to time, even now, particularly on Mothers' Day and his birthday.

One night, while I was still at Phil and Mair's, I descended into a real hell of despair and panic and literally felt, like the title of this book, that I really couldn't go on – promise or no promise to Ron, I was going to have to end it all. I crept down to the kitchen and took out a very sharp knife from the drawer, fully intending to cut my wrists, but a voice in my ear said sharply, 'What a terrible thing to do to these wonderful people, who have literally saved your sanity if not your life. Put it away at once.' Reluctantly I did and spent the rest of the night walking the floor, literally wrestling with the demons who were still egging me on to self-destruction and with a strong feeling that I could never face the future on my own.

Going back to school after Easter was very hard; I still felt weak, ill and tearful – but after an uneasy and awkward start, I fell back into the routine. But of course it was never the same. I had lost the bolstering support of John and my self-esteem was practically non-existent. I felt empty and bereft and cried myself to sleep every night. Nothing seemed worthwhile. I didn't want to go out socially any more, and life was channelled into work, punctuated by depression.

Chapter 11

The inevitable flow of life was imperceptibly beginning to stir again, like the green shoots that push up through the blackened landscape after a fire. I even managed to laugh occasionally which was great, because I sure had missed my sense of humour. The school kids contributed magnificently to my rehabilitation. I strongly suspect they knew I'd had a baby; in fact, one of them told me that he'd heard it was a certain member of staff who was the father. But overall they dealt with the situation much more easily and graciously than some of my colleagues. I resumed many of the extra-curricular activities I had previously run for staff and pupils, and as time went on, more and more pupils began to seek me out to tell me their troubles, and together we would find some way of coping.

Arising out of my own experiences, I had tremendous empathy with people going through difficult times, and this success made me see that there was a useful future for me after all, and maybe a training in counselling would be a sensible course to take. So most holidays, I enrolled on courses run by the Health Education Council, Marriage Guidance as it was then called, and the Department of Education. They were usually held in interesting and attractive venues like Oxford and Cambridge, and I remember one memorable fortnight at a beautiful old vicarage at Ecton in Northamptonshire. These courses were balm to my wounded emotions, as I learned all about the patterns of behaviour we lay down in childhood, how to recognise the sabotage and repair it as much as possible. I also met some very loving and loveable people, one in particular with whom I could have fallen in love, but as I have said, the cruise I had taken in 1968 had confirmed my decision to be celibate.

I still felt depleted, physically and emotionally, unable to take on a change of job or home, and developed a strong distaste for anything male, finding it quite difficult to go through the male underwear departments in the big stores. Confronted by a pair of Y-fronts, I would rush for the exit! This distaste has lasted, though not so strongly, all my life and I've never been able to get close to a man since. Although I have no homosexual tendencies, my experiences have really helped me to understand lesbianism in a way that was incomprehensible to me previously. I now see the body as a house in which the spirit lives during its sojourn on earth, and the male/female relationship necessary for the reproduction of more houses so that more spirits may live on the earth's plane.

This is not to minimise the importance of sex between two people who really love one another: who can explain the feelings of awe and wonder when the beloved stands before us naked and vulnerable, when our coming together skin-to-skin lifts us off the earth and moves us to say, 'Oh God!' at the climax of our love-making? One of the best descriptions of true love is found in Khalil Gibran's The Prophet.

'But let there be spaces in your togetherness, and let the winds of heaven dance between you. Love one another but make not a bond of love. Let it rather be a moving sea between the shores of your souls. Fill each other's cup but drink not of one cup. Give one another of your bread, but eat not from the same loaf. Sing and dance together, and be joyous, but let each one of you be alone, even as the strings of a lute are alone, though they quiver with the same music. Give your hearts but not into each other's keeping. For only the hand of life can contain your hearts. And stand together, yet not too near together, for the pillars of the temple stand apart, and the oak tree and the cypress grow not in each other's shadow.'

At this stage of my life, I became dimly aware that the destiny that shapes our ends was guiding me, as more and more children, staff and parents were seeking me out to talk over their problems. My love for, and interest in, the pupils at Westlain deepened and grew. I spent more and more of my spare time at school in taking them out to the theatre, to London shows, and the boys even took me to wrestling matches. I was usefully diverted by this as it took my mind off my own wounds. I became totally involved in counselling, and was able to experience an empathy with people that enabled me to develop a strong intuition as to what the best help for them would be. I have always believed in offering some practical suggestions to people as to what they might actually do regarding their problem. Whilst talking a problem through helps enormously, it's like bursting a boil – the boil still needs cleaning and dressing from time to time in order to heal successfully. It may leave a scar that lasts a lifetime, but scar tissue is much less painful than the original wound. Also, I could relate to many of the problems that were brought to me; 'a fellow-feeling makes us wondrous kind'. A woman who was having an affair with a married man said on her first visit, 'I don't think you'll be able to help me. You see, a woman like you wouldn't even be in a situation like this.' To which my reply was, 'You wanna bet?' And I told her briefly my whole sorry tale. She shot forward almost into my lap, and we were away: she reached a very successful solution to her dilemma.

So many problems arise from childhood, inconsolable grief after the death of a loved one, and terrible, terrible loneliness – and here again, my own experience was extremely helpful. I decided that I was much more interested in psychology than in Home Economics by now, and in a vague sort of way decided that maybe I would leave teaching and become a therapist. But as always, the problem was money – it is difficult to leave a feather-bedded job like teaching at nearly 50 and make a leap into the unknown without a reliable source of income. But yet another blow was about to fall.

Chapter 12

In late 1968, I began to feel a terrible pain under my left ribcage. It was uncomfortable to sit or stand, and I could only lie flat on my back on the floor – it was impossible to rest on a bed. The pain also interfered with my breathing, and I often felt giddy and faint. I always had a lift to school and back, but when I got there I had to sit on a stool in the middle of the classroom and direct operations. With twenty pupils, eight cookers boiling water, irons, knives and naked flames, it was all a bit horrific! But it was better than glooming by myself at home. The pain grew steadily worse; I lost over a stone in weight and my doctor became sufficiently alarmed to send me for an X-ray.

There was a shadow on my left lung which made the plate look like a replica of my late husband's, and I was rushed to Guy's Hospital for a bronchoscopy as there was an obvious possibility of cancer. I had to see the same surgeon who had been my husband's consultant, which vividly revived all the old nightmare experiences. Another trip to hell. And back, as it transpired, for the shadow proved to be a pleural effusion due to an undetected infection, and the search then moved to my spine. This was found to be degenerating and the cause of the referred pain in my rib cage, as vertebrae were pressing on nerves originating in the spine. I saw a specialist who said that, in a year's time, I would be in a wheelchair, and as I did not have a family, I would need to go into care. Disbelieving, I saw two more consultants but they came up with the same story, and all advised a neck collar and a spinal corset.

Now, whilst my sex life was at an end, I still had a strong predilection towards pretty underwear, and this was bad news indeed! Mair Smith took me to the surgical instrument-makers as I still couldn't walk, and there in the window was this revolting pink corset strung about with sadistic leather straps and buckles and a neck collar sitting smugly like a medieval instrument of torture. I stopped in my tracks with my hand on the door and said, "I'm not going in." And Mair said, "But what will you do?" I replied, "I don't know, but I know what I'm not going to do. And that's wear one of those things."

I was quite ignorant of natural healing then but I did realise that keeping muscles indefinitely supported would result in eventual atrophy and loss of function. That night, I sat at home facing a bleak prospect and feeling totally trapped. But I'm usually at my best when my back is against the wall; it always makes me want to fight back with enormous vigour. One of my friends who is a very eminent therapist says I'm stubborn. Maybe. I decided to keep going as far as I could and to refuse the suggested treatment. Needless to say, I was unpopular with the specialist and was given the patient's equivalent of being struck off. Once again, I felt very lonely and extremely apprehensive about my future. But what I was increasingly aware of was my inner voice which kept saying, 'Keep going. Knock on every door. There is an answer to this problem and eventually you will find it.'

I was meeting a lot of people and I asked the same question of them all. 'Have you ever had back trouble? What was it like? What did you do about it? Did it work?' Most of the answers were painkillers, corsets, lying on the back for weeks, sometimes months, all of which I somehow knew were not for me. Then one day in 1969, a friend was giving me a lift home, and I remained in the car while she did some shopping. When she came out of the supermarket, she was accompanied by a woman shuffling along with great difficulty on two arm-crutches, and looking as if she was in great pain. She was introduced as Kay and joined us in the car. It seemed that she had a very arthritic back and had experienced the usual palliatives, all to no avail. "But," she said, "I'm going to a naturopathic clinic next month, which uses only natural methods of healing, because I've certainly tried everything else."

When she returned, I contacted her and went round to tea, and just didn't recognise the woman who opened the door. The sticks were gone, she stood straight and tall, her hair was blonded and piled on top of her head in the most fetching arrangement, and altogether she looked a good twenty years younger, and fifty times as glamorous. I wouldn't have recognised her if I had met her in the street. She told me about all the treatments she had had which sounded pretty drastic, not to say alarming. But obviously they had worked, and I decided to go to Tyringham myself. I booked in for a fortnight during the summer holidays and was in such agony during the intervening weeks, I would have put up with anything to relieve the pain.

Tyringham was an old manor house, originally built in 1068, by a William de Tyringham who had come over with William the Conqueror and been given the original land as a reward for his services. The gardens and surrounding fields were beautiful; one approached over an old Norman bridge, passing a Norman church, also built in 1068, and up a tree-lined drive, flanked by fields full of farm animals living in natural conditions. The house had only recently been opened as a naturopathic clinic and was still in the process of renovation and refurbishment, so it was all a bit rough and ready. There seemed to be as many staff as patients, and everything was very relaxed and happy. I remember how we used to laugh. All these treatments were very new at the time and seemed to us to be most amusing. We all used to sit together in the sun on the front steps and exchange experiences. One story sticks in my mind of a huge, macho man who had come to help a disabled friend, not to have treatment himself. Apparently, he was persuaded to have a massage from a very large lady, even bigger than he was, and tottered out onto the steps, completely shattered, to relate the experience to us. "Well," he said, "First of all, she tore off my arm and said, 'You don't need that, for a start. We'll throw it away.'" We really were one large and very happy family.

I was bemused by the whole experience, and not a little scared by some of the treatments which at that time were so diametrically opposed to conventional allopathic remedies. First of all, I had weighed in at seven stone because of all the pain I had suffered, and was put on a fast for four days. Since my interpretation of fasting was for weight loss, I thought they were out of their minds! All I had was six cups of water a day, with a slice of lemon, and a teaspoon of honey. Since I had been brought up on the 'three meals a day or you will die' imperative, I was really apprehensive and by the end of the second day felt quite ill and faint. I was also having up to eight treatments a day – osteopathy, massage, radiant heat, ultrasonic, ultraviolet, acupuncture, steam baths, remedial exercises, peat pack, yoga, Scottish douche, sauna, wax baths, sitz baths and various therapeutic baths like seaweed and pine. There were also various outdoor activities like walking, jogging, swimming and breathing exercises.

I remember being absolutely intrigued by the name 'Scottish douche', and wondering if it were some sort of Gaelic contraceptive – but found it in fact to be a most stimulating and energising experience. You took off all your clothes and entered a tiled room where you held on tightly to a rail at the far end. A therapist then entered with a hose with which she proceeded to spray your spine up and down with a pleasantly warm strong jet of water. Having stroked you gently several times with this warm jet, it was suddenly turned to icy cold, and this was sprayed up and down your back several times before returning to the warm water. The screams that came from that cubicle were absolutely blood-curdling.

I had noticed a very interesting phenomenon in the sauna which was shared with five others. After about five minutes of baking, I noticed a most unpleasant odour, and would look suspiciously at my fellow inmates thinking that it came from one of them. On the third evening of my fast, I had decided to go home – because I felt so terrible – and had actually started to pack. Then I asked myself where else could I go to get rid of this racking pain in my back? And I reluctantly admitted that this place was more than likely the end of the road so far as I was concerned. Wearily, I slid down into my bed and was overcome by the same sickening smell I had noticed in the sauna – and it was me! I began to put two and two together and realised that something bad was being driven out through the pores of my skin. Could it be the poisons in my system that were causing my problems? Fortunately, we had a talk the next evening, in which the principles of fasting were explained, and this confirmed my theory. Apparently, when the body goes without food, it really rests, particularly from the enormous expenditure of energy required for digestion. Most people eat far too much; for instance, to 'break fast' implies we have been without food for a period of time. But this is only true if the last meal of the day has been taken at six o'clock in the evening, and breakfast is at seven or eight in the morning. But if we eat after nine o'clock in the evening, the digestive system will have barely finished coping with the evening meal before the next lot of food arrives in the stomach. And this constant onslaught makes people sluggish and lethargic.

Fasts lasting longer than 24 hours should only be undertaken under the supervision of a qualified therapist. By yourself, you can take a light meal at midday on Saturday, followed by purified water or unprocessed fruit juice until Sunday evening, and break the fast with a light meal on Monday morning. Fasting is one of the oldest methods of healing and is still instinctive in animals. Watch your dog or cat when they are ill – they sleep and refuse food. This instinct was probably strong in primitive humans, and is noticeable still if we are really ill. But it's become overlaid by the self-indulgent behaviour of the present day.

After four days on the hot water, lemon and honey, I progressed to a piece of fruit for breakfast, a bowl of natural yoghurt with honey and nuts for lunch, and a very small green salad with fruit for supper, punctuated by three cups of water, fruit juice or herb tea. I was beginning to look and feel exceptionally well and to take an interest in my fellow-patients, one of whom was a young man of 16 who was suffering from epilepsy. He was tall and looked older than his years, and he had been very friendly with a number of the younger patients until he had a fit whilst out with them, and had subsequently been ostracised. We sat together at lunch one day, and in a fit of laughter, I spluttered a microscopic bit of lettuce onto his plate. And because he was so hungry, he fell upon it and ate it! It certainly made me realise the effect that real hunger must have on people who are truly desperate for food. His name was Alan, and he and I grew very close. Artificial communities are hotbeds for emotion, and we walked and talked together for hours. It was one of those rare relationships where age and sex truly do not matter. In the light of further knowledge, I would say that we were soul mates, and had been together in a previous incarnation. Alan went home before me, and I saw him off in a taxi at seven o'clock in the morning. The parting was really painful as we knew we would not see one another again, on this plane anyway, and I felt quite bereft for the rest of my stay. I have never forgotten Alan and am often aware of him during meditation.

There were many other remarkable people staying there: Sir George Makarios was being treated for a strained elbow, and there were many visitors from the acting profession. I find it fascinating to see someone from the cinema or TV screen actually in the flesh – the third dimension adds a strange unreality somehow, particularly without make-up and styled hair, and slopping about in the clinic uniform of either dressing-gown and slippers or a track suit. It was the most one aspired to as far as fashion was concerned.

One lunchtime, I sat next to a very pleasant, funny guy, who had us all in stitches; and when he'd gone, I said to the rest of the group, 'Isn't he like Roy Hudd?' To which they all replied, 'It *is* Roy Hudd!'

Another remarkable young man who'd been at the clinic for some time was Richard. And Richard I will never forget, if only for his magnificent courage. He was 21 and suffering from multiple sclerosis which made him unable to walk without arm crutches, and he was doubly incontinent. The illness had started when he was 18, and progressed with frightening speed. He was virtually under sentence of death when he first arrived at Tyringham, and had been carried in on a stretcher. But after three months' natural treatment, and a very restrictive diet, he had improved enormously. He was the hub of the place in many ways, in that he reflected his own faith and bravery to everyone; we all felt so much better in his presence, and came away from him with renewed health and energy. He was very thin of course, and possessed one of the mostly saintly faces I have ever seen. He had a Beatle-type mop of dark hair and the most wonderful, dark, deep eyes, which radiated love, compassion, and a tremendous sense of humour. The people who gathered round Richard always looked happy.

He and I became great friends, and often went round the country lanes in his specially adapted car, to talk deeply about life, the universe, and everything. His wisdom was remarkable for such a comparatively young man. I never heard him grumble, not even when I had to walk away whilst he empted his colostomy bag. Just occasionally, he was inordinately sad, and his remarkable eyes would register a pain which had nothing to do with his physical disabilities. Obviously, he had a healthy interest in the many young and beautiful women there, and several of them went out with him, but he had decided that marriage was impossible. I was not convinced of this, and on one of my subsequent visits, I found out that one of the girls working there in the dining room was quite besotted with him, and he was interested in her. We talked about this at length, and he asked me to tell her she was wasting her time. I said I would do no such thing, and I thought it would be a great idea for them to get together. Anyway, with a little secret diplomacy, I convinced Susan to make the first move, which she did, and they had many happy years together. I visited them in Barnard Castle in the late seventies, and was touched and delighted by their obvious happiness, and by the tremendous bond between them. I heard recently from Susan that

Richard had died peacefully in hospital at the age of fifty. What a victory for Tyringham, and for Richard, whose indomitable faith and courage helped so many people, including me, to reappraise their lives and circumstances, to realise what was good and worthwhile, and to live a happier and more useful life.

At the end of the first week, a couple of friends I had made asked me to go into Olney with them for an illicit cup of tea. After seven days of hot water and herb tea, this seemed like a journey to heaven. So off we sped – and I have never enjoyed a cup of tea more! Maybe temporary deprivation is good; it certainly restores any kind of jaded appetite. My whole digestive system felt so healthy after the fast that I could have demolished the whole plateful of cream cakes which appeared along with the tea. But another advantage of fasting is that the stomach shrinks, so it is only possible to eat very small amounts of food – but those small amounts taste like ambrosia.

Since the pain in my back began, I had been compelled to wear the most ugly longline boned bras, because it was the only way I could sit up straight. But I was now so much better that I went into a shop in Olney and bought some delicate lacy bras and changed into one as soon as I returned to the clinic. My joy knew no bounds at this transformation. Don't be fooled by people who tell you that pretty underwear is only worn for men; I had no men in my life, but the sheer lift of spirits brought on by that underwear was amazing! I even stood up straighter. I took the three old boned monstrosities into the woods and set fire to them. I often wonder if I was actually the first woman to burn her bra!

I really enjoyed my second week at Tyringham as we finally had a hot midday meal of various vegetarian dishes as well as a large salad in the evening. I looked quite different: my skin glowed, my eyes were bright, and my flesh had been redistributed in all the right places. I can never be sufficiently grateful to the staff at Tyringham for putting me on the right road, not only to physical well-being but to a regime which led eventually to both psychological and spiritual health. I learned about many interesting and effective complementary therapies available, about positive relaxation, that you don't necessarily have to wear a steel corset but can 'grow' your own corset by strengthening your muscles, and you can keep your body clear of the poisons that cause disease by eating the right food. And that you must keep your body supple and strong with the right amount of exercise. This was where I found the real bliss of practising yoga which has kept me extremely mobile ever since and without any return of the severe osteoarthritis in my back.

I returned to Tyringham two or three times a year throughout the seventies, and the place never failed to restore me on all levels of being. I always met a crowd of congenial and interesting people with whom I felt at ease and happy. I also made friends with a member of staff who invited me to stay in her house, which was built in the sixteenth century. And it was there that I encountered a manifestation of evil which made a very deep impression on me, and also in the end freed me – eventually – from any subsequent fear of evil forces. I must admit that I had given no thought to evil forces whatsoever, and if anyone had told me the same story I am about to relate, no doubt I would have listened politely, but had grave suspicions of the story-teller's sanity at the same time! I was a very conventional soul in those days.

Anyway, the second night of my stay I went to bed as usual, and fell asleep about half past ten. The landing light was on and visible round the edges of the ancient door which had warped over the years, and left large gaps. I thought I had a dream in which a large, undulating, oily black mask had oozed through those gaps and covered my face. It seemed to be suffocating me, and I was in no doubt that it intended to kill me. I sat up suddenly, thinking I had had a nightmare when, to my horror, I found I could still actually see it hovering around my pillow. In terror, I shouted, "Go into the light. Jesus Christ is my protector." And it disappeared through the crack in the door. To this day, I don't know why I said this, as in those days I was very unaware of Jesus as an influence in my life. I can only think that He, and my personal angels and spiritual guides, were around protecting me, although I was not then aware of spiritual forces in any way.

I tried to convince myself that I had had a nightmare, but deep down I knew it had been real. In any case, I was rigid with fright and almost unable to breathe. Also, the room was icy cold. I had a small stick pin in the shape of a cross in the lapel of my suit which I had been given by Brother Mandus at the World Healing Crusade in Blackpool, and I stumbled out of bed to get it. I held it in my hand and knelt by the bed until it began to get light, begging for help from I knew not who or where. At five o'clock in the morning, I got back into bed, but moved the pillows to the foot of the bed, so that I would not have to put my head in the same place again.

Next morning, I didn't tell anyone; I didn't think anyone would believe me – I was afraid they would think I was showing signs of madness. But walking through the village later on, I encountered two sisters – very precise, very devout, and very involved in the Baptist Church, who, looking extremely concerned, said, "Are you all right?" "Yes," I said, "I'm very well – why?" And they told me they had been saying their prayers about midnight the night before, when suddenly one said to the other, "We must pray for Eileen Swan; she's in terrible danger." "What time was that?" I asked. And the time fitted exactly. I then asked, "What kind of danger?" And in unison, they both said, "Evil. Positive evil." Now these were two unimaginative, conformist village maiden ladies, so something must have happened. I attended Tyringham for treatment the day after this experience, and my osteopath commented on my unusual tension, and I told her what had occurred. "There are some very strange energies around this week," she said. "One patient came in for treatment for a broken leg, and two hours after his arrival, he tripped and broke the other leg. The yoga teacher has had a car accident on the way this morning, and the man delivering the yoghurt overturned his van and spilled today's supply all over the road." Although I was sorry to hear about all these mishaps, I felt somewhat reassured that I was not going mad! Had a patient of mine told me all this, I would have been sceptical to a degree and decided they were dreaming, hallucinating or telling lies in order to draw attention to themselves.

At the time, there was another patient at the clinic whom I will call Olga: a very beautiful Russian who seemed to dog my footsteps, and to stare at me with malevolence amounting almost to hatred. She never spoke to me – just glared unblinkingly – in this very disconcerting way. I found out that she was denigrating me to everyone, telling them that I was not qualified either to practise psychotherapy or to teach yoga, and that the latter was an evil activity anyway and should be avoided at all costs. One evening during that fateful fortnight, I volunteered to take a yoga class as the teacher was unavoidably absent. Olga arrived with a young woman in tow; they were late and immediately proceeded to giggle and make fun of all the poses and breathing exercises we were doing. I had borrowed a cassette recorder to play my own relaxation cassette at the end, and it just wouldn't work. When I had tested it beforehand, it was working normally. I talked the group through the relaxation myself and the whole time these two were laughing and audibly making fun of the whole procedure. I was very upset – much too much of a coward in those days to ask them to leave. It was quite obvious that this woman was doing her best to destroy me, and when I returned the recorder, we found that it was working normally. My unease was gradually turning into terror, and I thought seriously of returning home. The nights in my friend's house were still frightening and the room continued to be icy cold, and I dared not sleep in the bed – begging some then-unidentified force or strength to see me through the night. At dawn, I would creep reluctantly into bed, and sleep head to foot as before.

I still had an uncontrollable urge to pack my things and return to Hove. But some instinct deep within me compelled me to stay and see it through. I felt that the experience would pay enormous dividends, and it has. I feel that it is not too fanciful to say that I wrestled with the forces of darkness and overcame them. Certainly, I have been able to laugh away any subsequent supernatural experiences, and I can honestly say that evil does not frighten me any more, although I have great respect and sympathy for patients who now tell me of their own similar experiences.

During the second week of that particular stay, I went down to the beautiful little Norman church to find some solace in the stillness there. It was dark and deserted, and I knelt by the altar rail, trying to make sense out of these (to me then) bizarre events. Suddenly, maniacal laughter appeared to burst forth from the altar, which really froze my blood. As soon as I could move, I ran from the church and up the drive towards the clinic. Ahead of me were Olga and her friend. I found the friend in the library and asked her if they had been near the church. "Oh yes," she said, "Olga insisted on going up to the far end, all through the nettles, for some reason. And then she started to laugh like a maniac. I don't know what was going on." How relieved I was to hear this factual explanation, as I really was convinced by then that I was mentally disturbed.

I was so relieved when the fortnight came to an end and I could return home. Interestingly enough, further proof of evil forces operating was provided by a friend in Hove; a mediumistic healer who came to see me and said, "I must ask you what you were doing on Tuesday, the-whatever-it-was, of May." It was exactly the night when I had had the first terrifying experience. I asked her why, and she said she had suddenly shot up in bed from a deep sleep to be told to pray for me, as I was in mortal danger. So I was further assured that it had not been a nightmare or mental aberration. However, the effect on me was profound. I made a vow that if that was the kind of experience which resulted from yoga and relaxation, I wanted none of it.

So I gave up these interests for about six weeks, but was irresistibly drawn back by a dawning awareness of the metaphysical and the psychosomatic. It was blindingly clear by now that most, if not all, of my particular ailments were originating in my mind. So that if I could change my old entrenched patterns of fearful thought, I could liberate my physical body from the arthritic pain and the digestive problems and the many respiratory infections from which it constantly suffered. But how to change the thinking which by now had had years of uninterrupted confirmation and become habitual?

The two most helpful ideas that Tyringham taught me were the concepts of healthy eating and yoga. The dietary advice was comparatively easy to follow, and my angels worked for me again when I returned from the first visit. Jane was a collector of donations to what was then called The Spastics Society, and her immediate superior was a man called James McMahon, who used to call at the house from time to time. It was on one of these visits that I met and was introduced to him. It appeared that he had been so ill with emphysema twenty years previously, that he was lying in hospital with a prognosis of about three months to live. He was visited by a friend who was seriously involved with the teaching of yoga as a means of healing the whole person. He taught James some yoga breathing, called pranayama, and this simple therapy, practised devotedly, caused a miraculous improvement. Within another two months, James left hospital with only a few pockets of disease left in his lungs, and with such a dedicated interest in yoga that he was to train as a teacher and become one of the best in the country. Now, in our conversation about yoga, I learnt that he taught a small class in Hove on Sunday afternoons. So off I went the next Sunday, and was alarmed to find a group of young and lissom ladies sitting in the full lotus position and elevating themselves into a headstand with ease.

At that time, I could hardly manage to sit down on the floor, and was quite incapable of such feats of flexibility as kneeling or sitting back on my heels. However, James was kind and lovingly concerned about us all, and gradually my stiff spine and rigid joints began to ease, and I became more and more mobile as time went on. Combined with improved vital statistics and the emotional calm that yoga brings, I too became a devotee and practise to this day. I know that the combination of yoga and the right foods, adhered to over many years, is the foundation of the excellent state of well-being in which I find myself today.

Chapter 13

In 1972, my father died in hospital from a heart attack following a severe bout of bronchitis. I had been to Stafford to visit him several times a year and always at Christmas. It was a strange relationship; I suppose I was still hoping to find a story-book Daddy every time I saw him, and being sadly disappointed. Of course he hadn't a clue how little girls' daddies were expected to behave, and in consequence, was awkward and brusque. It is not surprising that fathers and daughters who do not ever live together cannot deal with the relationship; they have no previous experience on which to draw. Nor is it surprising to me that women who do not have a father or surrogate during their formative years appear to have a somewhat exaggerated interest in men when they mature, or even before, because they have been so starved of male attention.

In part explanation of my relationship with my father, let me tell about my experience one Christmas when, tired after a hectic term, I arrived to stay with him, laden with a home-made cake and pudding, a box of cigars and a large bottle of his favourite whisky. I cooked a complete Christmas dinner, of which I was quite proud. After surveying the table, my father said, "Where's the wine? Christmas dinner's no good without wine." So off I rushed to the pub to buy some. Every visit was marred by a similar put-down. I don't think he was conscious of this – it was just the way he was. He had been totally spoiled by women all his life, starting with his mother and ending, I suppose, with me…

When I arrived for his funeral, the hospital allowed me to stay in the old nurses' home which was so old, it was awaiting demolition, and my room faced the mortuary in which my father's body lay. I was the only inhabitant in the building which had accommodated sixty, and it was a quite horrifying night. I just lay sleepless, listening to every noise, imagining all sorts of terrifying apparitions. I was the only mourner at the funeral which took place in Stoke, an hour away from the hospital at Stone. Sitting alone behind the coffin brought back memories of Ron's funeral, and I struggled all the while to keep myself from disintegrating completely. My father left his house, his money and effects to the Royal National Institute for the Blind.

Meanwhile at school, plans were going ahead to amalgamate Westlain with Stanmer Secondary School, about a quarter of a mile down the drive which linked the two buildings. The actual merger was planned for September 1973. During the long summer holiday, I went on a course about the integration of two separate institutions, and became aware of what a very complicated exercise lay ahead. I wrote a précis of all this and submitted it to the Head, but I suppose it was all too late, as it was ignored. No one seemed to know what they were doing; the only preparations made for such a gigantic change were purely mechanical and material, like making certain classrooms larger and widening the doors. When all the children arrived on the first day of term, it was absolute chaos, bodies hurtling all over the place, and bewildered staff either standing marooned and swearing at the pupils or shouting hysterically at mobs of people who, because they didn't know what they were supposed to be doing, were making the most of the situation and behaving like lunatics. St Trinian's had nothing on us that first day of comprehension at Falmer High School.

My beautifully decorated and appointed home economics room was overrun by thirty bodies at a time who, if they had come over in the rain from the other building, were wet, bedraggled, dirty and smelly. There was a fashion at that time amongst the young for a particularly shabby long-haired fake fur which gave off a most offensive odour when wet. And since no extra cloakroom facilities had been made for these extra pupils, they piled these horrible wet coats on the well polished furniture in the elegant flat. I was devastated by the whole nightmare scenario. All my symptoms of stress returned in spades and I felt I was on the edge of a nervous breakdown. I was still counselling, and there was only one other counsellor for a school of 2,000 pupils and their parents. 'I can't go on' indeed, but this time it wasn't comic.

There were a couple of bright spots in the overall gloom. There was a group of eight 15-year-old boys, supposedly unteachable, and capable of wrecking, literally and metaphorically, any class of which they were a potentially explosive part. Still fired with counselling zeal, I elected to have these boys every Wednesday afternoon to teach them some cookery – and it worked. I would put on full make-up and a sparkling white coat, and together we made lots of 'comfort food' like steak-and-kidney pudding, apple pie, chocolate cake, fish and chips, hamburgers, etc. At the end of the afternoon, we would sit down together and eat, so learning a few social graces. They were quite Neanderthal in appearance and communicated mainly by grunting. After each session, they were also covered from head to foot in flour. However, we made progress and by the end of term, we had a deep and caring respect for one another. Is there such a thing as a really evil child? I wonder.

I recall one memorable afternoon when they were dipped in their usual coating of flour and the odd pellet of margarine, one of the masters from the other building burst in, seized one of them by the ear, and proceeded to manhandle him out of the room. By the door was a very heavy fire extinguisher on a bracket which this boy managed to lift off and swing at his persecutor. It rolled away down the room and the boy ran away, leaving the rest of us skipping like the high hills, to avoid having our toes mangled. I often think of those boys with affection and gratitude, for they taught me the valuable lesson of not always judging by appearances – and that if you really take the trouble to listen to someone, your whole perception of them alters.

The other bright spot was a discussion group which I ran for an equally 'unteachable' group of 14-year-old girls, all extremely aggressive, foul-mouthed, unhygienic and defensive. One of these was an embryonic harridan: brassy hair, no front teeth, the remaining ones black with nicotine, and a reputation of being the school 'cert', this epithet having nothing to do with examination success. Let us call her Mary. I thought I was wasting my time in a big way until one afternoon we touched on the subject of abortion, and it was as if I had let off a firework in Mary's brain. She went ballistic and became subsequently a fervent supporter of the Society for the Protection of the Unborn Child. When I visited Brighton in 1992, I ran into Mary who greeted me like a long-lost friend. I didn't recognise her; gone were the ghastly hair and unsavoury teeth – and in their place was a wholesome-looking, well-groomed young woman pushing an extremely healthy-looking child who positively shone with cleanliness. Once again I ask, is there really such a thing as a thoroughly evil child, completely beyond redemption? I don't know.

During the autumn and spring terms, many of the previous Westlain staff left, driven out by the ever-increasing chaos. I felt that someone should create an atmosphere in which these children could be taught, at least the rudiments of education, and decided in a rather sickeningly pious way to remain. But it proved to be a Canute-like task, as I was constantly overwhelmed by feelings of inadequacy and despair. But now there were no sympathetic colleagues in the corridor joining in the hilarious cries of 'I can't go on' to relieve the tension – only unfamiliar faces as white and strained as my own.

There was no social life outside school either. All my friends on the staff had left Brighton and moved fifty or more miles away. And I was too exhausted to make any effort to make new contacts. Life was grim indeed. I proceeded to get more and more nervously exhausted. I was tearful, irritable, sleepless, had a permanent headache and constant indigestion, but still deluded myself that I was an essential ingredient of the whole sorry mess.

However, a crisis was looming – as it usually does in any apparent impasse – which would blow me out of the water. In early May, I was looking forward to some free time in which to prepare the ingredients for a practical A Level exam. To my extreme irritation, I found I had to go across to the other building and sit with a class whose teacher was ill. Having no time for my coffee break, I set off in the wind and the rain and a filthy temper, only to be shouted at by four 12-year-old harpies under an umbrella. The gist of their four-letter-word instructions was the performance of various impossible physical feats, and since I did not even know these girls, I just couldn't understand their vicious animosity. I was so incredulous, I went towards them and asked them to repeat what they had said, which they did, with added embellishments. All the frustration, sadness, anger and pain of the last eight months rose in an uncontrollable wave, and collapsing my umbrella into a very formidable truncheon, I went for them, thereby losing more dignity and self-respect, as of course they quickly outdistanced me, and eventually withdrew to a safe distance, shouting further obscenities. I arrived at the other building wet, cold and bedraggled, to find thirty large boys shouting and pushing each other, some with their feet on the desks and smoking. Restoring order with difficulty, and the prospect of an imminent stroke, I asked them to get out their books to do the work that had been set for them. They quickly disabused me of any hopes I had of at least sitting quietly for fifty minutes, and calming my shattered nerves. "We ain't got no books," they said, "And we don't do nothing anyway." These were boys compelled to stay at school for an extra year, due to the raising of the school-leaving age, so understandably, they were considerably miffed. I checked with the school office to ask for paper and pencils, and was told, "Sorry, no – there's an economy drive on." So I tripped back and spent the rest of the lesson getting them to look for job opportunities in copies of the local paper which I had taken with me. I then asked them to imagine they were telephoning about the jobs or writing for an interview. (There were plenty of jobs in those days for school-leavers.) This worked up to a point, but gave rise to much muttering about, 'If I've got to apply for a job which I could get now, why the hell can't I leave and get it?' – revealing a certain amount of logic it's true! In my mind, I was asking the same question.

After this hour of terrible torture I was beside myself, and on returning to my own building I stormed into the Head's office and graphically repeated my story. I remember I wrote the swear words down as I couldn't bring myself to repeat them! What comparatively innocent days they were, and yet at the time they seemed apocalyptic. The Head was smoking his pipe, and reading The Times, very relaxed and insulated. He fixed me with a benign, avuncular gaze and said, "There, there! Let's not get this episode out of proportion," called me an old reactionary, and in general seemed surprised at my incandescent rage. "After all, it's only words – ha! ha!," he said.

So far as I was concerned however, I was out of there and gave in my notice to take effect at the end of August 1974. It was a good thing that I was so angry, as it stopped me worrying. After all, I had given up a secure, well-paid job, six years away from retirement – for what? I didn't know; all I knew was that there would be ten times more dignity and self-respect in scrubbing floors, than in subjecting myself to such vile abuse from 12- and 15-year-olds in a situation which showed little hope of improving; in fact, it seemed to be deteriorating rapidly by the day. I was reminded constantly of Kipling's If:

> If you can watch the things you gave your life to broken
> And stoop and build them up with worn-out tools ...

And:

If you can make one heap of all your winnings
And risk it on one last turn of pitch-and-toss,
And lose, and start again at your beginnings
And never breathe a word about your loss.
If you can force your heart, and nerve, and sinew
To serve your turn long after they are gone;
And so hold on when there is nothing in you
Except the will which says to them, Hold on.

That line has always made me smile; I get a vivid picture of a Kiplingesque figure clad in pith helmet, long khaki shorts and knee-socks, holding a flagpole with a tattered Union Jack, uttering the words, 'Hold on' in over-dramatised tones. Thank God for a sense of humour; it is an invaluable possession at any time, particularly in adversity, where it can literally make the difference between life and death.

I had frequent severe bouts of panic so that my symptoms of nervous exhaustion were acute, but the rest of the term was bearable because I knew it was coming to an end. I dreaded my last day and the unavoidable farewells, until a wise colleague pointed out that I was not leaving Westlain. Westlain had left me twelve months previously. And so it was! The two laboratory assistants, who were great friends of mine, took me down to The Hiker's Rest at lunchtime and poured sufficient whisky into me to induce a pleasant state of euphoria, and I sailed through the speeches at the following party without a single tear. All I felt was relief.

Chapter 14

My personal angel had been hard at work in the meantime, and I had been offered a job at Brighton Sixth Form College, teaching A Level part-time, so any fears of destitution had been laid to rest. I was also offered 2½ days a week as a teacher of Home Economics in a very pleasant comprehensive school on the outskirts of the town. There was already an established head of department and a full-time teacher, so I was right back on the lowest rung of the ladder with no say in the curriculum – which seemed to me to be uninspiring. Things were done entirely by the book and there was no discussion of the relevance of what we were doing – like testing out the new convenience foods which were beginning to flood the supermarkets.

It was a limbo time, incredibly dreary and very hard to endure. I didn't want to get up in the mornings, the school was a long way from where I lived, involving a difficult, complicated bus journey, and there never seemed to be any point in going there anyway. I knew I was being an incredibly bad teacher but I was paralysed by the whole situation, and my inevitable comparison of this job with Westlain made it almost unbearable. However, nothing could ever be as bad as the grief I suffered over my husband, so I soldiered on. Looking back, I suppose I have always been hopeful at heart, knowing that every bad time will eventually pass and life will improve. That optimism has now blossomed into a certain detachment from the world and its pain, in the sense that it's all a dream anyway – shifting into nightmare from time to time admittedly, but still a dream.

Life may be full of pain, suffering and difficulty, but in fact, all these are opportunities given to us to learn. It is only when we hang on to a situation, a person, a job, health, wealth, etc. that we shut off the possibility of this learning from change. If we shut off this possibility by clutching desperately at each apparently permanent solution to our problems, we will become closed to any real progress. Because impermanence spells anguish and terror, we are terrified to let go of any apparent solution to our problems; but learning to live is learning to let go. This is the tragic irony of our lives – the struggle to hold on brings us the very pain we are trying to avoid. There is nothing wrong in trying to be happy, but the situation we are trying to hold onto is by, its very nature, short-lived, and everything, good and bad, does pass. I of course was unaware of any of this at the time, but now look back and see how important it was in the gradual growth of my spiritual awareness.

After nine months of this incredibly dreary existence, I was asked to take on a group of sixth-form boys in their last year at school, and work out with them a twelve-week course to prepare them for leaving home and living in university or college accommodation, or perhaps a small flat or bed-sit. This was like a draught of sparkling water, given to a man dying of thirst in the desert. It was not only something innovative, but was left entirely to me to organise and carry out. So the tide began, imperceptibly, to turn again. We used to meet in the sitting room of a Home Economics practice house on Tuesday afternoons. I felt rather like the female equivalent of Old King Solomon when he was packed round with virgins! Their youthful enthusiasm, not to mention their exuberant masculinity, acted like an elixir to my dragging spirits, and I began to do my Phoenix-rising impersonation once more.

It was great fun, as well as being a great teaching experience. I taught them how to cook cheap, nutritious meals on a gas ring, to keep their clothes at least clean, if not well pressed, to sew on buttons and replace zips. I also called in various experts to talk with them on their particular area of expertise. We had a consultant on sexually transmitted diseases, someone from a building society, and someone from social services to discuss matters appertaining particularly to students. We had a bank manager and a solicitor, to talk to them about the law and the way it affects students. We had someone from the police, we made a visit to Sussex University and talked to the Union President, and we also covered many other areas of concerns of theirs. We also had many discussions on spiritual matters, relationships, their own personal fears in general, and about leaving home in particular, so it gradually became a counselling group which I like to think offered them some security and solace. For the first time since I left Westlain, I felt I was doing something useful.

A year later, this boys' school became a sixth form college, and girls were admitted. This meant some A Level Home Economics classes were added, which were small and quite delightful, although the girls resented being made to work hard, and I felt a certain amount of unaccustomed resentment coming my way. Having never experienced this before, except in the odd rebellious teenager, I was quite hurt and, due to my own psychological problems, didn't deal with it very well. However, when I told them in June 1978 that I was taking early retirement, and leaving at the end of term, their reaction was totally unexpected, even to the extent of tears! I expressed my surprise, and one girl said, "We really liked it that you never came to college in trousers!" (Remember this was in the seventies.) That really amazed me; their reasoning was, 'We don't want teachers to look like us – we want a barrier between us and you' – presumably to grumble about and kick against: the 'us and them' syndrome which obviously helps make youngsters feel secure.

So 1974 to 1978 were difficult years. Besides the strain of the uncoordinated teaching posts, the situation at home which had been so nurturing and secure since 1957, was beginning to deteriorate. Jane and Frida were beginning to show the inexorable signs of age. Jane, whose cerebral palsy was worsening, was left with the business side of the flatlet house when her brother-in-law died. Frida had always been the archetypal, charming, but totally dependent female of the upper class Victorian family: decorative and well-versed in the social niceties, but totally dependent in a material crisis. She was also beginning to suffer from glaucoma so the mantle of caring for both of them fell upon me. I would be at the sixth form college or the comprehensive school all day, sometimes take a yoga class in the evening, and arrive home to find Jane waiting in floods of tears, simply because the window-cleaner hadn't come – the ultimate tragedy on Jane's Richter scale of disaster!

Chapter 15

Once again, the fragile foundations of my life were shifting; if only I had known then what I know now! That nothing ever can last anyway – impermanence is the very nature of things. My stress symptoms returned in spades, tremendous difficulty in getting up in the morning, close to tears most of the time, what felt like a hole in my middle, sweating at the slightest demand made upon me, palpitations, insomnia, indigestion et al. One of the biggest problems with stress is that we are so bowled over by it when it first strikes, we disintegrate, and in that disintegration seem quite unable to let the first shock pass and then do something about it, like Dr Weekes' formula of Face – Accept – Float – and let time pass (as mentioned in her book). This little axiom never really fails if only we can do the exercise over and over again. I repeat: we must let the first shock pass. I knew about the Weekes exercise, having used it to such good effect when Westlain went comprehensive. But I drowned myself in the feeling generated by the onset of this further fit of nervous exhaustion.

I had taken early retirement that year and felt I had been cast adrift in a stormy ocean with no means of propulsion, entirely at the mercy of winds and tides. Looking back at these nightmare years, I wonder how I carried on, but when there is no one else to turn to, you either carry on or you disintegrate into nervous illness or suicide. I used to pass a hospital for nervously ill people every day, and the sight of these sad, pale people, wandering aimlessly around the garden in a state of drugged torpor always produced a strong reaction in me, and I would repeat in time with my footsteps, 'I will never go in there, I will never go in there, etc. etc.' Thus was born a steely determination right in the pit of my stomach, of which I am always immediately aware now when the going gets tough.

The spiritual help that I now believe was always there was at work all the time. One day, I walked into the house in Walsingham Road and met another tenant carrying a copy of The Brighton & Hove Argus which he passed on to me. Riffling through it in a fairly disinterested way, I saw an advertisement for a meeting of the Unity School of Christianity which gave a welcome to everyone of any faith. I forget the actual title of the talk – it was about life in general and faith in particular – but not just one limited narrow creed. I was reminded of Mervyn Stockwood's autobiography in which he quotes from A.J. Balfour: 'Our highest truths are but half-truths. Think not to settle down for ever in any truth: make use of it as a tent in which to pass a summer's night. But build no house in it, or it will be your tomb. When you first have an inkling of its insufficiency and begin to descry a dim counter-truth coming up beyond, then weep not but give thanks. It is the Lord's voice whispering, "Take up thy bed and walk."'

That meeting at Unity was a milestone in my life, a significant step along the road towards wholeness, or recognising and understanding my relationship with God. And if you want to know what I mean by 'God', I would define 'it' as 'a deep awareness of a benevolent non-physical power which appears to be partly or wholly beyond, and far greater than, the individual self'. This is a quotation from Alistair Hardy who is a zoologist and a founder of the Oxford Religious Experience Research Unit.

The people at the Unity meeting were a shining example of how to welcome a stranger in your midst. So many established groups take no notice of the newcomer beyond the first cursory greeting, and I am sure they have no idea of the hurt they inflict by such apparent rejection. I was reminded vividly of a Scottish dancing group at Shoreham which I attended shortly after Ron died. I had made an enormous effort just to get there, and stood inside the door feeling embarrassed, lonely and somewhat ridiculous. No one spoke to me for two hours! I wanted to run away, but decided that, surely, someone would speak to me. But they didn't. It is difficult to describe the raw loneliness and pain of that evening, so that the loving friendship of that Unity group was like healing balm on a festering wound. Unity is American in origin, and at that time the minister was in America being ordained. He was away for two years, so this friendly little group had no perceived authority figure; maybe that was why it worked so well. There was some jockeying for position, but as the group was so small – about 16-20 people – the friendliness overcame any potential ego trips. There was an outstanding couple called Grace and Fred Frost who organised the meeting. They became great friends of mine, supporting me through the frequent dark nights of the soul I was still experiencing with depressing regularity. But through the talks at Unity on Friday evenings, I began to perceive dimly there was something beyond human experience, something transcendent, beyond speech and intellect that is the ultimate illumination.

I first sensed this illumination way back when I was about 18. I was enjoying one of my much-prized holiday visits to Cropston and had gone for a walk through the fields by a natural reservoir. I sat on a stile; it was high summer – swans stretched their necks in stately flight over my head, waterfowl dipped and chugged, and the golden fields of August stretched away to the horizon. Over it all hung the sky, enveloping the whole scene and me in a new sense of awareness. I sat on my stile, and felt immeasurably happy and strong. Everything seemed warm and wonderful; I felt as if I'd been suddenly set down in Paradise. But these moments of insight come and go. Being young and much more interested in worldly things like clothes and men at that time, I did not pursue it. Unity, however, revived the memory and made me realise that the mystery of the universe and ourselves has to be experienced rather than studied, and this is where the difficulties begin, because we cannot define the meaning of life with reason and intellect.

At this time, I was also beginning to experience the benefits of yoga. I was attending James's group every week. The stiffness and pain in my back had practically disappeared; together with the correct food, I was improving by leaps and bounds. This was the moment when the fourth beneficial influence entered my life – the practice of meditation. After the yoga class, James used to light a candle and asked anyone who would stay behind to join him in meditation. Most of them left, being young and interested in a good time, I suppose; they had more exciting things on their mind. I used to stay because I felt he deserved some support after working so hard on our behalf. There was also one other student who was as dedicated to yoga as he was. We three used to sit cross-legged around this candle in the dark while he read from some obscure Hindu philosophy to us. I used to look surreptitiously at my watch and willed the hands to reach the hour of our release. It really didn't grab me at all. However, during those dark days of the late seventies, I reached a point where I was desperate for some kind of reassurance.

I walked into my flat one day after a desolate walk along the seafront and felt the terrible hopelessness which threatens total disintegration. In this blackness, I remembered the candle flame and also the Daily Word booklet issued by Unity which had some uplifting and reassuring messages within its pages. So I drew the curtains, lit a candle, intoning one of the Unity paragraphs to myself, and sat gazing at the flame, hoping to enter an entirely different plane of existence where all was peace and love. I was disappointed! Instead of the beautiful peace and oneness I now experience in meditation, I nearly went mad! My thoughts raced round in a mad jumble, I thought my head would burst, and really feared I was losing my reason. I drew back the curtain hastily and blew out the candle, feeling worse than I had felt before, not realising that this was par for the course at the beginning of meditation. I was tempted to forget the whole thing, but something greater than my will encouraged me to sit for just five minutes every morning when I first awoke. Mornings have always been a bad time for me; I nearly always wake with a feeling of foreboding as if something dreadful is going to happen as soon as I become fully conscious. I now recognise this as a symptom of nervous fatigue, and through working with Dr Weekes' suggestions over many years, do experience the occasional optimistic awakening and know how to deal with the bad ones in a satisfactory way.

I continued to attend the Unity meeting every Friday evening, and through this contact became aware of the works of Joel Goldsmith, a modern mystic whose books have been very helpful to me. In his book The Infinite Way, he says: "We are reminded in this book that the great power necessary to dispel the erroneous conditions which surround us must be sought within ourselves, and we are shown how it may be accomplished. We are seeking as never before that which will free us from the fears, anxieties and dangers of material living. We know that whatever it is that will give us mental rest and spiritual peace does not lie in the realm of human thought. We live under the illusion that material forces and human will are great powers, until we learn that within our own being there is a spiritual power which dispels this illusion. There is a 'Peace, be still' within our own consciousness which will still every storm in our experience, heal our diseases, lift us above the strife and weariness of human existence.

Our part is to recognise its presence within ourselves and let it fulfil its mission. This universal power of truth, life and love is ours, regardless of which church we attend, or not, or what philosophy we follow, but abides at the centre of every individual, saint or sinner, awaiting only our recognition."

Looking back, I see clearly now how this presence, this power of truth, life and love which had always been there, was beginning to make itself known to me, and was to grow into the invincible spiritual awareness which now orders my life and in which I now experience a general calm abiding. Of course, there are occasional descents into the darkness, but like the emotional remedies I use, I have my spiritual ones as well.

Also through Unity, I heard about The Seekers' Trust, a centre for prayer and spiritual healing, situated in the village of Addington in Kent. I contacted them and had my name put on their prayer list which at certain times was read out in their healing prayer circles. This practice of sitting still and quiet and with them in spirit, while saying the same prayers for healing was a significant step forward for me on my own path towards awareness. I was still training as a psychotherapist and counsellor and as my own deep psychological wounds began to heal, my ability to comfort and console became apparent and people began to ask me to counsel them. Although I was heartbroken many times over, I would never have survived if I had not been sternly practical and 'got on with it', as it were. So I tried to communicate this to people and they responded.

One woman said to me, "I have been seeing various therapists for two years, and all I am told is that my parents didn't want me, and I was left to the maids. No one has ever suggested anything *I* could do except take tranquillisers which by now are just spoiling the quality of my life." I began to realise dimly that this is the purpose of the bad things that happen – pain makes us ready to learn, and if we are wise, that is what we do. We feel a strong sense of compassion and love for people who are ill and in trouble. We learn humility and feel an inner strength which surprises us. Freda Naylor, a doctor who kept a diary as she died of cancer, says: "I have had to stop in my tracks, reassess and proceed. If we can reassess and proceed with these feelings, we are much more open to spiritual practice and true healing." I am sure many of you will be asking the inevitable question, 'If there is a Presence, a power, who does take care of us, why did this woman have cancer in the first place?' I will leave the answer to this for the section on spiritual awareness, which is a more appropriate place.

I had pursued my interest in The Seekers' Trust at Addington, and sometimes they had seminars on Saturdays on many diverse spiritual subjects – on out-of-body experiences, the meaning of dreams, the power of prayer, yin and yang, holistic healing, yoga, tai chi, shiatsu, meditation, reincarnation, et al. There I met Sir George Trevelyan, a true Gandalph-like mystic looking like an elderly angel and who spoke literally with the tongues of men and of angels. I remember at one seminar he shared the platform with a shining young professor of physics when they both set out to prove that all creation was actually light. So, although apparently coming from totally different standpoints (the purely physical as opposed to the metaphysical), they were agreed on the basic premise.

This was exciting stuff, and I decided to go and stay for a fortnight, to consider the possibility of joining the group permanently. There were about 28 residents, living in very pleasant flats or small bungalows. Visitors rented a smaller version of the bungalows, consisting of a bed-sitting room with curtained-off kitchen and a bathroom. These were ranged in a circle round a green space, in the middle of which was a magnificent Indian bean tree. What had been the stables of the original stately home had been converted into small chapels which fronted onto a most beautiful garden of remembrance. Members and friends were able to buy rosebushes, in memory of loved ones, which were planted in the garden. The atmosphere of peace and otherworldliness in that garden was indescribable, and I spent many restorative hours there, gazing at the roses and the trees, watching the cows and listening to the birds, and feeling my wounded spirit becoming whole again. I felt as if at any moment, I would lift my eyes and see some beautiful Presence walking in the garden. I used to walk for miles along the Kentish lanes and fields, stopping for lunch at some country inn, and falling into bed exhausted at the end of the day.

There was no TV, and it made me realise how much of a drug it had become for me. Sometimes at the Seekers, in spite of the radio and the many books I had, I would experience a sudden feeling of panic when it seemed I was the only person left in the world, and all my old fears would return. I also experienced some vivid, unpleasant dreams – all to do with loss, loneliness and persecution.

A very interesting episode happened at one of the seminars; a woman was speaking about the significance of dreams and how much we can learn from them. At the end, I asked her about a recurring dream I had in which I was frantically trying to get through a hole of some kind to the other side, but always stuck halfway and woke sweating with fear, and with my heart really racing. She said she thought it was a past-life experience, and would I go to see her at her home in Wembley. This I did; she went into a trance and after apparently communicating with some sort of spiritual guide, told me of an experience that had caused great trauma for me in a previous incarnation. She explained that I had been one of an aristocratic family during the French Revolution. When the revolutionaries arrived I had to be hidden in a hole in the yard, where there was a half-window which I had tried to get out of. She suggested that I was still experiencing this in the dream state. I make it a rule never to scoff, for after all, how little we really know or understand, but the main feelings I took back with me to Hove were scepticism and an amused superiority. 'Very likely!' I thought. However, I have never once had that dream since. 'More things in heaven and on earth'? It seems so.

I owe a great deal to The Seekers; staying there for a few weeks at a time gave me the opportunity to reflect on my life, and during these reflections to come to terms with the demons that still plagued me from time to time. The prayer circles, each consisting of six people, took place every half-hour throughout the day. The leader of the circle had a list of names, taken from the hundreds of people all over the world who had written to them asking for help. The six met first for a period of quiet, then filed silently into one of the small chapels to seat themselves round a central altar. Simple prayers for healing were said, the names read out, and a period of silent intercession ensued. I found the experience quite uncomfortable at first, particularly the silence. For the first time, I realised what a seething mass of thoughts were whirling around my head and how uncontrollable they seemed to be. This was the start of true meditation, of course, of which I was at that time so very unaware.

There were many dear people living and working at The Seekers whom I grew to know and love deeply. I owe much to their patient devoted instruction. Eventually, they asked me if I would join them and I thought seriously about making such a move. At that time, I was dimly aware of my own intuition which had been growing during my practice of yoga, and something within that intuition was uttering a very firm No. It is interesting to observe how a course of action often seems absolutely right in the conscious mind but on quiet reflection proves to be quite wrong. I have trusted my intuition (or gut feeling, if you like) for many years now, and it has never let me down.

It was at The Seekers that I experienced my own miracle. One frequently hears of miraculous so-called 'healings' but in most people's minds there is nearly always a sneaky feeling of disbelief. The mind which sometimes presumes to believe there is no such thing as a miracle is, after all, itself a miracle. My own healing miracle occurred one hot summer's day in June 1984 at a dedication ceremony at The Seekers. A mulberry tree, and the carved stone seat beneath it, were being consecrated. I had a very painful right hip joint which had been found to be so severely eroded by arthritis that I had been put on the list for a hip replacement. Attendance at the ceremony was by invitation only, so I felt I must go, but on the train from Brighton to Victoria, I was in such agony from the lance-like pain shooting violently down my right leg, I decided to turn round and head straight home as soon as the train stopped. Painfully, I descended, but I was overcome by a severe attack of the 'oughts' and 'shoulds', and so continued on my journey to Addington, hobbling and sweating with pain.

Once there – there were fifty of us – we assembled in the main hall for a short address by the group leader, after which we went outside and formed a circle around the tree and the bench. My hip and leg were still excruciatingly painful and I found it difficult to still my mind and feel the sense of at-one-ment necessary to feel compassion, healing and peace. After a few general prayers, our spokesperson asked us to come forward in fours, sit on the seat and send out our own silent requests to the Infinite for the healing of those who would come after us to sit on the seat under the tree and ask to be made whole again. When my turn came, I sat, and felt an overwhelming peace of body, mind and spirit. I felt as if I were expanding into immeasurable space, passing beyond all body. We returned to the hall for further general prayers of dedication, and I suddenly realised that my hip was entirely free from pain, and I was using my leg freely and unrestrictedly.

I notified the hospital on my return and they took further X-rays which showed that the bone was completely restored without a trace of arthritis remaining. Their explanation was that there had been a mix-up of the X-rays, but I think I knew better! Of course, there are spontaneous remissions, and disease does sometimes cease of its own accord, but this complete and dramatic change, together with the transcendent feeling I experienced on the seat in the garden seems to me to have been miraculous. Maybe it was because I stopped thinking exclusively about myself and my own pain for a time, and was willing to extend my consciousness to encompass the rest of humanity in the humility of love. If only I could step outside myself more often – if only we all could – what a Paradise this world would be!

Chapter 16

In the meantime, I made a significant step forwards. The principal of the local adult education college wrote to ask if I would be willing to replace a yoga teacher who was leaving unexpectedly. The reasoning was, that I was a qualified teacher and practised yoga myself – ergo, I was a yoga teacher, which of course ain't necessarily so. There's a bit of difference between home economics and yoga! I was terrified, but also attracted by the idea of doing yoga and teaching at the same time, as this was a combination of my two favourite activities, so with great trepidation, I asked if I could sit in on a class before making up my mind.

The evening class was held in a gym at a rather chilly primary school, but I was not just shivering with cold. However, the teaching was so uncaring I knew for certain that I could not do worse! The teacher, clad in heavy shoes, thick trousers and an enormous jumper and anorak, sat on the piano stool with a sheet of paper in her hand. Eighteen poor students in leotards and tights sat frozen on the floor, each with a duplicate sheet of paper by their sides. The teacher called out numbers from the sheet which the students tried to identify. Apparently, each number represented a yoga pose. But only a few knew how to execute them. After all, what do the cow head, cobra, locust, lion and gas ejection poses mean, for heaven's sake, to the uninitiated?! There was no breathing work done at all, which I think is an essential part of any yoga session. And after three quarters of an hour of uneasy shuffling about on the floor, the teacher bellowed, 'Corpse pose', departed at speed to light up a cigarette, and could be heard coughing in a terminal sort of way for the next twenty minutes. Not a very suitable accompaniment to the corpse pose, I felt!

I had no more doubts about my own ability to take the class; I knew I couldn't be worse and might even be a tad better. So began some of the happiest and most fulfilling times of my life, teaching yoga. Before the first class, I was terrified, and all my symptoms of nervous tension returned in spades – the dry mouth, sweating, a churning stomach, trembling hands, weak muscles, etc. However, after about ten minutes, I suddenly realised how competent I felt and how very much I was enjoying myself. There is nothing more rewarding than teaching a subject you love to a group of very interested people who are equally eager to learn. At the end, instead of shouting 'corpse pose' and rushing off to cough, I tucked them up individually in extra blankets and they were mine. So began many years of fulfilment from teaching yoga, which is still my favourite activity.

Among the great things that yoga does, if it is well taught, is to nurture people on all levels of being. As the body is soothed and relaxed by the physical process, the mind becomes able to sort out its problems, and many emotions can surface, sometimes causing tears and sobbing, and sometimes giggling and hysterical laughter. This is why classes should be small, so that the teacher is able to comfort and reassure on an individual level.

One night, about six weeks after my first encounter with the class, a woman who had always lurked at the back of the hall, waited until everyone had gone, before coming up to me and saying, "I don't know why but I feel that you could help me." So we met and it seemed she had a son who was suffering terribly from mental problems. He had been ejected from hospital as a hopeless case, and he was going out at night trying desperately to steal drugs from pharmacies. She and his wife were also going out, trying to find him and bring him home. It was a sad story, with nothing but blind alleys and apparently no real help from anyone. I told her that I would be more than willing to see her son, but it was another four years before he finally appeared, and we were able to do some useful work together. In the meantime, I was able to support his mother and his wife. When he finally came, I left my street door open and sat at the table, apparently writing but watching out of the corner of my eye. And finally a sad, defeated but incredibly handsome young man walked hesitantly back and forth outside for about ten minutes before he finally entered. He was trembling violently, looked pale and haunted, and my heart dissolved in compassion for him. After a difficult beginning, we were finally able to work together, to resolve some small part of his problems, and I grew to love and respect him for the effort he was making to sort out his life.

We started by using his pride in his remarkable physique, cultivating a respect for his body, and he began to swim regularly. Unfortunately, later on he developed some trouble in his back which made it impossible for him to continue his regular swimming. But he still fights on manfully to maintain some semblance of bearable existence. I am still in contact with him but not able to do as much for him as I would like, now that I am so many miles away.

This episode, arising from the yoga class, was the first of many such encounters along the way with troubled souls desperate for help, and I realised that it was not meant that I should seek out people to help, but that they would seek me. Now that I meditate a great deal, I receive a considerable amount of enlightenment to do with people in need, and have incorporated a form of absent healing into my meditations which does seem to help considerably. I receive tremendous insights into the causes of patients' problems and, not least, into my own. For instance, in a recent flare-up of arthritis in my hands, I kept seeing a picture of a wax bath on my closed eyelids. As a result, I was able through my doctor to have this particular treatment at my local hospital, and it eased the condition quite quickly.

Chapter 17

In 1979, Jane became incapable of looking after herself, and Frida was losing her sight, so the final decision to sell the house was taken. I found a nursing home for Jane and a small genteel hotel for Frida. For myself, I decided to move into a small hotel in Hove which took permanent guests during the winter. It was a sad, sad day in January when we went our separate ways, and my heart felt near to breaking as I arrived at my own particular destination – which was in a row of similar establishments in one of many typical, slightly rundown roads leading to the sea. I stood in my room, surrounded by cases and boxes, and surveyed my domain. It felt like yet another bereavement along my road.

However, I had been brought up on tales of heroes donning dinner jackets in the depths of the jungle, surrounded by salivating savages, and the received message was that one always changes for dinner, no matter what. Hadn't my own grandmother told tales of breaking ice on the water in which she washed herself before changing into some off-the-shoulder flimsy frock in which to shiver or roast, depending how near she was to the fire? So, feeling like a principal character in Separate Tables, I donned a bright flowered skirt, a smart black top and high-heeled shoes. Clutching my hand bag like a lifeline, I descended to the dining room, expecting to be met by bright lights and animated conversation. Not so! The dining room was in a basement, and the only other people present were an old man in trousers like elephant's legs and a stained pullover, and a woman in her sixties who looked rather like a bag lady in a pair of old, decrepit carpet slippers with dirty fur cuffs. They acknowledged my presence with little enthusiasm, and resumed their conversation – which consisted of a total condemnation of Hove Town Council, the government, the weather, the young, the social services, the bus service – in fact, the planet in general, and Hove in particular. As I ate my meal, my gloom deepened, and retreating back to my room, I thanked God for the television which I had brought with me. Having only a portable aerial, all the programmes looked as if they were taking place in a snowstorm. But I was so grateful for its hypnotic power to transport my mind away from personal problems into temporary forgetfulness.

With what was then my abysmal lack of self-esteem, I was convinced that the proprietress disliked me intensely, and crept around the place, trying to make myself as unobtrusive as possible. I frequently walked around outside in gales and torrents of rain so that I needn't go in. The year, 1980, moved on, and I spent much of my time visiting Jane and Frida in their separate abodes.

Jane was at first quite delirious with joy in hers; she was well looked after and receiving much more attention than she had ever had in her life. Before this time, she had always been dependent on people to look after her who didn't particularly want to, but now, at £250 a week – which was a good deal then – she was entitled to the dedicated care of people who were paid a salary, albeit small, and who could look forward to going home at the end of their shift, leaving their dedication behind. No one should be condemned to permanent caring, however much they love the object of their devotion.

Frida, on the other hand, was not happy; every time I met her, she moaned in a querulous, mumbling sort of way – which, being incoherent, was doubly difficult to endure. She had been allowed to take her dog with her, and the proprietor of her hotel went out of his way to be kind and helpful. But, as they say, people don't so much get old as just get more so. And she was becoming more dissatisfied by the day. She still maintained her smart appearance but found the modern clothes shops hard to bear, with their musak, their communal changing rooms, their racks of clothes and pert assistants who acted as if no one over 30 should have the right to be there! I remember one classic occasion when she ripped off the skirt she was trying on and stamped on it in a fit of anger and frustration. I think she found it impossible to come to terms with the ageing process. She had been a real beauty: slim, with red hair, huge violet eyes, a radiant complexion, and the prettiest nose I ever saw. It is sad to see such beauty crumble away as age takes its toll. I used to prattle on about inner beauty and character being more important than looks, but now the same thing is happening to me, I'm not quite so philosophical! It takes a real saint not to mind about the old lady in the mirror who has somehow surreptitiously taken your place.

The one bright spot in my life during this slough of despond was my yoga class. I had met a gloriously handsome West Indian at Tyringham the previous Christmas who was studying psychology at the Open University, so we had a common interest. He lived in London but decided to join my yoga class and travel down to Hove every Tuesday evening. One Tuesday I had the whole class upside down in a shoulder stand, when John collapsed out of it, emitting one of the most ear-splitting farts I have ever heard in my life! He just lay there in a totally unconcerned way whilst I struggled desperately to contain my hysteria.

I have always found emissions of wind from the anus (as the dictionary has it) hugely amusing, and been incapable of any reaction other than convulsions of mirth. As with many established patterns of behaviour, this reaction has its origins in my childhood. Uncle Tom was a grand master of the art and, on hearing classical music, was wont to say, "I could make a better noise with my arse." And in some cases, this was very true! Well, there I was with twelve assorted females in front of me expressing very different emotions, the more prim among them looking shocked and self-righteous, and those whom I regarded as my mates, struggling with varying degrees of hysteria. By then of course, everyone had collapsed out of the shoulder stand and I had to go back to the front of the class and take charge, but the sight of the prim, the paralysed and the hysterical was too much for me. After what seemed a lifetime, I managed to regain control, but it was one of the most difficult things I have ever done.

So, with frequent retreats to Tyringham, and my yoga classes, I managed to survive that winter of 1980 and continued to stay at the hotel where a growing friendship with the proprietress eventually resulted in her coming to my yoga class the following autumn. So much for my perceived feelings of her dislike! In the spring, the hotel began to fill up with summer visitors, and I had to move to a smaller room on the top floor. I began to feel restricted by this hotel life, and to want a place of my own once more. I am convinced that, when we need change, there are forces around us which bring the right circumstances into being. And so it was for me. Not by sitting back and waiting in an apathetic 'I don't have to do anything about this by myself' kind of way, but by knocking on metaphorical doors and, most importantly, letting everyone know exactly what you are looking for.

I had told my yoga class that I wanted to move, and one day in June 1980, this paid off. It appeared that one of my students knew a man who had a small ground floor flat to let in Hove. After mutually approving of one another, I moved in. It was a bit dark, and had bars at the windows as Brien my landlord was a jeweller who worked on the premises. However, net curtains obliterated the bars and I settled in quite quickly – Brien was such a kind and helpful person that it was a happy place for me. He had a workroom on the ground floor and gradually we become great friends. We used to meet for a coffee break in the mornings when I was in and discovered a mutual sense of humour which enlivened the times considerably. He was also a very attractive man physically, and it was a pleasant change to live in a more masculine environment. There were no sexual complications; I was fourteen years his senior and he was a man who definitely leaned towards the 'bimbo' rather than the older woman. He had been brought up by his father single-handed so maybe I was able to give him some of the mothering he had missed.

The flat was certainly a haven to which I could thankfully return and be at peace, but I was still looking after Jane to a certain extent in her nursing home, and also busy moving Frida into a block of sheltered housing. I used to walk the 2½ miles to see Frida twice a week, laden with a lunch I had prepared and food to stock the fridge. She was always pathetically glad to see me but maintained a steady flow of querulous complaints throughout the day. I would feel a tremendous sense of relief when I left and thoroughly enjoyed the walk home! Once the novelty of her new home began to wear off, Jane too, began to moan about her fellow-residents, but I found this easier to take. I felt that anyone with such extreme disability as hers was entitled to have a grumble now and again.

And of course, there was always my wonderful yoga class which gave me self-esteem, loving friends, healing and peace. I now had the same eight people coming every week and we had bonded together into a very strong unit. We were both protective and supportive of one another and always found something to have a really good laugh over. I always left with my shaky self-esteem considerably strengthened. We used to be together for 2½ hours, starting with breathing exercises, going on to the yoga poses, lying down in relaxation, and then sitting in a circle to calm our minds and be aware of the spiritual side of our nature.

Latterly, some strange things happened during the meditation; one day my voice changed into the deep, rich tones of a young man, and several times I was aware of a young man with a shaven head, dressed in saffron robes, sitting by the door. Once, one of my students went home and found her house full of ectoplasm. The group decided they didn't want to pursue this particular manifestation of meditation. It seemed to be a deviation from communion with the Infinite. So during my own times of deep meditation, I asked that these manifestations should cease, and they did. After all, we do have a God-given freewill and we should use it to determine the way we want to go. Even during the truly terrifying experience at Tyringham, I was the one who finally won control.

Don't ever believe you are entirely at the mercy of outside forces. You can find the strength and courage to take charge of your own life. As W.E. Henley says in For England's Sake:

> I am the master of my fate;
> I am the captain of my soul.

And:

> Out of the night that covers me,
> Black as the Pit from pole to pole,
> I thank whatever gods may be
> For my unconquerable soul ...
> Under the bludgeonings of chance
> My head is bloody, but unbowed.

Chapter 18

Soon after I moved into the flat, another significant event occurred in my life – another milestone, if you like. From time to time, I had been visiting an old colleague from Westlain who had become head of a girls' independent school in Malvern. Just before Christmas 1980, I wrote an article for Here's Health magazine, and in my complimentary copy I saw an advertisement for a small residential nature cure centre, also in Malvern. So thinking to kill two birds with one stone, I booked a fortnight's stay over Christmas.

Although I left home in brilliant sunshine, by the time the coach reached Tewkesbury, it had begun to snow quite hard and this was several inches deep when I disembarked in Malvern. I had arranged to telephone for a lift on my arrival, and the driver of the car that finally picked me up was not amused. Apparently, everyone else had cancelled their visit except two people who were already there, and a member of staff who couldn't get home, and the driver had had to dig out the car and make what had been a hair-raising journey. I don't think he ever believed my story – that I had started out in brilliant sunshine. But from this inauspicious beginning came one of the most enjoyable phases of my life since Ron was alive.

The Victorian house was charming, tastefully decorated, warm and comfortable, situated in a quiet cul de sac halfway up the beautiful Malvern Hills. From my bedroom window, I could see right across the Severn Valley to the Welsh mountains. It was one of those places in which one immediately feels at home. Win Jones, whose brainchild it was, was a truly amazing woman: small, bustling, beautifully dressed and attractive. She was a dynamo of energy, to whom I was instantly attracted. Obviously, she was the spark plug around which everything revolved in an extraordinarily competent way. The disgruntled car driver was revealed as Mike, Win's partner, who over the next few days, proved to be not only the best masseur

I have ever encountered, but also a kind and friendly soul. His sense of humour was great: his favourite epithet for people who upset him was 'arsehole', and because he invested it with such humour, I still apply it to people who irritate me. It never fails to dissolve my aggravation!

The snow continued to fall that Christmas, and we were totally cut off, so we got to know one another pretty well. The hills and trees turned into a veritable winter wonderland, and I went for some magical walks with the dog in snow so deep that sometimes only his long tail could be seen. It reminded me of the fairytale Christmases at Cropston, so I felt nurtured on all levels of my being. My body was soothed by the massage, the excellent food and the walking, my mind occupied by stimulating conversation, and my wounded feelings were healed by the appreciation and respect of the people around me. I found the naturopathic approach most acceptable and could not help but be aware of how much less arthritic pain I was in, and how much better I felt in general. I was also able to see my old friends who, when the snow began to disappear, took me in their car to all the beautiful places in Herefordshire and Gloucestershire. I really fell in love with Malvern, and from 1981 onwards visited Win and Mike at least once a year.

In 1985, Win suggested that I might join them as a therapist, using my skills as a teacher of yoga and relaxation, and also working as a lecturer and a psychotherapist. At that particular time, the seed fell on stony ground, but it had been sown. I felt then I was much too tied up in Hove; I had quite a number of patients and my lovely yoga students, my lecturing to various groups on topics as disparate as Understanding Your Emotions to Do I Really Love My Neighbour? and Yoga and Relaxation.

I used to give some talks to the London-based Unity group which contained a number of lovely black, well-endowed ladies, all wearing fantastic hats resembling baskets of cherries or bouquets of flowers. Every time I mentioned Jesus, the whole harvest festival shook and rippled to the sounds of 'Praise the Lord!' and I – not realising what they were saying – was quite convinced that some sort of protest was going on. 'Does anyone have a question at this point?' I quavered. But gradually the hands stopped waving in the air, the voices died down, and I realised that this reaction was quite normal for a West Indian audience.

At the end of one lecture on holistic medicine, a group of highly enthusiastic medical students kept me talking for two hours, and it has been good to see the enormous spread of this enthusiasm among the medical fraternity over the past twenty years or so.

So time scurried by, as is its wont, fully occupied with classes, counselling and lecturing. I also attended various seminars and conferences on matters metaphysical, and continued my visits to The Seekers.

Jane died suddenly from a heart attack in 1985, but Frida still needed a great deal of help. She complained constantly; she felt cheated that the people in the flats surrounding her were 'not (her) sort'. Consequently, she remained very lonely and isolated, repeating constantly that she lived only for my visits. So when I went to see her, I was irritated and drained of all my energy. And when I didn't visit her, I felt guilty. My landlord divorced his wife and remarried an incredibly sexy and attractive lady and began to talk about the possibility of a rent rise. Rents were skyrocketing in Hove, anyway; I knew the rent I was paying was not realistic for the late 1980s, and this made me uneasy. Frida fell and broke her hip, and the constant to-ing and fro-ing to the hospital without a car, as well as all my other commitments, began to take its toll. I was fast approaching 70 and it began to feel like it.

Every time I visited Win and Mike, I had more weariness to shed, and Malvern took on the aspect of Shangri-la. Win was still urging me to join them, and there was now the added attraction of Margaret, a nurse who, disenchanted with allopathic medicine and the National Health Service, had turned to naturopathy and trained as a masseuse and naturopath. She and I were attracted to each other immediately, and we spent many an hour together talking our heads off about our mutual interests in life, the universe and everything. So in many subtle ways, my life in Hove was being eroded and the way to Malvern made plain. My conscious awareness of this plan was in meditation, where I saw the place over and over behind my closed eyelids, and yet the thought of such an upheaval made me dismiss it out of hand. How could I face such a total change? Where would I live? I didn't even own a house or a property to exchange. How could I leave Frida? Obviously, fear was my dominant emotion and courage had flown out of the window. So I decided to ask my friend Jesus for guidance. Every night in meditation, I felt his presence and said, "I want to do what is right, so please tell me." Nothing. Night after night after night, I asked and I asked, and nothing.

After about six months of this, I was in Sainsburys, fascinated by a huge display of early strawberries. My thoughts were focused entirely on them: 'They're very expensive – can I afford them? – why are they ripe so early? – they have probably been irradiated – they look a bit dry', etc. Then suddenly, right out of the blue, I felt struck – literally – between the shoulder-blades with the overwhelming instruction, 'Go to Malvern.' These words went round and round in my mind from then on, until no doubt whatsoever remained; it wasn't my decision any more. I felt a bit shell-shocked and didn't say anything to anyone until the following October when I went to stay with Win and Mike. Win happened to be alone in the house when I arrived, and I told her about my decision. She told me I could have a room in the annexe – and that was that. It all fitted together like a dovetailed joint, and now, over twenty-five years later, it is very clear how right that instruction was.

During that momentous October visit, another event occurred which was also to have a profound influence on my life. Win introduced me to a slim, frail young woman who was preparing for a massive operation on her spine. This was Jane, with whom I was to find a great affinity, and who – with her husband and daughter – was to become my family. In other words, they were to adopt me as Mum, Mum-in-law and Gran – Supergran actually, so acclaimed because I was able to do the yoga headstand which raised me above all other grans for evermore. This has been such a compensatory relationship for me, and a wonderful confirmation of love's all-encompassing power. The world may view us as alone because we have no blood relatives, but that is no reason at all why we should not truly love and be loved.

My new friend Jane was in a great deal of pain which was visible in her beautiful, tragic eyes, but she managed this with dignity and courage. Obviously, she did not ever feel well and, as a wife and mother, was considerably frustrated. Her life was further complicated by the 'Iron Maiden', a frightening body support – all wires and straps which stood in the corner of her bedroom like an instrument of medieval torture. Her husband John turned out to be a kind and cuddly teddy bear of a man, and we loved each other on sight. Their daughter Hannah, who was five at the time, was a self-possessed young woman, wise beyond her years, who astonished

Win with a loud and clear, 'Hello, Win' although she had not met her before. Full marks for leaving Win speechless – a 'first' for anyone!

Of course, the actual move to Malvern was not easy. When I returned to Hove, I was overwhelmed by the enormity of what I had said I would do. But there was no going back – this inner compulsion was too strong. Frida was devastated of course, and used all the emotional blackmail at her command, but I felt strangely detached. My inner voice was so strong, it overcame all doubts. I had arranged to move on 30th November 1989 which gave me only a month to make my arrangements. I felt panicky and shaky the whole time, getting rid of things, including books belonging to my husband; putting furniture into store; and packing up clothes, all interspersed with recriminatory and tearful visits to Frida.

I had hired a car to take me and my personal effects to Malvern on 30th November, and that morning I woke, dry-mouthed, sweating with fear, convinced that I couldn't go. I'd have to cancel everything and stay where I was. I was paralysed with sheer panic, literally terrified. This feeling is one of the worst; it is what keeps so many people tied to the known and familiar, however unbearable and impossible, because the paralysis of terror literally binds them there. I overcame it by taking a long, hard look at the past few years and asking myself if that was what I really wanted for the future. This thought enabled me to lift myself off the bed with great difficulty and set about the business of the day.

I felt quite numb during the journey until we reached the outskirts of Malvern when my heart dropped like a stone, as I realised the enormity of what I had done. My spirits dropped further as I moved my stuff into my room: Win and Mike were about to go out, and Margaret was in the process of packing all her things as she'd had a row with Win, and said she was leaving. So, instead of a welcoming cup of tea and glad cries of delight at my arrival, I found an almost total lack of interest!

My spirits revived on going in to dinner with the patients, and as time went on, I realised that I had made the right move. I just lazed around for a couple of months, enjoying Malvern as I rested and settled in. There was an attractive young woman called Debbie at the clinic doing the cooking at that time, and she proved to be a very good friend to me. We went to the swimming pool together, and she chauffeured me around in her little car. In February, I started to take some classes in yoga and relaxation and to see some patients with problems. I met some interesting and brave people, some of whom were helped considerably by therapy. I made tapes of the yoga and relaxation classes, and of self-help for nervous tension, which they were able to take away and work with at home.

That spring of 1990 was a wonderful time for me. I was a working member of a like-minded group; I had praise and admiration from the patients, and truly beautiful surroundings. I walked on the magnificent hills and marvelled at the beauty of the trees breaking out into breathtaking blossom and delicate green leaf. I began to feel my spirits lifting, and there was a growing inner awareness during my meditation. But these times of total bliss and satisfaction do not last, of course. Everything on the earthly plane is in a constant state of flux, and therefore change is inevitable. I have changed in many ways since I started to write this book, and you have changed in many ways since you started to read it.

We knew that Win had cancer of the breast which had been developing over several years. As an extremely skilled naturopath, she knew the prognosis. She also knew she needed to take time off if it were to be treated successfully. But, involved as she was with the nature cure centre, she refused to leave the place. So she grew thinner and thinner, white-faced and tired, but with a fierce, almost fanatical, energy which drove her through the days. It had been suggested that the lower floor of the clinic be converted into a flat for me. At one point, in his colourful and varied career, Mike had been a builder – but I knew things were getting desperate when one day she took me aside and told me that this was no longer a viable idea. Her tone was somewhat brusque and dismissive, and at the time I was quite hurt, but of course the hurt was hers; I was just reacting to my 'I'll put you in the gutter' programming. How necessary it is to wait and think through the remarks that people make to us before reacting like a wounded animal which bites the rescuer's hand.

Some of my nervous symptoms reappeared at the thought of being homeless yet again. But at least I had Margaret and Debbie to talk to, and again, a growing self-confidence – born of success in the work I was doing. It was really good to see people change from apathy and despair to at least a modicum of peace and self-confidence. I was also putting into practice the techniques I was now teaching on a day-to-day basis. I combed the To Let column of the local paper and found nothing. I also contacted various Air Force associations to see if I could get financial help as the long-term widow of an airman. This experience was not a pleasant one: I felt I was asking for charity under false pretences.

Nothing was remotely suitable for weeks and weeks until one Saturday in May when Margaret said, "Don't bother to look in The Gazette – there's nothing." At first, I didn't look, but as the day progressed, my inner voice kept saying, 'Look anyway – go on, look!' So I combed the columns of To Let till I found it. 'One-bedroom bungalows to let in Malvern.' And a telephone number.

Chapter 19

I spoke to a pleasant woman who said yes, there was a bungalow belonging to a housing association. She told me where it was, and I found myself in a delightful close, containing 22 small dwellings each with its own small garden, arranged in a circle. In the middle of the circle there was a large lawn planted with various trees and shrubs, and including the largest and most beautiful cherry tree I have ever seen. 'This is most definitely for me,' I thought, and thanked the powers-that-be with fervour. Interestingly enough, I had gone under protest to a festival of Mind, Body and Spirit in Malvern a couple of months previously, and been told by a psychic that I would soon be living in a small bungalow, followed by an accurate description of the garden.

I couldn't look inside until I met with the secretary later on when the house was empty. At this point, my bubble burst: the interior filled me with dismay – a bright blue carpet, doggy brown wallpaper striped with darker brown, and an unbelievably ugly metal pipe leading to an ancient gas fire. I almost ran away! It was also very small, having only one bed-sitting room, and a microscopic bathroom and kitchen, largely devoted to the growth of various moulds and fungi. Apparently, the one-bedroom variety were only available to established tenants. With this promise in mind, I decided to take it and of course dipped into my meagre savings to refurbish it. The Association employed a competent general factotum and together we renovated the place until it underwent a complete metamorphosis, with a new white fireplace, pale green emulsion over wood-chip paper, a pale yellow-and-white bathroom, and a smart red-and-white kitchen. When my furniture arrived from Brighton, it completed a most attractive, albeit small, home. There were practical advantages too: only minutes away from shops and public transport. I had never owned a car, the clinic was now 2½ miles distant, and there was no bus that took me more than halfway there. As I was only going there occasionally now, I usually walked there and back which was enjoyable and relaxing. I have found many different ways of getting there, off the beaten track, away from the ever-increasing volume of traffic on the roads, with its noise and pollution. Up to now, I have found 45 different routes to take – over commons, through woods and fields, as well as the quieter roads, when rain makes the former too muddy.

I was pleased to find that this housing association was not restricted to old ladies, but encompassed a wide age range from the twenties to the nineties, and also included both men and women. One of the tenants was a biker, leather-clad and hirsute, of whom I was a little bit apprehensive until I observed how kind he was to the animals in the place, and how helpful to the elderly. Another was Barrie, greying and handsome, the perfect example of the attractive older man for whom girls leave home in droves in the land of Mills & Boon and Barbara Cartland. He had been in the Navy, and was no doubt continuing the tradition of a girl in every port by cutting a positive swathe through the women of the West Midlands. However, my own advanced years excluded me from sexual games, which means that at least real friendship is possible with men. And a true friendship developed between Barry and myself. He takes me hither and yon when I need transport, and being told, 'I never think of you as being old,' is much more flattering to me now than the facile compliments of men who were just trying to get me into bed. The people in the close made an interesting mix, and as I gradually got to know my neighbours, I felt more and more at home and at ease with them. They seemed to have the happy knack of caring for one another without ever intruding.

Just after Christmas 1991, Win finally died. Mike and Margaret carried on but it was a grim time. There were no patients in January, which was usual, and the house seemed unnaturally dark and gloomy. Whenever I stepped over the threshold, I felt as if someone had thrown a suffocating wet, black blanket over my head, and was wrapping me tightly in its stifling folds. However, time moves forward, and with the spring came the patients, and gradually a semblance of normality returned.

My work at the clinic continued to delight me, particularly the teaching groups. It was good to see people gradually learning to relax and let go. I was also made aware of the tremendous pain and fear so many people suffer from, and hopefully I helped to alleviate some of that suffering. A great bond of friendship emerges from these one-to-one encounters, and these friendships were like balm to my own troubled emotions. Empathy between patient and therapist is a powerful force for healing, although conventional training in psychotherapy insists on the therapist distancing him or herself both physically and emotionally. But to me, psychotherapy is not learned techniques, words or unconditional regard; it is to truly involve oneself in relationship. In fact, I think the success of psychotherapy depends on love.

As I have said before, we are embarrassed by this word 'love' because of the confusion between sexual love and the genuine love portrayed by Jesus. Genuine love involves an extension of oneself, and demands huge amounts of energy. But our energy is limited so we must be wise in expending it: to attempt to love everyone is not within our power. We may exceed our energy limits and spread ourselves too thinly, when this so-called 'love' becomes harmful to ourselves and the people who seek our attention. As a result of spreading myself too thinly, I became ill. The body has an innate intelligence which prevents us from overdoing things, and one week in May 1992, I felt very strange, weak, tired and generally not well. Eventually, I found myself in bed, unable to stand, with a tearing cough that kept me awake all night.

During this illness, I had a sort of hallucination or semi-waking dream. I saw three owls fly into the room, and take me out with them to perch in the cherry tree in the park opposite my bungalow. Sitting in the tree with the owls, I could see my body lying in bed. I felt a strong feeling of peace and that all would be well. The scene faded and I was back in my body in bed, but then saw the forms of my husband and my mother (I recognised her from photographs) by my side. My husband looked upset and disappointed; my mother loving and compassionate. I have read that many beliefs regard the owl as the bird of death, and many country folk have seen an owl sitting in a tree outside a house where someone is dying. I can only interpret this vision as a near-death experience, that my soul literally left my body but came back because I had work still to do. My husband would look disappointed and my mother compassionate under these circumstances. But it was a most uplifting and strengthening experience, and from then on I started to improve and regain my strength.

I continued seeing patients at the clinic: some sad, some bad, some just disenchanted and needing a kick-start out of their old ways into something new and interesting. Most of all, I loved the classes, the teacher in me responding like an old warhorse to the sound of battle. I became quite adept at making cassettes of my teaching and was frequently heard apparently talking to myself in the bathroom in the annexe, the only place where I could be undisturbed. The situation at the clinic continued to improve, but it was extremely hard work for Mike and Margaret, particularly Margaret as she was doing most of the cooking as well as seeing patients. The extremely high standard of the food and vegetarian cooking demanded a great deal of finicky preparation to be successful.

I occasionally visited a friend's natural healing centre in Bournemouth as a visitor, but available for teaching yoga. I loved Bournemouth, the sand and the pines, and was almost tempted to move there. But turning to meditation for an answer, it was always, 'No, stay where you are.'

This was good advice, as in November 1992 a larger bungalow became available in the close with a large sitting room, a dining alcove, bathroom, kitchen, and a small separate bedroom. I went to look at it and again experienced the shock of dark colours that to me were so depressing. The kitchen was a home economist's nightmare and needed complete restructuring. I would also have to recarpet all the floors again. Having seen all this, I sat down and wailed, 'I can't do it all over again. I can't! I can't!' Incidentally, this was to be the 32nd move in my life. However, basic commonsense and determination reasserted itself. I dried my tears and set about refurbishing this 'new' bungalow in Pickersleigh Close.

Barrie proved to be a tower of strength and redecorated the whole place (except the kitchen) with the pretty pastels and whites with which I like to surround myself and my patients. No one is right or wrong in their particular decorative preferences: we are all programmed by our past, so that someone's sunshine yellow may be another's bile green. I don't subscribe to the 'good and bad taste' dictum, choosing always only what makes me feel happy, warm and relaxed. It is interesting that there is now a huge industry devoted to the right use of colour and I think it is a good thing to consult an expert if you are unsure of your own choice.

At one point in the refurbishment, I was reminded forcibly of the inevitable influence of time on my appearance. I had to telephone an electrician who kept me talking for quite a while. I thought this was a bit odd until he arrived the following day and said, "Oh, I *am* disappointed – you sounded such a *young* lady on the phone!" I felt quite hurt until I managed to see the funny side. Once more, thank God for a sense of humour.

I continued to visit the clinic from time to time to see patients whom I now knew quite well, most of whom were a pleasure to meet again. There is always the odd pain in the neck of course, the ones who moan incessantly throughout the first consultation and continue to moan without ever making any effort themselves to improve their lives. My own self-esteem was once so low I always blamed myself for their lack of improvement – but now, after several meetings together with no sign of progress, I suggest another therapist and pass them on with a sigh of relief. Sometimes they return, and then I know I've struck pay dirt because now they have realised that effort is required and they are willing to make it.

I also continued to add little touches to my house and am particularly proud of a flourishing philodendron plant standing proudly in the corner of my sitting room. This was brought to me by a patient, a young man with many problems, who improved considerably during treatment. He finally shot off to Hungary to do voluntary work, and asked if I would look after the plant. Poor thing – its leaves were dusty and drooping sadly and it was giving off a very strong smell of marijuana! I felt genuine compassion for this poor plant and tended it lovingly, not just in a practical way, but talking to it and stroking its leaves whenever I passed by. It rewarded me by becoming healthy and strong and almost doubling in height. I swear too it missed me, as when I returned from a fortnight away, it was drooping and sad but revived after a few hours, and this was not because it was short of water…

Chapter 20

I made another trip to Tyringham, twenty years after my previous visit. Before Christmas, I had some sort of illness – what I would call a healing crisis, but what allopaths would call an acute viral infection. Whatever it was, I felt very ill and was left in a state of total apathy and exhaustion, all I wanted to do was sag in front of the television or meditate. I lost interest in everything – writing this book, food, exercise, friends, talking to people, everything. Again, meditation came to my aid. "What shall I do?" I asked. And finally, I kept seeing Tyringham. My conscious mind refused this image – the old nightmare experience of evil arose, and I told myself I was being stupid to ever think of going again. But the image persisted, like the urge to come to Malvern, the urge to take Brian's flat, the easy path to Pickersleigh Close, and the negative response to thoughts of moving to Bournemouth. A very strong impulse was saying, 'Do it now! Do it now!' So I picked up the telephone and made a booking for a fortnight.

My conscious mind immediately began to play absolute hell. Old patterns of panic, with its attendant physical symptoms, arose. I found myself dealing not only with the post-viral depression and weakness, but the sweating, the stomach-churning, the palpitations, the breathlessness, the dizziness, and the awful feeling of my mind being drawn out on a frail thread which would snap at any minute. With nervous exhaustion, there can be a terrifying feeling that one day the 'ultimate' will happen, that everything will fragment into chaos from which there will be no return to normality. I had three weeks to endure before going away, and it was hell. If I could have gone as soon as I put the phone down, it would have been bearable, because my anxiety could have been converted into action. But three weeks of worrying about where I would find the energy to wash my clothes, to iron, to pack, and concern about being too weak to stand the treatment, or how I should cope with people chattering all around me, and even about where the money was coming from, were stressful, to say the least. I hadn't had a holiday for nine years, and not even gone away for five, so I was very out of practice anyway.

I survived those three weeks with the support of meditation and by accepting that this was how I was at the moment: there was no magic wand which was going to alter things, and the only magic bullet was a tranquilliser. Incidentally, I find these helpful in an emergency but only to calm the storm temporarily. In other words, they mask the symptoms of an inner tangle of fears and self-doubts which only I am able to unravel. This is not to say that tranquillisers do not have their place; at times a temporary crutch is essential. When I felt I was going to fragment, I did take a few herbal tranquillisers but always only half the recommended dose. There is a lot to be gained for coming out of these bad times mainly by oneself. The strength and self-esteem it engenders is considerable. You feel a great sense of achievement.

Of course, there are times of nervous collapse when professional help is not only advisable but essential – for example, in a clinical depression arising from chemical imbalances in the brain or the terrifying grief experienced after enormous and paralysing tragedy. As in many of life's experiences, balance is the key factor, balancing how much help is needed against the vitally important input of the patient. Purely practical help is also significant: what can I or someone else actually do to relieve this situation? It is a good question to ask. So I took my small doses of tranquillisers, made sure I went outside every day if only for a walk round the block, practised calming yoga breathing, did a few gentle yoga stretches and practised the Alexander technique. Most importantly, I meditated. Sometimes my mind was so agitated that all I could do was concentrate on my candle flame and make an attempt to stand aside from this inner turmoil and just watch the thoughts that raced and tumbled through my brain. The most important factor here is the willingness to make the effort – and it is Herculean – to do something. Not in a frantic, desperate, panicky kind of way which only causes more tension, exhaustion and depression, but (and this may be aided by cautious tranquillisation) by endeavouring to let go and to float through to the other side of the problem. This is very hard to do but I recalled past bad times in my life which did pass eventually and remembered that time itself takes care of most things.

One night during a fruitless meditation, I felt so trapped and desperate I asked for a dream to tell me where I was going wrong. I had a clear and definitive answer. In my dream, I was lying on a plinth in an Egyptian pyramid. The High Priest came in with a large knife and proceeded to cut into my body from collar-bone to pelvis. It was not horrific or painful, just metaphorical. He then peeled back the flesh on either side and invited me to look inside my body which was filled with a thick, liquid, molten gold. I lay back again, and he beckoned to crowds of people on either side of me. They too were dressed as ancient Egyptians, but each had the face of a patient I had treated or a friend from the past or the present. These people all carried large soup ladles with which they proceeded to dip greedily into the liquid gold and slurp it up into their mouths, wasting a great deal of it in their haste. The Priest clapped his hands and they ran away. He looked at me and said, "Now do you understand?" "Yes," I said, "I think I do." With that, he poured more liquid gold into me until I was full again, and fitted a fastener into the incision which he pulled tightly closed. He put my hand onto the tag, and said, "Remember, you are in control."

What a wonderful explanation, strongly confirmed six weeks later by one of my soul mates, a fantastic lady whom I miss greatly who went to practise homoeopathy in California. To my great surprise and joy, she telephoned out of the blue because, she said, I had been on her mind so much and she felt vaguely uneasy. I told her what had been going on, and she said, "Now that you have restored your energies, release them slowly like an IV drip – one drop at a time and with total control over the flow." So I thanked the powers-that-be for giving me such a precise and explicit explanation, and such simple and direct instructions for the future. As it was said, 'Ask, and it shall be given you; seek, and ye shall find; knock, and it shall be opened unto you.' We really do only have to ask.

In spite of these elevated intimations, I was still deeply distressed, and became more and more stressed as the time for my departure drew nearer. I felt trapped in a Catch 22 situation, terrified of going away and equally terrified of staying where I was. Sinking slowly into a morass of fear, weakness and paralysing panic, I began to think, 'So this is it. This is old age whether I like it or not. It has caught up with me and there is nothing I can do about it. There is nothing ahead but carers and meals on wheels and eventually the dreaded home.' Then God spoke in the shape of a friend, who said, "You know, you are not yourself at all; you're not our Eileen any more – all this talk of wills, funeral pre-payments and memorial services – it's just not like you."

So the day of departure came, and after a sleepless night, I had to make myself get out of bed and prepare for the trip. The only way I could stop myself sinking back onto the pillow was by repeating over and over again, 'You have to go. You have to go. There is no alternative. If you stay here, that is the end. You have no choice but to go.' Barrie was his usual kind and caring self, and the journey was uplifting. And as we trundled through the Cotswold countryside with its faint green of incipient spring, I felt my spirits strengthening to meet the fortnight ahead.

I had a strange feeling of déjà vu, of coming home, as we turned off the main road through the gateway to the estate. And as the magnificent house came into view, I felt a lump in my throat and a tear in my eye. This feeling was much stronger than the apprehension arising from memories of the visit in 1979 during which I experienced evil. The magnificent house was even more gracious and inspiring. There had been many improvements and my own room had recently been refurbished with attractive dark pine furniture and a brand-new shower. The whole place exuded an aura of timelessness and continuity which seemed to reduce personal problems, not exactly into insignificance, but certainly into proportion. It was salutary to see photographs of the 14 original members of staff in 1969, and to realise that only the general manager remained, and he was retiring. How strange, I mused; it had all felt so permanent and immutable at that time. Now only the building remained, the people gone, like the inhabitants of a dream.

The present fine building which gave me such joy was designed by Sir John Soane and built in 1792. He replaced the old grey manor house with an elegant classic villa with a large copper dome, and various statues and ornaments were added at a later date. Will Praed died in 1870, and the estate was inherited by Roger Tyringham and purchased in 1906 by Frederick Adolfus König, a banker who spent a great deal of time in London as well as New York. In the late 1920s, he commissioned Sir Edwin Lutyens to construct the outside swimming pool, the bathing pavilion and the Temple of Music, and to do some extensive landscaping. These two pavilions, especially the Temple of Music, are unique to this country. König died in 1940 and his wife in 1951. Some of their descendants still live in the area.

During World War II, the house became a maternity home for evacuees, and after the war was purchased by the Australian and New Zealand Bank who used it as a weekend clubhouse.

In 1967 it was sold to a trust fund headed by Sir Maurice Laing, and Tyringham Naturopathic Clinic opened its doors in May that year, with thirty beds, eleven staff and only eight patients. When I visited it this time in 1999, there were 81 beds and 85 staff. As a registered charity, this beautiful building in its idyllic surroundings was now within the reach of everyone, rich and poor, as somewhere they might experience the undoubted success of natural healing. Unfortunately, Tyringham has now closed owing to lack of funds.

Responding to the changes, I realised the truth of impermanence. To try to hold on to anything is to become fearful and afraid to live at all. If I had gone to Tyringham expecting to find everything as it had been, my attitude would have negated any healing process. Accepting change, we discover that learning to live is learning to let go. However, philosophy was not on the agenda at that point.

I was sent for a consultation with a serene and smiling Asian lady who would determine what treatments would help the low condition I was in. It was a shock to discover that my blood pressure was high, but considering the weeks of illness and fear in which I had been wallowing, this was not surprising. I comforted myself with the memory of a patient of mine who came in a dreadful state to see me. He'd been told by his doctor that his blood pressure was high, and that when his time came, he would probably die of a stroke. The man was in a pitiful state, not surprisingly; his mind was frozen on the subject of strokes. He said he almost wished the wretched thing would come and get it over. Discussion with his doctor revealed a totally different interpretation. He had mentioned a stroke, yes – but it was only in years to come when death was inevitable anyway. The doctor was surprised at the man's reaction and said, "But he seemed such a sensible fellow." Aren't we all sensible, I thought, when it comes to other people's problems? The patient eventually relaxed sufficiently to lower his blood pressure and stop worrying about it. But it took patience, effort and time. I decided to accept the fact that my blood pressure was high and to relax as much as possible during the fortnight ahead. I didn't like it, but at least I was doing something about it.

At supper that evening, I met some interesting people, many of whom had far more problems than I had, and I began to see how introspective I had become. When we think continuously about a particular problem, it's like playing the same tape over and over. At first, we accept it as background noise, but gradually it comes between us and our work, our reading, and our making contact with other people. It not only takes control of our mind, it becomes our mind. Our mind has lost its resilience and becomes so tired that these unwanted thoughts race on automatically. So a large part of my therapy was mingling with the other people at Tyringham and a more diverse and varied a company it would have been difficult to assemble. I had spent so many weeks alone and desperately concerned with my own problems that at first I felt unable to make contact with them. It was as though they were in one world, and I in another. I felt I had a vacuum where my feelings should be, because I had been feeling such intense, fearful emotions for so long. I realised my emotions were frozen and needed time to thaw. I had also been experiencing an increasing tendency to think other people were thinking ill of me, and realised that this was another symptom of my own withdrawal. When the world seems black, it is not easy to admit that it is oneself that is out of sorts and not the world. In any event, there was not much time to be introspective at Tyringham; the day's programme is so full and one was shuttled back and forth between treatments, constantly on the move.

My treatments varied between enjoyable and relaxing seaweed baths and wax baths for my hands and feet, hot peat packs and infrared, to the more torturous treatments like CHT and Sitz baths. The former stood for constitutional hydrotherapy and looked harmless enough. A smiling kindly nurse ushered me into a cubicle, told me take off all my clothes, disappeared and returned bearing an enormous wet sheet which sparkled with ice crystals, which was not surprising because she had just taken it out of a freezer. Spreading its stiff folds over the plastic sheet on the plinth, she invited me – all in the nicest possible way – to lie face down upon the sheet. Gingerly I knelt, and even more gingerly, lowered the rest of my body, congratulating myself that I had not screamed. I began to relax – when the rest of the sheet was wrapped around my back! Great shivers shook my feeble frame, but relief was at hand in the shape of three hot peat packs which were distributed along my spine. I was then enclosed in the plastic sheet and lay like an Ice Age mummy for twenty minutes.

To my great surprise, I warmed up quite quickly, and my temperature was found to have risen a degree nearer normal, which was one of the many objects of the exercise. It seems to me that CHT is nature cure's answer to shock treatment: anxiety, tension and depression were among the many complaints for which it was recommended.

The Sitz baths, too, were a salutary experience: two large basins joined together, one containing hot water and the other cold, really cold – in fact, icy! I was required to sit in the hot water and to put my feet into the cold for three minutes. It was not too bad, I thought, even though my feet were frozen solid. A bell went off after three minutes, and a voice commanded, 'Change over.' So, warily, I lowered my bottom into the cold water and put my feet into the hot. This torture only lasted for one minute, so on the bell I leapt for the towel, only to be instructed to do the same thing all over again. But again, what results! Every organ in the lower abdomen tones and tightens, and there is improved function. There is also a great sense of achievement in natural treatments. Instead of passively taking a drug, and very often being devastated by its side-effects, you are in control yourself, and taking an active part in healing your own body…

Much more enjoyable was the warm seaweed bath, in which one was just required to lie for twenty minutes. Also the peat, or castor oil, packs where again, all that was required was to lie still while the pack did its healing work. Osteopathy and acupuncture were also easy and any slight discomfort easily outweighed by the obvious benefits. Massage was the most coveted of treatment; to lie on a specially designed body cushion whilst healing hands moved soothingly up and down one's spine, neck and shoulders until one was positively purring with pleasure. One morning, I was waiting for a massage when a prim, somewhat precise elderly lady burst out of her cubicle, pink-cheeked and bright-eyed, declaiming, "I've had a man! I've had a man!" Startled out of my Tyringham torpor by this unlikely event, I realised that a male masseur had been added to the usual female staff, since most patients were female, and how popular he was! I must say I felt quite elderly when I realised that it really didn't matter to me whether the hands on my back belonged to a man or a woman, as long as they were efficient. One could of course say that a man's hands are stronger, but I have seen women in this profession with hands like spades and arms like pile-drivers. Oh well! Vive la différence, say I, if it adds colour to the cheeks and a sparkle to the eye. Why not?

The other really enjoyable experiences were swimming in the large pool, exercising in the gym, and the yoga classes. I usually dislike being taught yoga because as a teacher myself, my ego tends to get in the way. But this lady was quite delightful, an excellent teacher, gentle and kind, with a beautiful voice. It gradually became apparent to the group that I was a yoga teacher, and this caused a strange reaction. Later on, I was approached by another patient who took me aside, looked pityingly at me, and said, "I must ask you to think again about teaching yoga. You are a nice person, and I have nothing against you, but yoga itself is sinful and an abomination unto the Lord. Please do not do it any more." I was stunned; I didn't think such prejudice existed any longer, but this was pure fanaticism in front of me. I explained that western yoga is not a religion; it is a method of complete physical, mental and emotional development, an attitude to life and to all creation. And its aims are the highest and most noble. All who study it, whatever their personal religion, will find something for themselves and will turn to their own devotions with increased spiritual awareness and understanding. But the fanatic is not to be diverted. From thenceforward, I was avoided and ignored as if, on contact with me, she might suddenly find herself with eight arms and legs in the lotus position! Would this fear of yoga turn to hate, I wondered, as fear usually does if it's nurtured long enough? And would this hate then be projected onto the whole Asian community associated with yoga? Most people fail to transcend the influence of their particular culture, their parents and their childhood. So humanity is full of conflict. Human beings, with vastly different views, each believing their own to be correct, must deal with each other. We are like blind men, each in touch with only one part of an elephant, yet each claiming to know the whole beast. So we squabble over our different opinions, and all wars are holy wars.

It was interesting to observe the microcosm of Tyringham and realise that it was in fact a somewhat superior part of the macrocosm. Most people who went there had to possess a fairly open mind to accept the unorthodoxy of its treatments, compared with the allopathic variety. The ubiquitous bathrobe too was a great leveller, as it was not easy to differentiate between luxury towelling and the cheaper variety at first glance. It was interesting too, to observe how important food becomes when this is not available. Some people were fasting or on a very restricted diet, and their interest in food became obsessive. They watched with hungry eyes as the more fortunate tucked into baked potatoes and the excellent vegetarian main dishes. Again, a sense of humour was a great asset. One man, trying to lose weight, looked longingly at an elderly lady demolishing a plateful of food, and said through gritted teeth, "I never thought I could contemplate mugging an old lady but now I would – just for that potato." The whole table collapsed into laughter whilst the lady unconcernedly chomped on, unaware of the potential potato pirate a couple of yards away.

Empathy abounded at Tyringham. Most people talked freely to one another about all sorts of things they would not have dreamt normally of mentioning to a comparative stranger. Much good resulted from this excellent therapy: shorn of outward appearance or professional qualifications, it was easy to accept people as they really were, and not be blinded by their credentials. (When I was young, they would have been compartmentalised by their accents of course. Happily, this no longer obtains.) Some people asked if I was a healer in the spiritual sense, so I explained the meditative practice I carry out in the evening. Many were interested and asked me to include them on my list. This has been most enjoyable for me, as I feel a oneness with them, even though physically we may never meet again.

Eventually, the time came for Barrie to bring me home, and we had a most enjoyable journey back through the beautiful Cotswold countryside, now showing the unmistakable signs of spring. I was so pleased to be back in my dear little house, that I actually stroked the wall and felt a sense of deep and lasting peace associated with 'coming home'. I thanked the powers-that-be for the incredible guidance that had sent me to Tyringham yet again; how absolutely right it had been. I resumed my activities with enthusiasm, and have continued to enjoy an active, interesting and enjoyable life, although I have acquired a pinned hip and a slightly deformed right hand and arm as a result of two quite bad falls. My spiritual awareness is increasing through extensive reading and meditation, and brings me great joy and peace – at least, most of the time. Physically, I eat well but wisely, and my beloved yoga keeps my muscles and joints in pretty good order. I swim, and walk, and it is all very enjoyable. So, although there have been many times when 'I can't go on' was a serious option, I have been able to counter these times with various

Desiderata

positive actions which I propose to share with you in the sequel to this book.

(Found in Old St Paul's Church, Baltimore, dated 1692)

Go placidly amid the noise and haste and remember what peace there may be in silence.

As far as possible without surrender be on good terms with all persons.

Speak your truth quietly and clearly and listen to others, even the dull and ignorant; they too have their story.

Avoid loud and aggressive persons; they are vexatious to the spirit.

If you compare yourself with others you may become vain and bitter for always there will be greater and lesser persons than yourself.

Enjoy your achievements as well as your plans.

Keep interested in your own career, however humble; it is a real possession in the changing fortunes of time.

Exercise caution in your business affairs; for the world is full of trickery.

But let this not blind you to what virtue there is: many persons strive for high ideals and everywhere life is full of heroism.

Be yourself. Especially, do not feign affection.

Neither be cynical about love; for in the face of all aridity and disenchantment it is perennial as the grass.

Take kindly the counsel of the years, gracefully surrendering the things of youth.

Nurture strength of spirit to shield you in sudden misfortune. But do not distress yourself with imaginings. Many fears are born of fatigue and loneliness.

Beyond a wholesome discipline, be gentle with yourself. You are a child of the universe no less than the trees and the stars; you have a right to be here.

And whether it is clear to you or not, no doubt the universe is unfolding as it should.

Therefore be at peace with God, whatever you conceive him to be, and whatever your labours and aspirations in the noisy confusion of life, keep peace with your soul. With all its sham, drudgery and broken dreams, it is still a beautiful world.

Be careful. Strive to be happy.

Book Two

I Can't Go On...

...Yes I Can!

Always we hope someone else has the answer,
Some other place will be better,
Some other time it will all turn out.
But this is it.
No-one else has the answer,
No other place will be better,
And it has already turned out.
At the centre of your Being you have the answer.
You know who you are and you know what you want.
There is no need to run outside for better seeing,
Nor to peer from a window.
Rather, abide at the Centre of your Being,
For the more you leave it the less you learn.
Search your heart and see
The way to do is be.

Lao Tzu

Preface to the Second Book

From My Life to Yours

Life is not cured, it is managed

So, what good could possibly come out of such a childhood, such a life? It seems that hell has many mansions too. Many of you will have had painful and difficult childhoods. Parents, being just people, are human beings; with the best will in the world, none of them can be the loving, protective, caring Mummy and Daddy of our fairy stories 24 hours a day, seven days a week.

At the moment, the average child spends thirty minutes a day actually talking with its mother, five minutes a day with its father – one third of whom are not present anyway – and two or more hours in front of the television. So it seems quite obvious who or what is bringing them up. I, for one, am not at all surprised by the apparent Midwich Cuckoos generation currently terrorising teachers and hanging about in mildly menacing groups on street corners.

Therefore, as adults, it is enormously important to analyse the painful events of childhood to understand their effects upon us so that we become stronger, both mentally and emotionally. Before you build a house, you have to make a plan and lay a foundation upon which the finished structure will depend. So it makes exceedingly good sense to examine and restructure this vital foundation, which is your childhood, before attempting to live the rest of your life.

In this part, I am looking back at the various therapies I encountered which were of significant help to me. Since a number of my life experiences are common to many people, it may be helpful for you to try out these remedies for yourself.

Individual Attitudes

However, please remember that you are a unique individual, a totally different entity from me: no two human beings are exactly alike. So a therapy that worked for me may not necessarily work for you, but there is a chance that it will.

I think the most important factor in any healing activity is your attitude towards it. If you approach it with an open and receptive mind, and in an expectation of success, it is far more likely to work for you. As Milton says in Paradise Lost:

> The mind is its own place, and in itself
> Can make a Heaven of Hell, a Hell of Heaven.

In more prosaic language, the way you think and feel about a situation makes all the difference, and generally you get what you expect. Consider two young women, both suffering from the common cold: one gets invited out by a charismatic young man for an exciting evening; the other faces an evening catering to the excessive demands of a selfish and querulous relative. Which one will go to bed early feeling miserable and dejected? Which one will feel much better the following morning, and which one worse? I know, because I've been there.

The Diseased Person

Before attempting any therapy, it is most important to remember that health is not just a matter of the symptoms of disease; indeed, real health is dynamic, and every so often may appear as quite violent changes in the status quo. For example, a man may pick and eat a deadly fungus which he thinks is edible, and if he is in virile health, he will react with violent sickness and diarrhoea, a vigorous and complete emptying of the stomach and bowels. The better the health of this man, the more dramatic this house-cleaning will be, and the more thorough and immediate the symptoms are, the less damage will be done to him by the poisonous fungus.

So the idea of administering some soothing and mollifying remedy in this case could be life-threatening to this man, however kindly intended. The same principle applies to most diseases. When a poison or toxin has gathered in any part of the body, a point is reached when the local tissues start to springclean the area in a number of ways. It can take the form of a simple cold, vomiting or diarrhoea, a rash or an abscess, or a more total crisis, such as a high fever; these are all indicative of the body's healing and cleansing forces.

So please give any minor episode of disease a day or two to get better of its own accord. Give the body warmth, rest and just a very little to eat and drink, and that should consist of only fresh fruit and salad, or even just water. Digestion takes an enormous amount of energy and your body needs that energy to return to a state of health again. But the mind is king, so I'm starting this section with psychotherapy and counselling, which, together with eating the right food (not necessarily dieting) yoga and meditation, have helped me to sail through some pretty rough waters.

Psychotherapy

With regards to psychotherapy and counselling, I must stress at the outset that the personality of the psychotherapist and your own reaction to him or her is paramount. No one is going to help you if deep down you feel uneasy with them. There will be an almost palpable curtain between you, and nothing will take place.

One of the best ways of finding a therapist is by recommendation from someone who has been helped by one. Even then, being individuals, that therapist may not be right for you. And that's OK – pay your single fee and find someone else. You should know after the first half-hour if you've struck oil and there's no discredit in shopping around. I was the thirteenth therapist one of my patients came to, and she went on to yet another. After all, it's your hard-earned money, so why throw it away? Qualifications are important, but not necessarily a true assessment of the psychotherapist's ability. Many lay psychotherapists I have met have been more successful than those with a string of highly impressive letters after their name.

If you know of a successful psychotherapist or psychoanalyst, or your doctor does, you could save yourself years of misery and ill-health by having a course of treatment. This will mean seeing a therapist for about an hour at least once a week, possibly for months. This will be costly, because it involves the therapist's sole attention. So if you can afford it, look upon it as an investment, and you will find it pays handsome dividends. The therapist will bring to light your inevitable resistance to cure.

We are all afraid of really knowing ourselves, and refuse to see the wood for the trees. Also, automatically you will expect from the therapist the same kind of treatment you received from your parent-figures. If they were cold and aloof, you will feel the analyst is cold and aloof. If they were dedicated to making money, you will feel the therapist is thinking more about his or her fee than helping you. If parental silence meant disapproval and dislike, then you may become uneasy if he or she doesn't say much. As you bring these feelings to light, your instinctive patterns of reaction will emerge, and in discussion of them, you can find a truthful and objective relationship with the people and the circumstances of your world.

The therapist will also teach you various techniques which you can employ whenever waves of depression, sadness, inadequacy, anger or self-pity, sweep over you and threaten annihilation. I have to say here that, although the therapist will be extremely valuable in the process of cure, he or she cannot do it for you. Only you can put these techniques into practice. Only you can work on yourself, and this work has to go on all the time, noting negative reactions, understanding them, and turning them round.

If you cannot find an affordable therapist or one with whom you feel easy and relaxed, and able to work with, then find a suitable minister, priest or wise friend. If you choose a religious confidant, make sure that he will not think it his duty to make you more aware of any guilt you may have or may have imagined. You are probably only too willing to castigate yourself. At this stage, you need comfort, not chastisement. Also, choose your wisest friend, who will not necessarily be your closest. Your closest friend will sympathise with you far too much.

I was totally ignorant of subconscious programming until I was led to a wonderful man in Hove who had trained as a psychotherapist after experiencing tremendous nervous suffering in his own life. His name was Edward Barker who, when he was 20, had a nervous breakdown and went through two years of hell, punctuated by violent attacks of tachycardia (loud, rapid heart palpitation) that made him fear he was dying every day. At that time, it was called neurasthenia, and when he looked it up in a medical book, he found that he was expected to suffer an increasing lethargy, leading to general deterioration until some fatal disease came along to finish him off completely. He changed his doctor a few times but always ended up with sedatives.

Finally, he met a young doctor who lent him a little book on psychotherapy. This led him to Manchester Central Library, where he pored over books by Freud, Adler, Jung and Thouless. These so enlightened him that he managed to complete his vocational training as a Methodist minister, but continued to experience considerable nervous tension in all that he did. Then his tension took a psychosomatic turn, and papilloma – fortunately benign – appeared on his vocal chords. Seven operations and painful radiotherapy were unsuccessful and finally his throat was cut and the vocal chords removed. This left him unable to speak above a whisper, so he retired and trained as a psychotherapist. During his training, he underwent exhaustive psychoanalysis with an eminent Harley Street psychiatrist, and this was the turning-point of his life. Nothing is ever entirely bad.

He discovered that his mother, who died when he was five, was herself a victim of a serious neurosis. He had been reared on the belief that she had been an angel in disguise. He admired his father greatly, who himself was the product of a difficult home, and had learned about life the hard way. His father was a self-made man, who had succeeded through sheer Yorkshire grit and determination. He resolved that his young son, bereft of his mother, should not only succeed but excel. So the standards and expectations set for the young Edward were high indeed. He, like me, was still a broken-hearted little child.

Once we both saw and understood our pattern, life began for us again. I was fortunate indeed to find Edward Barker, because there is nothing more helpful than a therapist who has experienced and conquered exactly what you are going through yourself. An injured leg needs a crutch: why not a shocked and tired mind?

If the spectre of cost rears its ugly head, you may find an NHS counsellor working with a doctor, or you may find help through the CAB; and there are some therapists who work voluntarily. However, try not to do what I have done in the past – bared my soul to anyone who will listen, fellow-occupants of a bus or train, tradesmen or total strangers. This is tempting but unwise, as you are so impressionable that the wrong advice or contemptuous criticism could be most upsetting and hinder your recovery. Listening to so many opinions is contradictory and confusing, and it can also be incredibly boring to the captive listener. Most people have enough troubles of their own.

Love

Psychotherapy must be a process of genuine love if it is to succeed, although this is an heretical point-of-view in traditional psychiatric circles. Genuine love is intangible, supra-rational, not measurable in scientific terms – and in my opinion successful psychotherapy demands that there be a loving relationship between therapist and patient. This is not unconditional positive regard, nor is there any magic wand; it is involvement and it is hard work. In Scott Peck's words,

It is the willingness of the therapist to extend him or herself for the purpose of nurturing the patient's growth, willingness to go out on a limb, to truly involve oneself at an emotional level in the relationship, to actually struggle with the patient and with oneself. In short, the essential ingredient of successful, deep and meaningful psychotherapy is love.

We are talking here, when we speak of love, of the Greek word *agape* (pronounced A-ga-pay), which means general feelings of gentleness, mercy, kindness, compassion, peace, joy, non-judgement, and a genuine concern for other people. There is an inevitable confusion of the word 'love' with sex. The media often present us with a scandalous story about affectionate relationships between psychotherapists and their patients, and because of the loving intimate nature of psychotherapeutic relationships, it is inevitable that some strong sexual attractions do develop. However, in my opinion, any therapist who has a sexual relationship with a patient, is using that patient to satisfy his or her own needs, and since the job of a good therapist is to be of use to the patient, and to lead him or her towards independence and a separate identity, such behaviour is extremely detrimental both to the patient's progress and the therapist's professionalism.

Taking the medicine

Since a prolonged period of psychotherapy is often not possible, because of insufficient money and the spare time it demands, I have devised the self-help programme based on the teachings of Dr Claire Weekes, which I have found extremely successful. But it's no good reading through the programme once; it must be read and read, and practised and practised, until it is known by heart, so that the mind automatically presents it in time of need. Personally, I have put it on tape, and find the spoken instructions to be much more powerful than the written. On the rare occasions when I cannot sleep, I listen to the tape, and on the even more rare occasions when my nerves really start to jangle, I listen to parts of it three times a day like medicine taken three times a day after meals, and I can assure you, it works!

Nervous Exhaustion... Stress

Introduction

Nervous exhaustion is hell. The hardest thing is its loneliness. No one understands, save those in the same boat, then you can talk and swap symptoms; but a fellow sufferer cannot give you the answers. He has not found the way out himself.

Everyone is full of advice - "Oh, pull yourself together", "Cheer up, it will be all the same in a hundred years time!" So bloody what? And one's heart sinks into one's boots.

If you suffer from a broken leg or appendicitis you will get flowers and sympathy. Not so the nervous sufferer! He is 'weird', he wears people out with his strange freaks and phobias, and none of them know how they wear him out with their advice and sheer misunderstanding. But this nervous illness is becoming more and more of a problem in today's busy world, and its common name is 'stress'. Stress is caused by anxiety, and most of us would agree that we are anxious at some stage in our lives. The word 'anxious' comes from the Latin *anxius*, which means being upset or worried by some future happening whose outcome is uncertain.

If we are constantly in a state of anxiety, our nerves can become trigger-happy and fire off at the slightest stimulation. They can be so aroused that they record emotions with increasing intensity and swiftness, such that fear can seem to strike with an almost physical force, causing physical symptoms such as a quickened heart beat, churning stomach and nausea, cramping bowels and diarrhoea, muscle pains, sweaty or cold hands, difficulty in swallowing, and pain and tightness in the chest wall, leading to breathlessness, dizziness, blurred vision, panic attacks, muscle jerks, light-headedness, tingling in the limbs, skin irritations, and a frightening vibration of the whole body like an electrical buzz.

If you are sceptical about the effects of your thoughts on your physical body, try this: close your eyes, and imagine you are holding in your hand a fat, juicy lemon and a small, sharp knife. You roll the lemon on a surface, squeeze the skin, and feel the juiciness within. Then you take the knife and cut the fruit in half. Raising one half to your lips, you take a large, deep bite of tangy, juicy flesh. Now do you believe me?

Just to underline the point, close your eyes again, and imagine you are sitting in a classroom looking at the teacher standing by the blackboard. You notice that she has extremely long, talon-like nails. Suddenly she turns to the board, and raising one hand, she drags her nails from the top to the bottom. By now, your physical reaction should be fairly apparent to you, and you can see clearly just how thinking about a situation affects your body in no uncertain way.

Recognise some of the physical reactions I described? Right! Let's sort them out and find the explanation, because knowing the enemy is half the battle.

The other half is knowing how to deal with these alarming symptoms yourself. After a childhood of being constantly exposed to fear, it was not surprising that I was a total neurotic by the time I was eighteen. I well remember being terribly, mortifyingly, sick on many occasions. If I was actually ill, the abuse stopped for a while and I received a modicum of care, so I began to associate illness with this care and attention. As understanding is the forerunner of cure, what was going on?

Blame

Understanding is vital, because it is the beginning of recovery. There is nothing to be gained by recrimination, blaming others and withholding forgiveness. I hear so many people blame all their troubles on parents, God and other people. "If it hadn't been for so-and-so, none of this would have happened," they declare self-pityingly. Or, "Of course, it's all my mother's fault," or my father's, or my brother's, my sister's, my boss's, et al. "Why me?" is a favourite one, to which I reply, "Why not? What makes you so special?" These statements are destructive in the extreme, and can seriously hinder emotional and spiritual maturity.

Some parents or carers are possessive, jealous and envious of their child's chances in life; some parents are still very dependent themselves, and if they have no parents to hang onto, they hold onto their children like a lifeline. Some parents, who feel that life has passed them by, want to live their lives through their children. Whatever, it's in the past, and it is the present and the future that are important.

When I am feeling really sorry for myself, and tend to blame circumstances or other people, I tap my chest firmly and say, "Eileen, the buck stops here. What are *you* going to do about it?" We all have the priceless gift of free will so that, no matter how devastating the situation in which we find ourselves, we choose how we will react to that situation. You may be paralysed for the rest of your life by a drunken driver, and this is almost beyond bearing, but you still have that choice as to how you will react. Of course, the driver has committed a criminal act, and hopefully will suffer for it. But it is you, lying paralysed on a bed for ever, who have to deal with your reactions. This book is based on how I coped with my particular circumstances.

For many years, I didn't, I just limped through life, trying one crutch after another, trying to find a man, a surrogate mother, a therapist, a pill, go on a course on how to deal with problems, finding a man who would make everything right by taking care of me like the little child I still was – but a crutch is only a crutch, and can't work in the sense of making whole. I shopped around but never found quite what I was looking for because it wasn't outside of me; it was inside me all the time.

Who am I?

Freud and his successors proved that nervous distress is always the result of emotions in conflict with one another, because you are not one person but three. There may be many more of you, but three will suffice for the moment. Before you scoff, think how many times have you said, "I was beside myself with rage"? Who was beside you? Or – "I am sorry: I am not myself today." Or – "It's just not like me to do something so awful." After acting without thinking, we say, "When I came to my senses, I was sorry." What do I mean when I say, "During meditation, I look right into myself"? What is our better nature? Who is I, and who is myself?

The most obvious is the everyday self, the self we recognise and are conscious of. This book is not a psychology textbook, so I will call it the 'central self' (1). The central self is usually a sensible, realistic, acceptable person, with a few foibles like worrying about what other people think, and trying to keep up with the neighbours, but in the main it follows tradition in the normal way of life.

However, the 'hungry self' (2) is much less sure of itself and very vulnerable about its place in society; it lacks confidence, is on the defensive, feels shy, awkward, indecisive, dissatisfied and unable to make friends; it would rather help in the kitchen at a party than be involved in the party itself. Alternatively, if the person is female, she will retreat into her shell if she cannot create a sensation and be the belle of the ball. It is as if, somewhere along the line, these personalities have suffered an incapacitating blow; their sense of inadequacy is brought about by the existence of two other selves at war within them, of whom they are not aware.

Let us call this state of mind the 'hungry self' – much less alarming than 'libidinal ego' or 'id'!

The hungry self is definitely not an OK guy, but is very, very powerful. Every now and then, we catch a glimpse of the hungry self, are strangely disturbed, and replace the lid as quickly as possible. I see my own hungry self in sudden, almost uncontrollable rage which really frightens me. This hungry self is like the classic picture of two children out in the snow with their noses pressed to the window of a warm and welcoming room in which their more fortunate peers are seen happy, well dressed, surrounded by food and presents, while two handsome, adoring parents cater to their every whim.

The hungry self is the result of the frustrations of babyhood. All we wanted when we came into the world was the deep, intimate, sensual satisfaction of our mother's breast. Offer us a win on the Lottery or a holiday in the Caribbean, and we couldn't care less – but take us from our mother's breast before we were ready to sleep and we would scream blue murder. Breast feeding isn't in itself necessary, although preferable, it's the holding and the nurturing which are important. If this primitive hunger is satisfied at the time, the baby can move forward into more mature and balanced relationships. But deprive him of it, and a raging, intolerable hunger arises that persists throughout life, and very often this hunger shows itself as anger, hate, cruelty, suffering, and an overwhelming sense of self-pity. How often have I succumbed to the 'poor little me' refrain which is being sung within.

As the baby grows older, he is forced into more civilised behaviour, but though he may appear to be a model citizen, scratch the surface and you will find the hungry self screaming, "I will have what I want – all of it! If I can't get it, like Elizabeth Bott in the William books, I'll thcream and thcream and thcream until I'm thick."

The third self is the condemned, condemning self (3) – the anti-libido ego or super-ego in psycho-speak. This is the self that says to us, "If life is to be endurable, I must conform to all forms of authority," and we are miserable and guilty if we do not conform. It has its roots in those early years, when our very existence seemed to depend on total obedience to other laws, such as saying 'please' and 'thank you', washing our necks and performing various loathsome chores which seemed to have little point. But if we didn't obey these laws, we were outsiders, unloved and unacceptable. Few children can survive such terrible and terrifying isolation.

All nervous suffering can be traced back to the very early years of life. Inevitably, it concerns the backlash between the hungry self (2) and the condemning self (3), where the intelligent and mature central self (1) is not sufficiently in control. But if the sufferer can be made aware of what is going on, he has a chance of helping himself out of his dilemma, by strengthening his central self and bringing his emotional affairs under stable and peaceful control. Why is he not aware of all this going on? Mostly, because the pattern is unconscious, and secondly, the central self is weak because of damage during the early years when it does not understand what is happening. This pattern always brings some warped substitute gratification to the sufferer, which doesn't make sense to the conscious intelligent mind.

As you have seen, the hungry self rebels against the condemned/condemning self, or the condemning self punishes the central self and the hungry self. Or your unconscious mind may find irrational ways of fulfilling the desires of the hungry self without the central self's consent – and the result is chaos. If you cannot fulfil yourself in love, the energies of that love turn to hate, humiliation, sadism, masochism, perversion or self-hate. The condemning self may insist on punishment from which your central self recoils, but the central self may be too weak to resist, and break down under the pressure of the other two personalities. So your emotions are harnessed to despair or suffering instead of happiness.

This dilemma needs to be clearly understood in the first place. Understanding alone will help you to understand the peculiarities of someone else's behaviour, but the pattern of your own is totally unclear. During your early life, your emotional problems were so threatening for you to face, you put blinkers on the eyes of your mind. Thus, your hungry self was able to get emotional satisfaction secretly, and your condemning self was also able to punish secretly. So the second step in the process of healing is insight. This is a sudden flash of awareness into your emotional condition. You see suddenly what your unconscious mind is doing with you. With practice, you can stand outside yourself and watch your emotions in action gradually recognising your own patterns of behaviour. If this sounds ridiculous and unlikely, let us look at my own particular pattern. This is not egotistical, it is just that I know myself better than anyone else.

I have had this experience in fact myself by realising that my intense desire to help everyone and make everyone happy arises from the hope that this will bring me the love, admiration, appreciation and security that was so lacking in my infant life. Wanting to help people is a very praiseworthy goal, and obviously one to be encouraged, but it is not appropriate when an adult is seeking the emotional satisfactions of a child. So in me it had its repercussions. I would work flat out at school with pupils, or in counselling with patients, but when working hours were over, instead of enjoying my well-earned leisure, I would sink into gloom, despondency, despair and overwhelming waves of self-pity. Or I would boil with injustice and anger, particularly on Bank Holidays when everyone seemed to be enjoying themselves with partners, friends and family, except me! I would find myself fuming, fretting, blaming other people and ticking off someone in my mind for their imagined part in my frustration. I felt let down, and would go for a solitary walk by the sea or on the Downs which only intensified my feelings of lonely isolation.

"Everyone's all right but me – it's not fair! All I do is work and put myself out for other people, and what do they care? Here I am on a lovely sunny Bank Holiday all alone, and no one gives a damn…" etc. I would struggle against this – after all, I was a psychotherapist, wasn't I? And deliberately try to enjoy myself, but after a few seconds, there I was back in the hell of injustice. Now I have insight into this situation, I don't do it any more – well, not often anyway. I saw that, while my conscious mind wanted to enjoy the walk, my unconscious mind was pulling me back relentlessly to my fury and sense of injustice. There was something deep inside me that insisted on my making a meal of my injuries. My throat hurt and tears welled up into my eyes. But I couldn't cry – why not? Because so many times I had been held between strong knees and shaken by the shoulders while Auntie Alice shouted, "No tears! No tears!" from a distorted mouth in a red and furious face.

So many times I had found myself in bed without supper – the bad, ungrateful girl whom nobody wanted because she was so bad and whose mother everyone had 'hated'. It was as if my whole life had been one big tragedy of frustration, injustice and failure: there was no hope – everything had to end in devastation. So finally and painfully I recognised that, though I seemed consciously to be intent on a successful and fulfilling life, happiness and peace of mind, my unconscious mind was devoted to an orgy of failure, heartbreak, disillusion, injustice and revenge. This was why I fumed and raged against people and circumstances in my mind. This was something I would not let go of, because it was my meat and drink – it was my unconscious life, the hungry self at work insisting on its satisfaction.

For so many years, these energies had been flowing into this kind of negative emotion. This was why I couldn't enjoy life and loved to retreat into morbid self-pity. My baby self was realising its satisfaction, my energies – which I was unable to pour into anger – went into self-hate, causing me to become submissive, self-effacing and self-disparaging. The energies of my hungry self were finding an outlet in humiliation because, during my early childhood, I believed every other door was closed. All my life, the part of me that could take pleasure in fulfilment and happiness was dominated by the part of me that wanted to feed on tragedy, self-pity and self-hate. And so I became a prime candidate for 'nerves'. I saw that the nervous sufferer is a victim – someone who has had a raw deal very early in life.

Fear

In its primitive form fear is life-saving. Faced with a mugger, for example, copious amounts of adrenalin pour into the bloodstream and cause our heart rate to increase, our blood pressure to rise, and our breathing to quicken. This enables more oxygen to be absorbed, digestion ceases, muscles tense, and we receive urgent messages to empty our bowels and bladder. If we use these preparations of the body to act physically, all is well, but if we neither fight back nor run away, we are left with the effects which are most upsetting. Such a conflict leaves our mind in a turmoil and our body with the physical symptoms previously mentioned. Unfortunately these feelings can cause more fear because we are ashamed of them.

If they can be explained or discussed with a counsellor or wise friend, it is often possible to find a way to live with them, or maybe even to solve the conflict. But if we do not allow even ourselves to recognise the cycle of fear we are in, then the conflict continues and our misery is endless.

Fear is common to us all. Like death, it is the great unmentionable. After an event of great physical danger, everyone will agree that no one panicked because there is great shame attached to admitting to fear. The result is that the fear gets buried deep in the subconscious mind and causes nightmares, agoraphobia (fear of going out) or claustrophobia (fear of small spaces), allergies or frequent illnesses.

The fear of actual danger is bad enough, but the fear we have buried so deep inside us so that we no longer identify it, is far worse. We feel excruciating shame, anxiety and guilt for no apparent reason, and we are further afraid to tell anyone for fear they would think we are weak or mad.

Sometimes I wake at 2 am and lie in a sweat of anxiety over who will look after me if I become senile and incontinent – after all, I am already in my eighties and am enough of a realist to know that old age does bring indignities and inadequacies. I learn from my patients that this is a very common experience, waking in a sweat of fear in the early hours of the morning. So I gain some comfort from knowing that, all over the country, people are lying awake experiencing the same uncertainty and loneliness, feeling they are falling and dissolving without hope of rescue. Some people, like me, wake completely alone, or even if a figure does lie beside them, it refuses to wake and comfort them.

The main thing is to face the fear, not run away from it, by turning it into an anxiety like, 'Who will look after me when I am old?' 'The lump in my breast is certain to be cancer,' 'I should have done more for that patient or that friend before they died,' 'I don't feel well enough to do all the things I've undertaken to do tomorrow,' 'What if I have a heart attack in the supermarket or a stroke in the street?' And so on. I have to face the fact that I'm experiencing the terrible loneliness of being, which has the wonderful name 'existential angst'. This ridiculously pretentious name makes me smile, so I tell myself that I am experiencing 'existential angst', and find laughter in the midst of fear.

I began to see the reason for my phobias — like a fear of heights, terror of travelling in a lift, and a mortifying inability to go on the more terrifying rides at a fairground. Fear is natural and protective, but phobias are not. If I live on the edge of a cliff which is gradually crumbling into the sea, the sensible thing to do is to leave and move further inland. Remove the cause of fear, and it no longer exists. But a phobia strikes terror where none exists. It also has a symbolic significance in that it shows clearly the buried reasons for our irrational reactions. Lastly, in a phobia there is not only conscious fear but also unconscious hunger: we want a repetition of the very thing we fear.

A phobia is a desire in disguise. I realised that my fear of heights was symbolic of the struggle between my three selves: the hungry self where all my desires were, the highly moral condemning self where I felt my 'duty' lay, and the central self which was weak and divided. I felt I must live on the heights, which was my condemning self, but all my desires were down below with the hungry self. So I became busy; I retreated from the problem life had given me into 'nerves'; the conflict in my emotions was like the danger of looking over a cliff which can be dangerous if we go near the edge. My conflicts were so painful and made me feel so agonisingly alone that I 'converted' them into a fear of heights which it is much easier to accept.

A claustrophobic patient once stayed in a small hotel room and woke in the night, panicked by the fear of asphyxia. He got up and broke the sealed window, took several deep breaths, went back to bed and slept soundly and deeply for the rest of the night. When he awoke, he was astonished to find the front of a bookcase broken, and the window intact! A go-getting American friend of mine suffers from claustrophobia in England because she feels it is so small.

Fear will certainly return, so you must be prepared to be afraid, not in a tense and apprehensive way, but with true acceptance. Recognise it, face and accept it, float through it (we will examine floating later), and be prepared to let it do its worst. It is the apprehension and intention that are creating the very fear you fear. A habit of fear can only be broken when it is faced and accepted. Take these steps slowly to give yourself time to remember and practise what you have been taught.

When you attempt to overcome fear, start slowly and continue at a steady pace throughout. Go even more slowly when panic reaches its peak. Hurrying creates agitation, and agitation creates panic. Acceptance means a certain amount of resignation, and resignation implies a certain amount of peace.

A criminal who finally gives himself up to the police at least finds some peace, and this is how the nervously ill person feels when they finally decide to surrender to the worst fear can do, when they decide to accept and not fight any more.

Courage

Life is a journey and this implies a continuous travelling forward. In order to maintain this progress, we have to cultivate courage, and you may say, 'But I have no courage; I am not brave – I am a coward.' But courage comes from the heart; the Latin **cor** means 'heart'. It is not so much defiance, or being brave; it is an extraordinary quality possessed by everyone if they want it truly and earnestly.

If you want to be courageous, you will be. You may have failed in the past because you have misled yourself. You did not really feel the urge to meet your situation with true courage. The feeling must override all other feelings and not be weakened by vague 'if onlys' and futile wishes. It has to be established and cultivated until it becomes a part of you.

Sit or lie still and close your eyes. Think of something or someone you want very much in your life. It is here, where you feel this yearning, that you will feel courage – in the pit of your stomach. At the start of this practice, be satisfied if all you feel is the yearning for courage, and in time – with practice and perseverance – it will become courage itself.

It is interesting that this feeling is felt in our middle and not in our mind. If you give your wish to be courageous sufficient concentration, it will set into a rock-like determination to succeed. But of course, you must be willing to put these ideas into practice many, many times before they produce a permanent result. When you finally have this courage, it will always stand as your shield against adversity and failure.

Try this experiment when you are feeling mortally afraid, having an attack of tachycardia (heart palpitations), have lost your temper or are panicking, any time you are feeling overcome by your own particular nervous symptom. If it is possible, give yourself half an hour, switch off the phone, and don't answer the door.

Lie or sit down in a comfortable place and relax as much as possible. There are methods of relaxation in another chapter. If relaxation seems impossible, feeling jumpy or fearful as you do, just gently make the attempt. Relax as much as is possible for you at this moment; then allow your feelings to take you where they will – even if you feel you are about to die or have a stroke, or a heart attack, or finally topple over into insanity.

Now ask yourself, 'When have I felt like this before?' Not the many times you have felt them recently, but during your earlier life – perhaps early in your career or at the start of your life with a partner, perhaps in adolescence, schooldays or infancy. You may find it takes time but do persevere, giving your imagination and feelings complete freedom to go where they will.

This process of association is a natural one, and will bring memories of the past that you have forgotten. From this practice, I realised the intensely painful feelings of a very frightened little girl. I remembered situations where I felt totally unloved, inadequate and unable to succeed. If I expanded these feelings further, I realised I had compensated for this intolerable inadequacy by being overly submissive, excessively thoughtful, unnaturally attentive, and precociously deferential to my aunts' and my grandmother's needs. I realised that my way to fulfilment in love had been totally blocked during my childhood, and so these energies of the hungry self – which must be satisfied, remember – had found expression in martyrdom, despair and emptiness. I felt this emptiness physically as an aching chasm in the pit of my stomach; it was as if someone had cut away my flesh and left a gaping, bleeding hole, over which I bent literally in agonising pain. Not only do we need to recognise the course our emotional energies have taken, but also to feel it happening. We may be 20, 30, 40, 50 years old, or even older, but in our emotional life, we are stuck. The energies that should be going into success, peace of mind, love and appreciation of the wonder of life, are still flowing into self-hatred, and self-punishment. Without knowing it, we have been feeding on this emotional meal all our lives, but when we see the secret ways of our emotional life, we can harness these energies to the enjoyment of life, to health and success.

After using this exercise, I felt an immediate release of my symptoms, both physical and emotional, but of course, one swallow does not make a summer. And for any sort of permanent cure, it must be practised over and over until it becomes a habit, until you gain a permanent insight into your problem. To make this possible, you must realise again and again that *it is not your fault*. You are not responsible for the way you were programmed during an impressionable stage of your life.

You are only responsible when you have the understanding and the capacity for insight, when the enemy forces are clear to you and the weapons of their destruction put into your hands. Unfortunately, many people are unwilling to take this responsibility because it means work, and most of us are lazy – I know I am: as I sit here writing, my hungry self keeps whining that it wants to stop and have a drink or, better still, go and have a walk, a jog or a swim. If I realise what is going on here, I will let my central self reinforce the decision I made to sit and write for two hours, and then do what my hungry self wants – to have a drink or to jog or to swim – which is necessary for the balance of my personality. All work and no play will make Eileen a very dull girl. But you see in this trivial example how vigilance has to be maintained all the time, and this is hard work. But what a reward it brings!

Such peace of mind and such positive enjoyment of the whole of life, from the sheer breathtaking beauty of a magnolia flower, the awe-inspiring majesty of an ancient tree, the bulbs bravely breaking through the darkness of winter earth, to the joyful appreciation of the heartbreaking brevity of life itself. How many excellent schoolteachers refuse the responsibility, obligations and duties of being a headteacher, how many well-qualified sergeants have no desire to become an officer? It is no wonder that so many of us do

169

not want the work or the responsibilities that accompany genuine mental health.

Abandonment

My experiences in childhood laid down the foundations of constant fear due to my strong sense of being abandoned, starting from my birth experience of literally being discarded as dead. This sense of abandonment is the opposite of being safely and securely held, which was how we felt in the womb. Being suddenly expelled into the world is our first experience of being abandoned. Mothers who are given their babies at once can hold them close and secure, but babies who do not have this may feel deprived and abandoned. In my case these feelings were constantly reinforced throughout childhood, to such an extent that I was unable to recognise it. Therefore I interpreted it as, 'I am thoroughly bad, I am so horrible, no wonder nobody wants me,' instead of saying, 'I am being punished unjustly by my aunt.' In order not to be abandoned, I felt I always had to please everyone, to be well organised, reliable and sensible, and to do everything perfectly. Even now, my house and my appearance have to be immaculate, my garden trim and neat, and visitors given home-made food served correctly. I do relax my standards when I am alone, but not very far... if you were to look in my cupboards and drawers...!

Everyone needs to be completely and securely held throughout their lives, and if we are not physically held, we need to know that we are loved and accepted by the people around us. There is no word in English for this need, because in our country, people who have it are considered weak and contemptible; we only admire the strong and the competently independent. Sir John Falstaff said, 'A plague on sighing and grief. It blows a man up like a bladder.'

So we hide this deep and vital need to be held secure in loving arms – not just literally held, but also to have the assurance of someone else's secure and indulgent love, coming home to the welcome knowledge that you can be yourself and totally accepted as you are. The husband who takes you in his arms when you look disgusting because you have the flu, the mother who gathers up her son's filthy football shorts from the bathroom floor, the granny who allows a sticky toddler to climb on her new dress for a cuddle. This is the security of loving arms which is needed by us all, but so often is missing from our lives.

Feeling abandoned can cause us to become either an extrovert or an introvert. Extroverts obtain their security from being part of a group, and feel annihilated on their own; introverts experience reality by being absorbed in the study and development of their own inner experience. Many introverts learn the skills of social interaction, and many extroverts learn the skills of experiencing and understanding their inner reality.

I used to think I was both, but when my back is against the wall, I know that I am an extrovert in the final analysis. I know I need people, so I meet this need by being extremely friendly, sometimes overly so, and by doing a job that involves close contact with other people, and catering to their need for support and genuine caring.

Nerves

To understand stress, we have to know how our nervous system works. The nervous system is divided into two – the voluntary nervous system and the involuntary nervous system. The voluntary nerves – as their name suggest – are under our direct control, and we move our muscles as we wish. The involuntary nerves, helped by hormones from our glands, control the workings of our organs – lungs, bowels, heart, kidneys, brain and so on. These nerves are not under our direct control but respond to our mood, and create some of the nervous symptoms mentioned earlier. If we are afraid, we go white, our heart races, we feel sick and breathless, and our blood pressure rises. A hormone is a substance formed in some organ of the body and carried to another organ or tissue, where it has a specific effect.

We have no power to stop these reactions consciously; but – and this is very important in understanding nervous illness – we can calm these symptoms by changing our mood. This is most important! *We can calm these symptoms by changing our mood*, because our mood is under *our* control. This can be done either with mood-changing drugs or by relaxation and meditation. In the past, I took valium, librium and seconal from time to time, but apart from making me feel muzzy, dopey and unable to cope, they were not really helpful. As soon as

I stopped taking them, my nervous symptoms returned in full force, magnified by the side-effects of the drugs.

Involuntary nerves consist of two divisions – sympathetic and para-sympathetic. When the body is peaceful, these two divisions hold each other in balance. When we are afraid, excited or angry, the sympathetic dominates so our heart races, our blood pressure rises, our breathing alters, and we are in a 'fight or flight' situation. The sympathetic nerves are aroused by hormones, several of which react to stress.

There are numerous hormones in the human body, but the chief hormone is adrenalin, which seems to be the prime mover, and so for the sake of simplicity, I will speak only of this.

Nervous symptoms over a period of time can be so upsetting and confusing that we become more afraid of them than of the anxiety and fear that caused the original stress. So by adding extra stress to an already frightened state, we stimulate the release of more and more adrenalin, and other stress hormones, and intensify these awful symptoms that we dread so much. This is what Claire Weekes calls the 'fear – adrenalin – more fear' cycle, in which we become trapped, and once trapped, we are well on the way to becoming nervously ill.

The original upsetting situation causes a physically expressed flash of panic, of which the sufferer is so frightened that it causes a second flash of fear to occur, thus prolonging the strain on his nerves. He thinks he is experiencing only one terrible spasm of panic, and is therefore much more ill than he thought. His lack of understanding is his worst enemy because now he is so afraid of his symptoms and their constant renewal that he is paralysed by them.

This is how agoraphobia starts: first, there is fear of symptoms, then there are places where they may occur, like leaving the safety of home, so that the sufferer will not go out any more but will stay indoors in a state of terror, which again intensifies his symptoms. If he lost his fear of his nervous symptoms, the situation would heal itself.

OMGWIs

The spiral of stress can also involve an over-active imagination, where the person develops what I call a severe case of the OMGWIs, which stands for 'Oh my goodness, what if?' For instance, 'I didn't sleep a wink last night' (he probably did), 'Oh, my goodness, what if I never sleep again?' 'That pain in my stomach' (which is actually sensitive nerves). 'Oh my goodness, what if I've got cancer?' 'Palpitation in my heart – oh my goodness, what if I'm going to die – what will happen to my family?' And so on, and so on.

It's so easy, and no doubt you recognise yourself in some of these examples. It's no good some well-meaning person telling you over and over again that you'll be alright, don't worry. Because at the time you know that it certainly won't be alright, that you are almost prostrate on the floor with worry. I used to feel as if I were moving in some other dimension, terrified – almost literally – out of my mind, feeling cut off from everyone. Once I felt as though I had a lump in my throat, had great difficulty in swallowing, imagining that my throat was swollen, and again was convinced that I had cancer. But once I realised that this was merely a muscular spasm of nervous origin, called *globus hystericus*, that is 'hysterical lump', I was able to relax and accept it as such. And it gradually disappeared.

The Heart

Symptoms in the area of the heart are particularly frightening because your heart is the centre of your being, and any malfunction in its beat seems to threaten life itself. So no wonder you feel so scared and think you are going to die. I must emphasise here that if you are worried about any persistent physical symptoms, particularly connected with your heart, you must go to a medical practitioner and have a complete physical examination. Only when you have his or her total assurance that there is nothing organically wrong with you can you go ahead with my suggestions with complete confidence.

I have had patients who were not reassured by one medical examination, so I therefore directed them to another practitioner for the same examination. If this too is satisfactory, then go ahead with self-help, and let any OMGWIs gently float away out of your head. And in time, such frightening thoughts will go away. We will speak more about floating later.

Stop watching, waiting and taking your pulse. It's a waste of time because your thoughts cannot harm your heart; it's a strong, thick, powerful muscle, temporarily overstimulated by your own fear and anxiety. Your heart is responding faithfully and normally to your stimuli by putting you into a situation of readiness for fighting or running away. When we lived in caves, these reactions literally made the difference between life and death. However, in the modern world, the threat has become fear of unemployment, fear of the boss, vague concerns about our health, anxiety about our children, our parents, and our complicated and often upsetting domestic situations. In today's world we cannot kill or run away from the boss, our family, pollution, congestion, etc. Well, we could but we would rapidly find ourselves in worse trouble! So the symptoms of stress remain; we become afraid of the symptoms and so a permanent condition of stress is established.

So, your heart is racing, thumping, banging and shaking. But in reality, it's probably not working much harder than any other healthy heart. It is only disturbing to you because you have become so aware or sensitive to its beating that you cannot stop thinking about it. If you have a comprehensive examination of your heart as I suggest, and the result is satisfactory, then stop resting for fear of harming your heart, go out for a walk, a jog even, or play tennis or badminton. It is more likely your heart will calm down and beat more slowly while you are doing this.

So be prepared to live with this erratic beating until your nerves calm down, which they will do as you understand the adrenalin theory, and accept the rattling, racing, banging and thumping as part of your recovery, and you will be getting better all the time. Once again, I stress, do have an examination by a medical practitioner to assure you that there is nothing organically wrong with your body, and particularly your heart. And once again, I stress that there is no magic wand to wave, no magic bullet to take, so that you must not be impatient with time. If you find acceptance difficult, then a mild sedative prescribed occasionally by your doctor or herbalist can be a great help. I only preach acceptance, not masochism!

Emotions at War

Such is the strength of the condemning self in nervous suffering, that whenever the central self tries to take the initiative, the condemning self pounces on him and takes over. So you have the central self being harassed by these two secret selves, who are not only at war with it, but also at war with each other. The hungry self is screaming uncontrollably, "I will have what I want," and at the same time the condemning self is saying, "You are wicked and worthless, and you must do exactly as you are told, or else." If the central self is strong, and the two secret selves remain within bounds, the personality stays strong and reasonably decisive: it can cope. But if the other two selves are constantly waging war and making impossible demands, all hell is let loose in the personality, and nervous trouble is the result.

It is rather like a situation in a 'western' movie: there is a gang of totally lawless and amoral young men who decide they are going to rampage through the town and turn it upside down; anyone who gets in their way will be knocked out of it in no uncertain fashion. This gang represents the hungry self. But of course the established citizens of the town won't stand for this: they represent the condemning self. They have their land and property to protect; they have their traditions – they will not allow young hooligans to bring violence and lawlessness to their town. They will fight to the death if necessary to keep law and order. So, in the first instance, they seek out the sheriff – that is, the central self, and demand that he clear these young hooligans out. So it all depends on the strength of the sheriff. If he can command respect from both parties, he will ride the storm and come to some agreement. He will concede in some but refuse to budge or yield elsewhere. So he may come through without bloodshed. But he needs to be strong to avoid serious trouble.

This situation is going on in every human life, and if the central self is weak and doesn't know his own mind, there is tension. The hungry self is making outrageous demands; the condemning self insists on a miserable, cheerless obedience to outworn principles; and the central self is at his wits' end and can't make a decision. So we get 'nerves'. So many good people suffer from this state of tension.

Let us take a hypothetical case. She is the only child left living with her widowed mother in the country, and has two brothers, both married and with homes set up abroad. She is thirty years old and would like to marry and have children. She has a job, poorly paid, in a small town nearby, but always feels compelled to go straight home as her mother is chairbound with arthritis. Her hungry self shouts, "You are meant for love and a family. Leave your mother – get a better job in a larger city where you will meet people and find a partner." But the condemning self is quite appalled by this, and shouts, equally loudly, "Leave the mother you say you love to manage alone – after all she has sacrificed for you for so long? That is unforgivable. And if you do leave, you will have nothing but the remorse and unhappiness you deserve."

If the central self is strong, if this woman has a mind of her own, she will find a solution, not an easy solution, but a solution. However, if the central self is weak, tremendous tension will result. She will become angry and impatient with her mother, then suffer an orgy of remorse. She asks for forgiveness and feels it is right to stay at home. But soon the hungry self says to her, "Why should I bury myself here? I must leave home and live my own life." So the struggle is renewed. After a while, she develops blinding headaches which show that one part of her is banging against another. Her central self cannot make a choice. She says to me, "I tried to walk over the wooden bridge the other day, but I was so terrified of falling that I had to go the long way round."

This panic is the symbol of these three struggling selves: down below is the hungry self, and up above, the highly moral condemning self where she feels her duty lies. The central self is weak and divided, feeling she must take the higher way, over the bridge, but all her desires are down below, so she becomes giddy. The conflict in her emotions is like walking over a bridge that isn't safe. So she now has a fear of heights and migraine headaches, which will be alleviated by pills and potions, but not cured until she understands her basic dilemma – that her central self can take over the problem and reach an intelligent decision.

As a footnote, one might hope that the mother in this situation would have sufficient love and understanding for her child that her central self could take over and make arrangements for her own care, thereby giving her daughter the freedom which is her right and which she deserves.

So nervous distress is always the result of emotions at war. But we now know that this battle starts in the earliest months of a baby's life. In these primary crises, we evolve our personal strategies, and these become habits which may persist throughout our lives. Take an example – Danny, aged two, wants an ice cream. His mother says no, so Danny whimpers and grizzles, and the more he complains, the more his desire for the ice cream grows. To himself he is saying, "I will have an ice cream, if it's the last thing I do." His Mum makes it very clear that she doesn't like little boys who whine and cry for ice cream, but Danny rants and raves and screams and scratches until his Mum's already frayed nerves snap and, for the sake of peace, she gives it to him. "All right then, here it is, and mind it doesn't choke you!" So Danny has won, or has he?

After he has eaten the ice cream, he realises that he has won his ice cream, but lost his Mum, as she doesn't like little boys who whimper for ice cream, and he not only whimpered – he screamed and he scratched. So he is quite sure his mother doesn't love him any more. And not to be loved for a little boy of two is a very serious matter indeed. He has lost his whole security and he is enveloped by a paralysing fear. This fear affects the nerves of his stomach, so that he has a bilious attack and brings back the ice cream. "There you are!" says his mother, "You see what happens to little boys who scream for ice cream when their mother says no."

So, because of this episode and probably others like it, a sequence of events begins that is to affect Danny for many years to come. If his hungry self wants something badly enough, he will do almost anything at all to get it. but at the same time, the mother within him – the condemning self – is disapproving and condemnatory. So at first, he is pleased with his success, but soon his pleasure turns to insecurity, alarm and discomfort. He probably suffers from nausea and butterflies in his stomach; he may give away what he has gained. He is remorseful and depressed, so this habit of making excessive demands of life by the hungry self, followed by gratification and ultimately remorse and the need for punishment by the condemning self, becomes his normal pattern of behaviour. He is not conscious of this, because it is buried deeply in his unconscious mind.

Accept

The whole treatment of nervous illness may be summed up in one word – ACCEPT. Whatever happens, provided you have been pronounced organically sound by a medical practitioner, accept it all as part of your healing, but be patient. It has taken you months and years to be programmed this way and it is going to take time for you to be deprogrammed.

Hearing the satisfactory explanation of your condition, you may lose your fear of it and recover quickly. But remember that you are always vulnerable to the tricks that memory can play, and therefore liable to setback and the return of all your distressing symptoms. Just as the conductor in an orchestra can stop all the instruments with one tap of his baton, so you can calm all your symptoms with one word – ACCEPT. Take a mild tranquilliser if you must, but it's the *acceptance* and the *floating* that will heal, and remember that you are *practising* floating through, not testing to see if you can.

An agoraphobic patient of mine arrived in great distress: 'I travelled into town so well yesterday, and yet today I panicked as soon as I shut the front door – why?' Well, it was because yesterday's journey was so successful that she was defeated today. Yesterday's success had made her over-anxious to be as successful again this time. So she started the journey apprehensive and tense; it only took memory and maybe a minor incident on the way out to bring panic. This convinced her that the journey would be a failure, so she despaired – more emotion, bringing more stress and more vulnerability to total failure.

So practise, practise, practise – never test. If you have panic after panic, take each one in the right way: accept it, don't fight it, and float through it, and that journey made with panic will bring you nearer to recovery than one made without panic. You will never lose what you have gained if you practise the right way. But you must keep practising; however tired you are, however ill you feel, keep accepting, keep floating, keep practising. Have the occasional rest for your body's sake, but even then, read this section – or listen to a recording of it – over and over until you know the procedure as well as you know your twice times table.

When you are programmed in this way, you will automatically recall the procedure when panic strikes suddenly or you are going through a setback. This is a simple method, but it is not easy. You will need your own determination to succeed and that determination has to be a really strong resolve, a total willingness to accept, an ability to float, and patience with time; don't be impatient with time!

I wish you well in your endeavours, and remember the Chinese proverb: 'Trouble is a tunnel through which we pass, and not a brick wall against which we must break our head.' Remember also not to run away from fear; see it as no more than a physical feeling with which you can now deal successfully.

This acceptance must be total and complete acceptance, without a trace of resignation. It's no good saying, 'I have accepted the rocks in my stomach but they are still there – so now what do I do?' because that means you haven't accepted them at all. You're still dwelling on them and subconsciously expecting them to get worse. You have to be so truly accepting of the rocks that they no longer matter. Then the nerves releasing adrenalin are freed from the stimulus of tension and anxiety and will gradually calm down, thus dispersing the 'rocks' over a period of time until they disappear altogether. You have to change your mood from fear and apprehension to total acceptance. That's important, it needs repeating: *you have to change your mood from fear and apprehension to total acceptance.*

Don't expect immediate results; it will be some time before your body reacts to your new mood of acceptance. You may have been frightened and tense for many years, probably all your life, and it will take time for your body to accept this new mood, and be calm and peaceful. So don't give up on these methods of self-help. Keep going and praise yourself frequently for your courage and your will-power. I buy myself a small treat for every victory – a bunch of flowers, a new paperback, a bar of chocolate, a bottle of wine, a new T-shirt, or I go for a swim or a walk over the hills, or for a special meal.

Make sure you don't just think you are accepting; if you can feel sick and let your hands tremble, your head ache, your heart thump, without paying them too much attention, then you are truly accepting. As I look back on my own symptoms – my hammering heart, my uneasy stomach, my sweating hands and inability to take deep breaths – I realise these symptoms were with me all the time. Other symptoms like spasms of fear, 'missed' heartbeats (they aren't missed, in fact, they are just out of sync), pains in my chest, giddiness, vomiting and diarrhoea, came at intervals in sudden attacks, so the ever-present symptoms were the result of constant fear, whilst the periodic attacks were caused by an increase of the intensity of that fear. What I was doing was shrinking away from my feelings, instead of facing them – desperately shying away from them and tensing myself against them. At the same time, I was anxiously listening in, causing a severe attack of the OMGWIs. All these reactions caused more and more adrenalin to flow which in turn stimulated all my symptoms, and made me feel worse and worse – a vicious circle indeed. What was so sad was that I was wasting my talents and my time in this useless flogging of my body and my nerves, when I could have used that energy, imagination and drive to improve my life and the conditions around me. But there is nothing whatsoever to be gained in morbid retrospection; there must be no looking back to find excuses for time wasted and opportunities missed. Do not be impatient with time.

You have probably realised by now that your devastating physical symptoms can only be made worse by fear of them. So there is a limit to their intensity. But what if I faint, vomit, suffocate, I hear you ask? These extremes are highly unlikely to occur, but even if they do, I still say, accept. I know what courage this takes, but it is the only way. Once you have really mastered the art of acceptance, you will be well on the way to an enjoyable and fulfilling existence. It is like taking a bin bag off your head, and seeing the vast and exciting possibilities of life for the very first time. Joy takes over from fear, interest and imagination replace self-doubt and terrifying insecurity.

Ten years ago, I was found to have high blood pressure. This had come about after a very difficult situation arose in the close in which I live. This left me with a severe attack of the 'Oh my goodness, what ifs?'. What if this is what my life is going to be like from now on? At the time I was nearly 80 – 'I'll have to go into a home', I thought. With the help of a fortnight at Tyringham, I managed to turn my thoughts around and face and accept and float through. When I thought, 'I've a dreadful headache, my vision is blurred, I feel very muzzy, what if I'm going to have a stroke? If I have a stroke, what if I'm helpless and dribbling, at the mercy of impersonal professionals for the rest of my life?' That was the signal for me to walk on through thinking, 'So what if any of these things do happen?' Why threaten the mobility and comparative health of the moment with stressful thoughts about an unpredictable future? And it worked. I was also helped by a very firm belief in infinite love, the presence of my personal guardian angel, and of course the purely practical help of the Tyringham treatments.

Floating

Floating means that, instead of being even more frightened by the symptoms of your fear than you were of the original fearful situation which started it, you remind yourself of what is actually going on in your mind and body. You understand that they are just the normal symptoms that a healthy body produces when reacting to fear and then you accept it as normal. You then react by *floating* through the situation instead of fighting it.

Floating means just what it says: floating forward through the situation without resistance. You can float on a cloud, or on water, on a ship, a raft, on angels' wings, or just on air. So you close your eyes, and ask your mind to conjure up a picture in which you are floating safely and peacefully.

Your visualisation is better than mine because we're all uniquely and wonderfully made and my visualisation may awaken unpleasant associations in your mind. I once suggested yachts billowing along the horizon of a beautiful blue sea to my yoga class in Hove, and felt quite pleased with myself as there was a regatta going on at the time, which made the visualisation quite easy. After the class, one of my students came up to me, looking quite disturbed, and said, 'Please don't use that picture again. You see, when I am on the beach, I have two little boys under five, and it's all a nightmare in case they drown or run off. So no way could I relax into that picture.' So your own feelings and pictures of floating must be used.

My own feeling and picture of floating is of kicking off from the side of the swimming pool into the breast stroke and feeling that first wonderful sensation of floating and support, but with a movement forward at the same time. Not making any movement, with no stress – you are not fighting your way along, you are just being supported and moving forward without any effort. Floating is relaxing, but it's more than that: it's relaxing with acceptance and understanding. It is as if you step out of your body, and let it find its own way out of the nightmare.

When you cut your finger, you clean it and cover it, and then leave it to get better, and this same healing will heal your over-sensitive nerves if you let go of the OMGWIs and rise above it. The cut finger takes time, it doesn't heal overnight, and in the same way you will release enough tension to loosen your muscles and gradually slow down the production of adrenalin. I have found floating an enormous help, particularly first thing in the morning when I used to feel very depressed. I used to attempt to get out of bed, only to sink back on my pillow, completely defeated by the way I felt. So I decided to float instead, to make no tense effort with gritted teeth, but to give way to the feeling, let it all happen, stop struggling and let my body float up out of it and into my clothes. No grim determination, no sweating, no anxiety, no forcing and no pushing. Fighting is exhausting and will make you worse, but floating is relaxing.

If you are so tense that you cannot even begin to float, then imagine yourself doing it – even this will help. Don't try to float past a real problem. It is essential to find a good friend, a good therapist, or counsellor, to help you find one point-of-view that brings you some peace.

Floating needs practice. You have to do your part and learn the process until it becomes automatic. All this will take time; like the cut finger, all healing must be given time. Don't get impatient; impatience means tension, and tension is the original cause of your illness. It is a chemical process that is going on, and it will need time for readjustments.

This step is just as important as accepting, because you are floating through a stressful situation instead of fighting it, which is what you have been doing up to now. Having faced your symptoms and really accepted them, you then float through them to the comparative peace on the other side. What kind of picture does the word 'floating' evoke? Sailing ships, birds floating through the air, yourself floating on the sea, clouds floating through a clear blue sky, swans floating on a lake? – the images are endless. Whatever your personal visualisation, floating is certainly the opposite of fighting. Floating means no forcing, no pushing, no aggression, no clenched teeth, no grim determination, but just letting your body sag, go slack, taking a deep breath and exhaling slowly through an open mouth. At the same time, you imagine yourself to be floating through the fearful situation, using a picture of your own choice. Your choice of picture is much more effective for you than anyone else's suggestion because it is individually tailored, as it were, to your needs. Once I suggested to my yoga group that they imagine their problems to be a swarm of bees, literally buzzing off and flying away into the distance, as they breathed out. The next minute I was approached by a white-faced individual who said, 'Please don't talk about bees again; I have a phobia about them – they terrify me.' I once suggested to a patient during deep relaxation that he should imagine himself floating on his back on the blue sea of the Mediterranean and feeling the hot sun enveloping him in soothing warmth. He sprang up from the couch as if stung by the former bees, sweating and trembling. 'No, no, no,' he shouted, 'Not water. I'm scared stiff of it. I can't swim.' So, you see, your own picture is better for you than anyone else's suggestions. (And the patient with the water phobia eventually lost it and learned to swim.)

Let us look at these 'ultimate' experiences and face them together. Fainting is unpleasant and weakening. Vomiting and diarrhoea are unpleasant and extremely degrading. But these experiences will pass and be forgotten and, most importantly, *they may never happen*! In spite of a long life, overshadowed to a greater or lesser degree by these fears of public humiliation, they have never actually happened to me. I have fainted, vomited, had diarrhoea, but have always managed to reach a private place before performing these activities.

So having faith and accepted that your difficulties are all rooted in fear, how do you float through it? Some people find the cause of their fear and try to conquer and control it, believing that if they remove the cause, their fear will go. For example, a patient of mine succeeded so well in losing his fear of dying during an attack of palpitations, he lost his fear of the palpitations at the same time, and they ceased. But in my opinion, tackling one fear by itself, does not really cope with the situation, because in overcoming one fear, you may uncover a Pandora's box to put in its place. So it is much more successful to attack the feeling of fear itself.

For example, a woman patient of mine was afraid to go shopping. When I asked her what she was afraid of, she reeled off a whole list: the bus stop where she once collapsed, meeting an unsympathetic neighbour who treated her problems with contemptuous amusement, waiting in the checkout queue at the supermarket with trembling, sweaty hands and a racing heart, feeling that her mind was being pulled out like a frail thread that would snap at any moment – the list was endless. To discover the source of each fear would have taken months, maybe years, of painstaking research. While this could be a most remunerative exercise for a therapist with a rich clientele, most of us do not have sufficient time or money. So it is better by far to find a common approach to all the obstacles, and unmasking fear itself is such an approach. No longer afraid of the physical sensations of fear, my patient can now float past the bus stop, the unsympathetic neighbour, and even stand in the supermarket queue because she knows how to unmask and float through the fear, and go on floating through it *until it no longer matters*.

If you can learn to face fear when it first strikes, stand your ground, relax into it, and see it through, floating without panicking, you will see it quieten down and eventually disappear. It has to, because you have not added further panic and tension. You have not tried desperately to control it, and soon you will be amazed that a feeling of an iron band around your head, rocks in your stomach, sweating, trembling hands, etc, should have frightened you so much. You begin to see that these are purely physical feelings triggered entirely by your own thoughts, and that these physical feelings will gradually disappear with understanding, acceptance and letting go. If you can analyse and understand your fear, you will find that only a bogey remains. If, after trying this method of facing, accepting and floating fearlessly for some weeks or months – together with some herbal sedation perhaps – you are still no better, then I would suggest you need help from a professional.

Set backs

Sometimes memory will strike and the symptoms you dread will return so vividly that you think you will never recover. This causes a setback because your body is still tuned to give too quick and too exaggerated a response to fear, and then adds the second fear of the symptoms.

I once experienced a bad setback after months and months of feeling that I could tackle anything. It was triggered – remember those over-sensitive nerves that fire off at the slightest stimulus – by a very painful abscess over one of my front teeth. Appearance is possibly over-important to me; maybe it's vanity, maybe a lack of self-confidence, maybe a mixture of both. Anyway, my spirits sank lower each morning as I regarded this monstrous face in the bathroom mirror. It's bad enough to look old in today's youth-worshipping society, let alone like a elderly pig.

Eventually, the gathering pus broke through into my gum and appeared externally. My dentist was reluctant to extract the tooth, so I took a course of penicillin which really disturbed my digestive system. After a further three weeks of painful apprehension, the tooth had to come out with more pain accompanied by a considerable amount of unpleasant rubbish in my mouth for a further few days. This was aggravated the night before the extraction by the news that my oldest and dearest friend in Hove had died suddenly.

However well you are coping, the combination of emotional and physical shock may inevitably cause a setback, and boy – did I set back! It was so bad one morning about two o'clock that I sat up in bed, started to cry, actually said the title of this book, I Can't Go On, and thought seriously of telephoning the Samaritans. But my mental picture of myself sitting bolt upright and quoting the title of my book made me laugh, albeit weakly, and I decided I would help myself. I adopted the self-help method outlined above – understanding, acceptance, floating with relaxation – by lying flat on my back, consciously letting go of my muscles and listening to a recording I had made of the process over and over again until I dropped off to sleep.

This setback not only took the form of the physical symptoms of fear but I also had a very severe attack of the OMGWIs – 'Oh my goodness, what if I'm not going to be able to look after myself any more?' 'What if I have to go into an old people's home?' Etc, etc. The next morning I felt much better and was able to laugh even more at the behaviour of the previous night, and continued to listen to at least part of the tape until I had calmed down. I also spent more time than usual in meditation – of which more later.

So, how do I cope with the setbacks? There I am, peacefully walking through the garden of my life, appreciating its beauties to the full, when metaphorically I step on the prongs of a rake which is hidden in my path. The heavy handle springs up and hits me full in the face, knocking me for six. Obviously, I stagger on and am close to falling, but I remember how to regain my balance; although shaken and bruised for a while, I manage to continue my walk. Perhaps I even learn how to look out for and deal with dangerous obstacles in my path before they hit me in the future.

The fear of setbacks is of course habit. I have had the habit of fear all my life because of my early upbringing. If you always carry a briefcase, and were suddenly told that you must go empty-handed and never carry it again, how would you react? For months you would feel lost, panic-stricken, and automatically keep looking for it. Recovering from fear is the same. If you lose your fear for a while, your hungry old self is so used to making a meal of fear that it will go looking for fear to feed on, but if you can recognise what is happening, that is face and accept and float, you can then use your self-conditioning technique to float through the fear and out into peace. Habit dies very hard, but die it will in time if you can see it through steadfastly, however violent its attacks may be.

Anger

Above all, don't hate and blame other people for your problems; that hate and blame only comes back to you in the end, often in the form of high blood pressure, stomach ulcers, irritable bowel syndrome, and many other stress disorders.

One of the most therapeutic ways I know of letting go of hate and anger is to clear out your china cupboard. Collect all the china you no longer use, or buy some from a car boot sale or a jumble sale, take yourself off to the bottom of the garden, wait until the family are all out and then give yourself a really 'smashing' time!

Another way is to beat the hell out of a pillow or stout cushion, or isolate yourself to shout and scream at the top of your voice. When I first became aware of the anger in myself, I bought a child's punchball on a stand at a jumble sale and started hammering away at it – extremely therapeutic! I gave the ball away about twelve years ago, and on the fairly rare occasions when I experience terrible anger inside, I now walk briskly or jog gently, and still find a good loud scream works wonders!

If you are angry, you do need a physical outlet. It does not respond to gentle, understanding words. A friend goes into her garden and hacks at overgrown branches; anything that involves hard physical effort will do. If you cannot perform physical action, you can always bash a cushion in your lap or scream. Watch a toddler realising for the first time that he is not the king of the universe, and you have the perfect example – but make your reaction adult and discreet.

Resolution

Your recovery does not necessarily depend entirely on you – so don't take any notice of the 'Pull yourself together' brigade. Do accept professional help if you need it – you can't always do it yourself.

Never accept defeat, however old you are or however long you have suffered with your nerves, it is never too late to be healed. Have no self-pity and don't waste time on 'if onlys' and brooding on past hurts and mistakes. Let them float away.

The real key to overcoming nervous problems is to reach a stage where it no longer matters. That is, you have changed your attitude towards your symptoms or, if you like, you have changed your mood. A nervously ill person is greatly influenced by the mood of the moment because their body reacts so acutely and so quickly to it.

Practising moving slowly is a great help here. I have spent years rushing from task to task like a demented hen, which has dissipated my energies considerably. So if I wake feeling depressed, I would now just take some slow, deep breaths, and think, 'I make no attempt to get up, I'll go with it gently, and I'll float up out of bed and into the shower.'

Here's the difference between fighting and floating. Fighting is exhausting, floating removes tension, and in time the physical healing of trigger-happy nerves will happen. So keep on repeating to yourself, 'Move slowly – let your body go loose – breathe slowly and deeply – accept and float. Accept and float.'

Some pessimistic therapists say that complete recovery from nervous disorders is impossible because the shock of memory brings back old symptoms so vividly and so often. But these setbacks, I think, can be your best teacher. They give you the space to recover by relearning the process all over again, and practising with renewed vigour. Don't let anyone accuse you of not wanting to get better in these setbacks. It's just that not enough time has passed for a protective layer of these curative responses to have formed.

Nothing can be forced in nervous illness. You have spent months, even years, fearfully concentrating on yourself and on your symptoms and 'Oh my goodness, what-iffing'. In no way can you force yourself to suddenly forget it all. The only way to lose this constant, anxious, introspection is to accept it and any thought that comes into your mind, however bizarre. So think about yourself and your illness as much as you like, but realise all the time that it's only a habit fostered by mental fatigue. The key to recovery is in no longer mattering, and for this, you must be prepared to let time pass.

After World War II, a Dutch writer said that the Dutch were suffering from a spiritual sickness which could only be healed by time and understanding. He said that suffering could not be erased the moment the war ended and peace began. Time was needed for the people to regain their balance and their ability to be in charge of their own lives. He said, 'Be patient with us – we have to grow into liberty.'

So must the nervously ill person grow into recovery, with practice, practice and more practice at accepting and floating and being content to let time pass. I say again and again throughout this section on self-help, there is no magic wand, no magic pill, no electric switch, no overnight cure.

It is so much easier to take a tablet, to drink alcohol, to smoke excessively, to over-eat, to do drugs, to go from one casual relationship to another, than it is to take yourself in hand and exercise self-discipline. It sounds very harsh and forbidding, but in fact the dividends are enormous in terms of physical well-being, truly loving relationships, and a dawning awareness of the path to spiritual growth.

Re-education

After this invaluable insight and understanding of the problems of nervous suffering comes re-education. The greatest tragedy of nervous problems is the feeling of total helplessness; it is like fighting an unknown enemy in total darkness. But if you can see and recognise your enemy in the light of understanding, you have a chance of winning.

Once I saw the pattern at work, I could choose to refuse it and replace it with something constructive, although it was not going to be easy. I could alter the course of my own nervous energy away from misery, depression and helplessness – into happiness, joy, success, ambition, love and peace of mind. Obviously, recovery does not depend entirely on the exhumation of buried memories; in fact, if that is as far as it goes, it could make matters worse and leave you with resentment and hatred for your parent figures and an overwhelming self-pity for yourself. You cannot get rid of your legitimate aggression by beating up two doddery, arthritic old people and trashing their bungalow in the retirement complex!

I found the experience of reliving my childhood painful but necessary and important, because I felt a tremendous release, a catharsis, a purging of damaging emotions, rather like the physical equivalent of purging the bowels. But this release was only temporary, until I discovered my 'pattern' and started to practise the re-education of my emotions on an almost moment-to-moment basis. The process of re-education is lifelong, and neither quick nor simple, because it is concerned with not only mental but spiritual growth as well.

I am not committed to any particular school of psychotherapy and I do not believe there is a single easy answer. The journey is a long one, but we can all learn together. And if we have companionship along the way, how much better it is. My aunts and my grandmother sacrificed love in order to dominate and control me during my childhood, so that feeling totally abandoned, I grew into an excessively fearful adult who perceived the world as a very dangerous and frightening place – unpredictable, uncaring and ungiving. The message I had received was, 'If you don't do exactly as you are told, I shall put you into the gutter, and you can work out for yourself what that will mean.' When parent figures do not, or more likely cannot – because of their own problems – give genuine love and care to their children, those children have an uphill struggle through life, constantly trying to obtain these gifts from other people.

'This is all very interesting,' I hear you say, 'But what did you do about it?' My methods took time, patience and perseverance. I didn't really believe that I could ever shake free of my physical symptoms, my depression, lack of self-worth and the awful destruction of loneliness. I felt I had no love, no life, no anything. I hated, despised, loathed and feared myself. Then I very gradually came to realise that the central self and the hungry self must work in harmony with one another, and the condemning self must be destroyed and replaced by ideals and principles that we have created for ourselves out of our experiences. In this way, I was able to leave my false pattern of self-punishment, self-loathing, misery and fear – for a life of reasonable satisfaction, some success, and most importantly, an inner peace.

Self-discipline

Self-discipline has its roots in love, which is a form of will. If you love and respect yourself, you will nurture your physical body as well as behaving with self-discipline towards another human being. Self-discipline does not mean the total annihilation of one's feelings; your feelings should be your slaves – they are the source of your energy with which you perform your daily tasks. So you should treat them with respect. If you do not discipline them – that is, give them no direction, set them no limits, and don't make it clear that you are the boss – then they will stop working for you, you will be their slave and live in the resulting chaos.

On the other hand, if like the guilt-ridden neurotic, you are terrified that your feelings will get out of hand and are determined that they will not cause you any trouble, you will beat them into submission and punish them severely as soon as they arise. The correct management of feelings lies along the middle path, balancing them with constant judgement and adjustment. You listen to, nurture, but at the same time organise and limit them, leaving no doubt as to who is in charge and who will make the final decisions.

Freedom and discipline are kissing cousins; without the discipline of genuine love, freedom can be annihilating and destructive. And don't ever look back. If you think you have slipped back, don't fight, and try to discipline your feelings. All you have done is to slip into the wrong groove. Your thoughts are like a needle stuck in the wrong groove of a disc, so stay in the groove willingly and once more, understand, accept and float. The way is always onwards and through with no desperate fighting.

Muster as much self-acceptance as you can over all shocks and symptoms – which will take a lot of courage, patience, perseverance, time and picking yourself up from the depths of despair over and over again. But one day, I can assure you, you will have the wonderful feeling of things no longer mattering. Memory will bring shocks from time to time but move forward with acceptance until the feeling of no longer mattering is permanent and you can regard your old self with rueful amusement.

One of my patients gained sufficient insight to deal successfully with a difficult family relationship. 'I felt really good about it all,' she said exultantly; 'I wish I could feel like that all the time.' 'So you can,' I replied, 'Now you understand how they are trying to manipulate you, how they distort the truth, and how devious they are, how their demands are totally unrealistic. If you can extend this understanding and this awareness into other areas of your life, you will feel really good about it all more and more.' She looked at me with great misgiving and suspicion written all over her face. 'But then I'd have to think all the bloody time,' she shouted. I agreed with her that it was only through a lot of thinking that this good feeling would grow and be established so that she would be free of her depression and lack of self-esteem. 'I didn't come to you to have my life made more difficult; I just want to relax and enjoy myself; you expect me to become some sort of nun or something,' she roared. Sadly, she terminated her treatment, terrified of the demands that mental health would make of her.

This patient suffered from the common misconception that recovery from nervous problems depends almost entirely on the recovery of buried memories. Although this is important, and helps us to experience catharsis, or release, it will not cure or even ameliorate your nervous symptoms unless you discover the particular nature of your problems and practise recognition and re-education of them all the time. A favourite aphorism of mine is, 'Life is not cured; it is managed.'

You may say this is all very egotistical but at least you are working on not destroying, but rebuilding yourself. If you are not willing to undertake this consistent work, then you'll stay in your Slough of Despond and never really know the exciting, glorious, challenging, useful and worthwhile life that is your birthright. Most people do not want to achieve such a worthwhile goal or work so hard in life – it seems too difficult. They're content to be ordinary men and women, and do not strive to be god. But here I am straying onto a different chapter – the way of spiritual development with which I am not concerned here.

Sleep

A patient of mine was so exhausted by years of panic and fear that although she understood my instructions very well on an intellectual level, her body was just too tired to accept her mind's instructions. What she needed was complete rest in the form of continuous sleep for a few days. Obviously, she was unable to sleep naturally, so this was a case for supervised sedation. Her doctor prescribed a sedative at night and she slept. When she awoke, she bathed, had a light, relaxing meal and was given another dose of sedative to ensure further sleep. After a very light lunch, she was usually able to sleep again without sedation. If she couldn't, then more was given. This regime continued for a week, at the end of which she was sufficiently restored to put the Face-Acceptance-Float theory into practice herself. Obviously, the sleep cure must be supervised by a doctor. Don't try to do it yourself.

The bogey of addiction raises its ugly head of course, but in my experience, most nervous sufferers take a delight in doing without sedatives, often too soon, because sedation is particularly necessary if you cannot sleep – and sleep is such a powerful healer. In my own case, I find that half the recommended dose of a herbal tranquilliser is enough to enable me to cope when I am going through a particularly rough patch.

Dreams

It may also pay dividends to look closely at your dreams: for the end of a dream is always the goal of your unconscious mind. The dream itself is working out the problems of your personal situation and most of the dramatis personae in the dream represent different facets of your own personality like the hungry self, the central self, and the condemning self.

To illustrate this, here is a dream brought by a young man being treated for depression.

I was in the sitting room with my father; he looked afraid and said to me, 'There is a woman hiding in this house; go and kill her.' I found a woman and killed her, then asked my father what I should do with the body. He showed me a large cupboard in the corner and together we lifted the corpse into the cupboard. We heard a loud knock on the door, and I opened the door very apprehensively. A handsome young man swaggered in, dressed in black leather, with a trendy haircut and one earring, and he made straight for the sitting room, shouting, "Where is my girlfriend? Where is my girlfriend?" As he searched the room, coming ominously close to the cupboard, my whole body began to tremble, and I was filled with panic. And as the panic became unbearable, I woke up.

So who are the people in this dream? The father represents the condemning self in the young man's personality; he was quiet but he dominated. He had tended to repress any attempts by his son to make relationships with women. He had always ridiculed and put down his son's interest in the opposite sex. The woman that the son was instructed to murder stood for the desire for sexual fulfilment that was constantly in the young man's mind and imagination. In killing the woman the young man in his dream is obeying the dictates of his condemning self. Once this desire is exterminated and hidden away in the cupboard of his mind, a loud knock is heard at the front door of that mind and in walks the representative of himself as a man who demands sexual fulfilment and who will brook no delay in finding it. This facet of the young man's personality obviously porrays that part of him that we call the hungry self, and as we know, the attitude of the hungry self is one that says, "I know what I want, and if I can't get it, I'll scream blue murder." The man in the dream (the central self) is obviously ina quandary. The condemning self demands one thing, the hungry self insists on another. The dreamer's central self is not strong enough to deal with these two mighty forces within him and his only solution is to fall into panic. So we can see that this weak, unsure central self is utterly incapable of dealing with this battle between the condemning self and the hungry self, and the end of the dream, his panic, represents the nervous collapse about which he is consulting me.

The end of the dream is always the goal of our unconscious mind. The conscious mind has one goal and the unconscious mind is seeking some goal of a quite different nature. The end of the dream therefore gives us the dénouement of out detective story.

Self-Esteem

Introduction

I once saw some graffiti on a wall in London which said, 'It's never too late to have a happy childhood.'

Jean-Paul Sartre summed up this aphorism when he said, 'Freedom is what you do with what's been done to you.' And, 'It is more difficult to understand one man than to understand mankind'. The point he is making is that *you* are in control of your life. And although what has been done to you may be devastating, almost to the point of annihilation, *you* can turn it around.

Childhood

A baby or a small child can soon sense whether it is welcome in the world. The absence of being cuddled and held, the absence of a response to its cries, the absence of hearing sounds of love and encouragement, all confirm that it is not welcome. At this stage, the infant has a right to feel that he or she is the centre of a world that is totally dependable.

Later on, the child needs to feel self-esteem that is fostered by approval, knowing it is good at something, compares well with others, meets expectations, and is able to go on to even more challenging things out of sheer interest and enjoyment. This conviction of being loved and loveable, valued and valuable, just as we are, is the beginning of self-esteem.

The trouble with the problems of childhood is that they are not easy to resolve, and yet they are always at the root of adult difficulties. I have dandelions growing between the paving stones in my garden. If I chop off that part of the plant that shows, it looks fine for a week or so, and then the plant grows back, bigger and stronger than before. In order to clear them out completely, I have to dig down really hard, and take out the entire root. This breaks my nails, bruises my fingers, and takes time and patience. Also, it gives me backache, but it solves the problem – at least, until the spring. (I don't use chemicals because of their side-effects.)

It is just the same with childhood problems. It's no good cutting away at the symptoms; you have to go right down and remove the whole root, and very often this causes temporary pain, and certainly takes time and patience. Pills and potions are like chopping off the part of the problem that shows, and they also have undesirable side-effects. In any case, who wants to go through life like a zombie? Personally, I'd rather suffer than just feel nothing – what's the point? If you want to be happy all the time you'll have to have a lobotomy!

My Story

However, in my case, and in millions of others, self-esteem was not fostered; I only received very faint praise for doing tasks that were always assigned, for obeying to the letter, for fitting in, for serving the purposes of my aunts and my grandmother. So I created a totally false self in order to earn approval and to avoid punishment and derision. Punished for having an opinion, punished for what was seen as wilful, and praised for a false docility and smiling obedience, I built a false, deflated, spurious personality which manifested itself in sucking up to teachers at school, as well as the adults at home.

The pressures and expectations of adults in the life of the child cannot be resisted if the child is to survive. So a true sense of self is never experienced. This creates the terrifying feeling of emptiness inside, which no genuine and well-earned approval later on in life can ever fill. I was like an emotional 'black hole' into which all external rewards just disappeared without trace. By being punished so severely at 3, 4, 5, 6, and 7, some part of me remained at 3, 4, 5, 6, and 7 until – with the help of therapy – I returned to that child, recognised her and set about mothering her, or reparenting her myself. As Ernest Hemingway said in A Farewell to Arms, 'The world breaks everyone, and afterwards some are strong at the broken places.'

Places broken in childhood hurt more in setting and take longer to knit. But like scar tissue over wounds, these broken places can become stronger. My father's erratic and ill-tempered parenting contributed to a need for fathering from every other male in my life. It was fortunate that my husband understood this need and was able to deal with it so successfully. He had that rare ability to love unconditionally, to say, 'No matter how the world may judge you, I will always love you for what you are, for yourself.'

Nevertheless, the depths of emptiness within me were so deep that even such a rare love as Ron's could not fill it completely. This emptiness showed itself in a terrifying depth of depression two years after we married. I was mortally afraid that I was quite incapable of coping with housework, shopping, etc, and holding down a teaching job at the same time. I felt sick, breathless, as though all the nerves in my body were being stimulated by an electrical buzz.

Even more terrifying was the isolation. Not even Ron's gentle love, sympathy and concern could break through the walls that imprisoned me, while inside the walls, I tortured myself. It was as if his words, his touch and compassion were coming to me across a yawning gulf, and no human contact was remotely possible. I felt as if I were at the bottom of a disgusting black pit and however hard I tried to climb out, just as I put my hand over the edge, an enormous spiked boot would crush my hand, causing me to let go and fall back, screaming with terror to the bottom again.

The following poem, by Portia Nelson, illustrated this very well. She was asked to write her autobiography in five chapters on a 5 by 7 card, at a seminar concerned with self-awareness. This is what she wrote:

Chapter One
I walk down the street
There is a deep hole in the sidewalk
I fall in
I am lost – I am helpless
It isn't my fault
It takes forever to find a way out.

Chapter Two
I walk down the same street
There is a deep hole in the sidewalk
I pretend I don't see it
I fall in again

I can't believe I'm in the same place
But it isn't my fault
It still takes a long time to get out.

Chapter Three
I walk down the same street
There's a deep hole in the sidewalk
I see it there – I still fall in – it's a habit
My eyes are open, I know where I am
It is my fault
I get out immcdiatcly.

Chapter Four
I walk down the same street
There's a deep hole in the sidewalk
I walk around it

Chapter Five
I walk down another street.

Hitherto, there had always been some respite in sleep, but sleep was now punctuated by nightmares that led me to contemplate suicide. This recurring, waking nightmare was made even more unbearable by the torment of knowing what my suicide would do to such a kind, loving, unselfish and patient partner, and I hope, in retrospect, that it was my loving concern for him that stopped me. Depression is a living hell.

Finally, the day came when I was referred to a psychiatrist. In 1950, there was still a certain amount of shame in this. You were supposed to 'pull yourself together' and 'snap out of it', to 'look on the bright side', to 'count your blessings', and more darkly still, I was told, 'You will lose him, you know, if you go on with this. Men just won't put up with this kind of nonsense. And you're not ill – you're just selfish.'

I believed the last two statements, and this intensified my agony and fear. Depression at best was seen as an illness, to be treated with pills and Electro Convulsive Therapy (ECT), but depression is something more than being ill. You don't just feel the misery and inconvenience of being ill; you also agonise about life and death, what's the point?

I was ushered into a bleak little room by a man wearing a starched white coat and a somewhat stern expression. The room had bare grey walls, and in the middle was a small metal table, and two metal stacking chairs. The doctor waved me towards one of these, and sat down in the other. An interrogation about my childhood followed for an hour and summing up, he said, 'Well, obviously you have never been properly mothered. So what you must do is mother yourself – you must be your own mother.'

Sounded fine for another psychiatrist, but for me? I left the hospital feeling bemused, thinking, 'How can I be my own mother? Can I get inside my own self and come out and be reborn?' I was totally bewildered. But at least I had someone to talk with once a week and someone who realised I did have a problem. There was tremendous healing in talking it all out. After all, this is the bedrock of all psychiatric treatment. As Shakespeare said in Macbeth, we 'Pluck from the memory a rooted sorrow, raze out the written troubles of the brain, and … cleanse the stuff'd bosom of that perilous stuff which weighs upon the heart.'

However, this was only the beginning. Being told to be my own mother – although a positive pearl of wisdom to the initiated – should have been the final sentence after weeks, months, possibly years, of intensive therapy. I did try to put this into practice; I listened to Listen with Mother on the radio, and pretended I had my own mother with me. I took myself for a walk, pretending my mother was holding my hand and talking to me. But this pretence left me feeling even more confused and not a little stupid. Was this another step along the road to total madness?

I had six sessions with this psychiatrist and only the medicine and the talking did any good. So that, when it suddenly stopped, I was left feeling more hopeless and dejected than before. Desperately seeking solace, I latched onto the idea that London was the cause of my despair, and that if we could only live by the sea, I would be well. The theory came from the effect a holiday always had on me but, of course, it was just an escape symbol. I did not realise then that, wherever I took my body, my mind and emotions would come too.

So living by the sea in Hove was not the answer. This is the devastating part of nervous suffering – that, however many ways you try to ease the situation externally, nothing works; they are all coming from the outside. It is like covering suppurating wounds without removing all the dirt and infection first. Under the dressing, the bacteria proliferate, and the festering damage spreads inwards and outwards.

The only thing that saved me from suicide or total breakdown during those years was my marriage. How sad that a literal heaven on earth was so threatened and spoiled by the snake of nervous illness. How sad the whole wonderful and glorious experience of life is so spoiled by the same problem for so many people. How many people tell us, 'It's my nerves, you know?'

No one understands except fellow-sufferers but they cannot give you the answers because they don't have them. Pills and potions will not cure it, and psychiatry and counselling – although on the increase – are not available to everyone. So what can you do for yourself?

W R Houston says, 'Many of those who suffer from nervousness are persons of fine sensibility, of delicate regard for honour, endowed with a feeling of duty and obligation. Their nerves have tricked them, misled them.' I would add that it isn't your fault; you are a victim, not a hypochondriac, or work-shy, and there is a way out – there is a way out.

A nervous sufferer is a great asset to the community when he or she is better. The forms that nervous illness take are many: patients have described them to me as, 'I have an iron band around my head', 'I have a heavy lump of dough in my stomach,' 'My stomach feels as though it is full of small rocks,' 'My heart is either shaking or it beats eratically,' 'I can't keep still; my chest is so tight that I can't breath,' 'I feel as if ants or worms are crawling under my skin,' 'I find it difficult to go to sleep, and when I do, I have terrible dreams,' 'I can't go out unless I know a lavatory is close by – I feel I am going to be sick or have diarrhoea all the time, or I have a constant urge to urinate,' 'I can't go out because my hands sweat and shake, and I'm embarrassed,' 'I'm so tired and weary that I can't take an interest in anything,' 'I have pins and needles in my hands and feet,' 'I have a lump in my throat which is choking me and making swallowing difficult,' 'I can only sit on the end seat at the back of the theatre because I must be able to get out quickly,' 'I dare not climb a ladder or look over a cliff,' 'I forget names and put salt in my tea; I must be going mad,' 'I have to go back over and over again to make sure I've turned off the gas,' 'I cannot make up my mind about anything – I spend an hour deciding which tie to wear or where to buy my baby's orange juice, or whether to go on holiday or whether to take an umbrella.' This is called folie de doute – it becomes a compulsion. All these experiences are frightening and, of course, the more fearful we are, the stronger they will become.

The first important step is to see your doctor and have a thorough physical examination, and if you still feel that your troubles have some dire organic cause, then get a second opinion. If this confirms your physical good health, then you can begin to work on yourself in the ways I have suggested.

Malnutrition?

Another misconception is that your nervous system is starved and that the nerve fibres lack nourishment or vitamins. If the trouble is caused by malnutrition, then it is easily put right. A course of nutritional supplements and you should be as strong as an ox, and radiating well-being. But nervous illness is not an illness of the nervous system as such; it is an illness of the emotions. So if you have received a diagnosis of nerves, 'neurosis depression', or an anxiety state – agoraphobia or claustrophobia – you can be quite sure that whatever strange tricks the nerves of your body are performing, the cause is not nutritional deficiency, but it's in the mind and emotions that control the nerves.

It is easy to see how our emotions play tricks on our bodies. I was staying with friends in the country, and their daughter had just returned from a week's work in London, and was lying exhausted in a deck chair. Her mother suggested that they mow the lawn together. 'How could you suggest such a thing?' she said reproachfully. 'You know how tired I am.' Looking injured, she sank even further into the chair and closed her eyes. Ten minutes later, a girlfriend arrived with two attractive young men in tow. Waving tennis rackets in her face, they said, 'Would you like to make up a foursome?' She regarded them thoughtfully. 'Well, perhaps I could do with some exercise after being stuck in an office all week.' Going upstairs, she changed and dashed about the tennis court like a mad thing for about two hours. Her physical energy was totally controlled by her interests and emotions.

A young writer was referred to me for help with severe cramp in his right hand, for which a neurologist could find no physiological cause.

The cause lay in his chaotic emotions. I asked this young man to write his name on a piece of paper; his brow furrowed and his muscles tensed. The lines on his face were strained. He held his pen lie a chisel. His hand shook and suddenly the pen shot off the paper altogether. His emotional turmoil turned out to be a struggle between conformity and protest, between dependence and independence, created by possessive and quarrelling parents. As we worked together, he was able gradually to give up this struggle in favour of maturity and independence. The writer's cramp was the outward signal of his inner turmoil.

If your car behaves erratically at a crossing, lurching forward and stopping suddenly, and this happens several times, you might conclude that there was something wrong with the car and take it to the garage. If however, after being pronounced mechanically sound, it still behaves in the same erratic way, you would have to conclude that the trouble lay with the driver of the car, not the car itself.

Work

Recently I have become aware of an important factor affecting my own mental health, and that is the job that I am doing. If I attempt a job which imposes too much strain on my nervous system, I become physically and emotionally ill. This means spending time at home, worrying about my absence from work and the extra strain this is imposing on my colleagues. So a vicious cycle of worry and sense of failure is set up, aggravating my symptoms even more.

Being a perfectionist doesn't help either. I need to get my happiness out of my work, and if I am attempting to do too much, then I cannot be happy. So look carefully at what you choose to do and don't be afraid to change jobs until you find the right one. It is better to enjoy a job that gives you less pay than have a well-paid job that makes you ill. Occupation in the company of others is vital for mental health. So that doing enjoyable work in the company of others is better for you than sitting depressed and lonely by yourself.

A patient of mine was a highly competent physiotherapist in complete charge of a residential clinic. This meant that, not only did she have large numbers of patients to treat, but also found herself doing numerous other jobs, such that she became totally exhausted which necessitated giving up the job for six months. During that time, the clinic closed, and so there was no job waiting for her when she recovered.

However, being made of extremely stern stuff, she found a job as a care assistant at an old people's home. Her hours are long and arduous, clearing up urine and faeces, heavy lifting, bathing, feeding, humouring – not an ideal way of spending one's time. Add to all this, a wage which is a risible insult and most people would rather run a mile from such a job. But she has found fulfilment in this work and looks as contented and happy as before she looked strained and ill.

I too, although living on a very small pension, am now more contented and happy doing far less with other people and working much more on my own, than I was rushing around, massaging my ego and other people's with psychotherapy, teaching yoga, lecturing, attending seminars, et al.

You need to look carefully at what you have in your psycho-emotional account and not overspend. Give out more than you have and you will bankrupt yourself into nervous exhaustion, psychosomatic illness, or even breakdown.

Death

We are all apprehensive about dying – it is such an unknown quantity – any information we are given can seem like pure speculation. Maybe you will be helped, as I was, by the development of spiritual awareness and the practice of meditation. If you are pathologically afraid of dying and death, you would be well advised to discuss your fears with a good counsellor. But choose that counsellor wisely – someone with very rigid religious beliefs could frighten you even more than you are frightened now.

This terrible fear arises because we are all members of a 'tribe', the family, the social group, the religion to which we subscribe, etc., and tribal thinking over many millions of years sees death as the great unmentionable. We have an enormous dread of being annihilated, of no longer being here, or not mattering anymore. This, of course, is sheer egotism and one of our most difficult tasks is to subdue the ego and let our 'better nature', or spirit, take precedence and lead us.

But most of us are governed by the rules and thinking of the tribe – for instance, the favourite mantra of the tribe is, "But what will they think?", and another, "Success depends on looks and money." So the tribe inevitably thinks, "We don't talk about death or dying," the reasoning being, "because we believe talking about it will precipitate our own demise." I am constantly amazed by the replies of intelligent people when I talk about my own closeness to death, that I have arranged and paid for my own memorial service, carry a 'Living Will', and in general accept the facts that I am old, I am tired, and I shall be glad to leave this crumbling body behind. No one is ever happy to go (except in rare circumstances of extreme agony perhaps) because many things in life seem so much more wonderful and miraculous as one ages. But most people react to talk of death with, "Oh, you don't mean that!" Don't talk like that!" "Please don't leave me." "Whatever will I do without you?" Many people dying in hospital often wait for their relatives and friends to leave before allowing their souls to depart, and the medical profession, alas, is much more concerned with the *quantity* of life rather than the *quality*.

I feel too that a benevolent Providence has mercifully allowed everything to deteriorate during my lifetime; the seasons are no longer identifiable, the music gets noisier and more senseless, the buildings uglier, the roads more nightmarish, the trains dirtier and more unreliable, the government sillier, clothes more ridiculous, and news more depressing. Good things like glow-worms, barn owls, nightingales, farmland, hedges, fish shops, white gloves and girls who enjoy being called beautiful – are slowly withdrawn. The process is no doubt a merciful one, because as I come to the end of my allotted span in a world grown so remote from the one in which I grew up, I think I shall be quite glad to go!

In case this last paragraph causes the reader to think, "Oh Lord! Just another miserable old fart," or to consign the book to the bin, I would balance it with some more positive observations.

First of all, people are so much cleaner these days; when I first started Teaching Practice in the 1940s, the smell of unwashed clothes and bodies was overpowering! Whoever thought the Berlin Wall would come down, Communism in Russia com to an end, Nelson Mandela be released from prison to become President of South Africa, black people in general to have much more equality, smoking be banned in public places and women gain the liberation they now enjoy.

I noted the ultimate change recently, on an aircraft, when a man appeared from the galley pushing the drinks trolley, whilst a woman's voice came over the intercom giving us information regarding the flight as she piloted the plane.

Grief

Obviously, my subconscious sense of abandonment was intensified by the death of my husband. The loss of a spouse is one of the most severe forms of psychological stress anyone can experience and caused a major psycho-social transition where my picture of the world and my own part in it had to be totally reassessed.

I was in great need of protection, reassurance and time to recoup, and I had none of these things. I was defensive, over-sensitive, vulnerable and unreasonable, and how I longed for an understanding and supportive friend or counsellor! But most people approach grief with enormous anxiety and a subconscious fear that it may be catching. Many societies have found it convenient to send a widow into the next world along with her husband, and ritual suicide has been widespread in Asia, Africa and America, Australia and Europe. Mourning is treated as if it were a weakness, a self-indulgence, a bad habit, instead of a psychological necessity. We do not burn our widows – we pity and avoid them. People who had been friendly and approachable were suddenly embarrassed and strained, and offers of help were certainly not followed up. The stress of bereavement emphasised the pattern of nervous exhaustion which had already been laid down during my childhood. One of the symptoms I suffered from, and still do from time to time, was palpitations and a feeling of fulness in the chest. And these are the normal concomitants of anxiety; bereaved people often suffer from them, which gives rise to the 'broken heart' theory.

In 1835, the American doctor, Benjamin Rush, wrote: 'Perceptions of persons who died of grief show congestion in, and inflammation of, the heart, with the rupture of its auricles and ventricles.' However, grief itself is not a cause of death, unless it aggravates conditions which would have occurred anyway. But it is a predominant cause of nervous fatigue which gives rise not only to palpitations and fulness in the chest but also to many other alarming feelings such as anger and irritability which can be accompanied by a general feeling of ill-health, manifesting as headaches, digestive upsets, asthma, panic attacks, insomnia, difficulty in swallowing, excessive sweating, dizziness, blurred vision, skin rashes, vomiting, heavy menstrual periods, frequent infections and general aching.

No later light has lightened up my heaven
No second morn has ever shone for me
All my life's Bliss from thy dear life was given
All my life's bliss is in the grave with thee.

But when the days of golden dreams had perished,
And e'en Despair was powerless to destroy;
Then did I learn how existence could be cherished
Strengthened and fed without the aid of joy.

Then did I check the tears of useless passion –
Weaned my young soul from yearning after thine,
Sternly denied its burning wish to hasten
Down to that tomb already more than mine.

But even yet I dare not let it languish
Dare not indulge in memory's rapturous pain,
Once drinking deep of that divinest anguish
How could I seek the empty world again?

Emily Bronte
Remembrance

And:

I love thee with the breath,
Smiles, tears, of all my life – and if God choose,
I shall but love thee better after death.

Elizabeth Barret Browning
Sonnet XLIII, Grief

Self-Conditioning

The fourth step in your general progress is auto-suggestion or self-conditioning – self-hypnosis if you like. Every advertisement on hoardings or the television bears testimony to the success of this technique. We are all influenced powerfully by suggestion. How many times do you buy a certain washing powder, breakfast cereal or chocolate bar, apparently without thinking, and then remember later that you saw it advertised on television the previous evening? When we are suffering from nervous problems we are particularly susceptible to suggestion. The secret hungry self is making so many subtle demands that you are prey to every proposal, good or bad, that is put to you.

I once had a patient who just could not sleep. She took stronger and stronger drugs to no avail, and was quite desperate. With the co-operation of her doctor, we decided to give her two saccharine tablets, but coated in a very bright red gelatine capsule, and to tell her, 'Take one of these tablets when you go to bed – they're so strong that you mustn't take the other one unless you are still awake after an hour.' 'You'll sleep,' we told her. Next morning, she phoned me early, ecstatic after what she claimed was her best night's sleep for years. 'I only took one tablet and I was asleep immediately. They must be very powerful.' I didn't tell her the tablets were saccharin until sufficient time had elapsed for her to establish a healthy and habitual pattern of sleep.

A doctor friend of mine had a patient who was allergic to cut flowers in the house, and inevitably developed an asthma attack whenever they were brought into his sitting room. He telephoned my friend in great distress, wheezing and gasping: a new housekeeper had brought in a vase of gladioli. 'I'm choking to death,' he said. 'I've taken adrenalin and it hasn't helped at all. I'm coming round to see you now.' My friend always has flowers in his consulting room, and he deliberately didn't remove them. When the patient saw them, he went into paroxysms of coughing. My friend led him into a treatment room and gave him an injection, and finally his coughing stopped. 'How could you do something so cruel and so dangerous?' he gasped. 'You know how sensitive I am to cut flowers.' My friend went back to his consulting room, took a flower and tore it to pieces in front of his patient. 'It is made of paper,' he said, 'And the injection you had was sterile distilled water. Not adrenalin – water. You have asthma, but it is not caused by flowers. It is caused by neurosis.' Every nervous patient is at the mercy of suggestion – a rose may trigger off an attack of asthma, a small windowless room or a lift may trigger an attack of claustrophobia, but the connection is in the mind and the emotions.'

Many nervous patients have habitual thoughts that constantly give them negative suggestion. If I am convalescent after an attack of flu or a bad cold, I can easily wake up in the morning, thinking, 'Oh God! Another day to be got through. How am I going to do it? I am obviously getting 'past it'. What's the point? I'd be better off dead.'

First, I have to learn to recognise my morbid chain of thought, and replace it with a positive suggestion, and a constructive idea like, 'I'm sure to feel better after another night's rest, even if I haven't actually slept much. Today is going to be a great improvement on yesterday. I have life, love and some energy. Certainly, I am improving all the time.'

Secondly, I had to find a prompter in my unconscious mind that would cause my thoughts and imaginings to flow automatically into positive and constructive channels. This is where the technique of self-conditioning comes in — not a complete substitute for psychotherapy but very effective as an auxiliary treatment. It acts on the personality rather like the self-starter in a car, and works very well if followed faithfully. Every nervous pattern is at the mercy of suggestion. The trouble arises because the suggestions are the wrong ones. Flowers trigger off a violent asthma attack, and a journey in a lift causes claustrophobia, but the connection is in the mind and emotions. It has this overpowering effect because of an automatic chain of associations, a pattern that we have very often created in childhood. Our minds have become chained to unhappy associations and these associations are triggered off in the first place by self-programming. Many of our habitual thoughts have the power of negative suggestion. So, first, we must gain an insight into these morbid chains of thought, and replace them with more positive suggestions and ideas. Secondly, we need to programme an automatic reaction to positive suggestions and constructive ideas into the incredibly efficient computer that is your brain. You may react with derision and scepticism, and at one time this did seem impossible. But we now know the amazing work done by the Russian scientist, Dr Pavlov, in the conditioned reflex called self-conditioning. I say again, it is not a substitute for psychotherapy, an understanding of self, but it is incredibly useful in a supportive role. I found that it worked well, but only if followed faithfully.

I cannot repeat often enough that none of the therapies or suggestions in this book will work unless you put them into practice. Only you can do it. It is not enough to read about palliatives and cures; you have to work at them. Look at a great musician: how did they become great? Only by practising, hour after hour, day after day, month after month, year after year. Certainly not by reading books about music! Your body is the most wonderful instrument – isn't it worth doing whatever it takes to obtain the very finest performance from it? In order to put this self-conditioning technique into practice, you must first spend time forming a picture in your mind of the person you wish to be. If you are fearful, you see yourself as courageous and confident. If you are depressive, you see yourself as contented. If you are inhibited, because you care too much about what people think of you, see yourself as independent, fearless and capable. If you suffer from lethargy, or put off doing things, you see yourself as energetic, strong-willed and efficient. If you constantly punish and put yourself down, the obvious picture is one of success, self-confidence and a zest for life. If you hate everything and everybody, then your desire is for a more positive attitude, an acceptance of people as they are, and a friendly disposition.

Once you have decided on the person you wish to be, in contrast to what you are, the next step is to make up a simple statement which will link up your present unhappy and morbid state with the one you desire. The statement has three parts:

A statement of the particular problem which is causing your tension.
A description of the way you want to be in the future.
The signal which links the two together.

Having written down the formula, you memorise it so well that you could repeat it in your sleep. I can hear you saying, 'That's ridiculous! How could a formula like that have any effect? I could repeat it a thousand times, and it would be of no use whatsoever.' But the whole point is that it is being introduced into your unconscious mind as an instruction. It is important to do this in a state of profound relaxation not during our ordinary, waking life, so that such a formula finds its way into the unconscious mind through a back door, as it were.

So what would be an effective formula? I personally use the following. WHENEVER I FEEL DEPRESSED, SELF-PITYING, WORTHLESS, A FAILURE – THAT IS THE SIGNAL TO ME TO BE CHEERFUL, POSITIVE, APPRECIATED, OF

INFINITE VALUE, AND TO ENJOY THE GOODNESS OF LIFE. Another example might be: WHENEVER I FEEL WORTHLESS AND HOPELESS, THAT IS THE SIGNAL FOR ME TO KNOW THAT I AM LOVED, APPRECIATED AND OF INFINITE VALUE.

So, having formulated your verbal statement, the next step is to relax. See the section on deep relaxation which links with meditation, but here is a short and simple method to use at this point. It may help to make a recording of this relaxation because when your voice is talking to you, it does have quite an impact. Preferably, lie on your back. If this is not possible, sit comfortably in a very cosy and familiar armchair, feet firmly planted on the ground. Rest your arms on the chair arms, or clasp your hands loosely in your lap. Say to yourself, 'I am relaxing my toes, my ankles, legs, knees, body, back, stomach muscles.' Pause for about two minutes. 'Now I am relaxing my shoulders, arms, elbows, wrists, hands, fingers, thumb.' Pause again. 'Now I am relaxing the nape of my neck, my whole head, jaw, mouth, tongue, nose, eyes, ears and forehead.' Pause. Having relaxed your body, you next go on to relax your mind and spirit. Let everything go and say to yourself, 'When I have counted to five, I shall be in a state of deep relaxation.'

> 1. Deep relaxation. Pause.
> 2. Deeper. Pause.
> 3. Very deep. Pause.
> 4. Deeper still. Pause.
> 5. Deep, profound, total relaxation.

By now, you may be almost asleep, but don't give way to it. Just feel this wonderful peace of mind and body – maybe the peace that passes understanding.

Now is the time to repeat the formula you have already learned by heart. Learn it so well that you do not have to make any effort to remember. Right on the borders of unconsciousness, you deposit your vital instructions and leave them there. Repeat the formula two or three times, then allow the deep peace of the relaxation to envelop you once again. You will be in such a deep state of relaxation that you will need to wake yourself before attempting any activity. So say to yourself, 'When I have counted from five to zero, I shall be wide awake and feeling great. Five, four, three, two, one, zero. I am awake. The effects of this conditioning technique will surprise you if you follow it, and don't allow your own lack of self-discipline to divert you from your practice. If you find yourself constantly diverted, this is a measure of the strength of your unconscious mind. The last thing your unconscious mind wants is to let go of your symptoms, and live a normal, positive, enjoyable life with all its responsibilities. Some patients fail again and again. 'The cat jumped onto the bed.' 'I lost the paper with the formula written on it.' 'I fell asleep after the relaxation.' 'I try really hard to relax but I can't.' 'The phone rang and I had to answer it – it might have been an emergency.' 'Someone came to the door, so I had to see who it was.' Look closely into all these excuses, and you will see at work the tremendous fear of love, fulfilment and happiness, and also the overwhelming desire to avoid the responsibilities of a normal existence. Peace, poise, and power over events are far less exciting to the unconscious mind than the subtle control of events brought about by misery.

There is a story told about the Storming of the Bastille during the French Revolution: the doors were opened wide, and the prisoners told that they were free. One of them had been in a small, damp cell at the back of the building, with only rats and mice for company for many years. As he emerged half-blinded into the sunshine and the shouts of the crowd, he panicked and rushed back to his cell again, preferring the solace of the rats and mice to freedom: he could not take the wholesale change his liberation involved. We nervous sufferers can behave very much like that man: when we recognise the method that is likely to bring us liberation, we shrink from it because the path of our previous satisfaction in frustration, hatred, humiliation, masochism and rejection, is so very well-worn. We go back to the cell with the rats of frustration and the mice of misery through no fault of our own, but because happiness, power and self-esteem look like a terrifying wilderness to us.

So it is not that the cat jumped on the bed, the phone or the doorbell rang, you forgot the formula, you can't relax, you fell asleep, but that right on the brink of positive change, you moved back once again to the old familiar satisfactions of misery and despair. So this is a test of your desire to be well because no one can stop you but yourself. No matter what happens, you will find as many five minutes during the day and the night as you possibly can to practise this conditioning technique effectively, constantly, faithfully, knowing it is the way to a totally new and liberated life. While you are practising this self-conditioning, or self-hypnosis if you like, it is almost certain you will continue to experience the physical symptoms of nervous tension, like the list I compiled earlier in this section – upset stomach, palpitations, headaches, sore muscles, raised blood pressure, dry mouth, sweating, inability to swallow, et al.

There is a most successful technique for dealing with these unpleasant manifestations of nervous tension devised and taught by Dr Claire Weekes in her books which I recommend *highly*. The technique is concerned with the way you feel instead of running away from it. If, for instance, your heart is racing, your stomach churning, your body vibrating and shaking, your head swimming, your sight blurred, your limbs aching, you feel as though you are about to snap, you face the situation, accept it, and then float through to the peace on the other side of the experience, which is within yourself. Before you consign the book to the dustbin in total derision, let me explain!

You have to face again that cure lies within yourself, with guidance and help from outside, but by *your* effort. You also have to face the things you fear and not run away from them for fear of making them worse. Running away is not facing. If, for instance, you are afraid to go far from home (agoraphobia), you may have been advised to go as far as you can and return at the first sign of panic, or you may have been given tranquillisers to help you. But these methods are crutches, not cures. Again, I repeat, cure lies within yourself. By facing the fear, by accepting it, floating through it and not worrying if cure doesn't happen overnight. After all, you have learned this behaviour over a lifetime so it is going to take time, perseverance and patience to unlearn. But you can do it. I did – and although it took me a long time, it has changed my life completely. Also, while you are working with the problems, you are taking charge of yourself and not being dragged helplessly through a hopeless miasma of fear and insecurity, over which you seem to have no control.

So here is the practical help for dealing with your physical symptoms as they happen. Notice what is happening to you as you sit in your chair; imagine that you are shrinking away from the feelings which threaten to overwhelm you. At the same time, you are watching apprehensively because you are sure they are going to get much worse. You must do the exact opposite! Let your arms and legs feel like lead and sag into the chair, and at the same time breathe through your partly opened mouth, as slowly and as deeply as you can. While you are breathing this way, instead of shrinking away from these upsetting feelings, do the exact opposite – take each one and describe it out loud to yourself. For example, you may say, 'My stomach feels as if it is full of jagged rocks and I feel sick.' Don't flinch from this feeling – relax! And just watch the feeling without tension. Is it really so terrible? If you had sprained your wrist, you would get on with your life as well as you could, without being too upset; you might even be rather proud of yourself, and bask in the admiration of your family and workmates for carrying on under such difficult circumstances. So why is this feeling in your stomach so frightening? After all, it is only the result of over-stimulated nerves releasing too much adrenalin which you yourself are making worse by worrying. This terrible thing which almost paralysed you with fear whilst you sat in terror thinking about it, is actually no more than a weird physical feeling which is not a symptom of serious digestive malfunction and will cause no real harm. By now, you may find your attention wandering away from yourself, but don't make the mistake of thinking that it is better now and will go away. You may cease to fear it but your nervous reactions are still programmed and it will take time for that programme to be wiped out; like the sprained wrist takes time to heal, so will your nervous system. But if you are no longer afraid of being sick or the 'rocks' being an early symptom of cancer, you are bound to improve. If you cease to stimulate your adrenalin-releasing nerves to produce more and more adrenalin, you will break the rocks and feeling sick/adrenalin/rocks cycle. In other words, the fear/adrenalin/more fear/more adrenalin cycle which feeds itself.

After describing your symptoms, try to make them worse. You will find it is impossible. Obviously, the power of your adrenalin-releasing nerves is limited. Yet you've been living in fear for so long, and it has been that fear and its accompanying tension that has intensified your symptoms. If you look at them from the outside with interest instead of fear, you create a respite from tension which has a calming effect. As Dr Claire Weekes says, 'Symptoms can be intensified only by further fear and its resulting tension. Never by relaxing, facing and accepting.'

I repeat again: it is essential to have a thorough medical check-up to eradicate any organic reasons for your symptoms before attempting any self-help programme. If you are still worried, then get a second opinion. There must be no, 'Oh my goodness, what if … my heart stops / I have an attack / my higher blood pressure gives me a stroke / this pain in my leg is a thrombosis / my headache is a brain tumour / my trembling hands are the start of some terrible motor neurone disease / my stomach problems are cancerous, etc, etc.'

So, you have faced the unpleasant feelings by describing them to yourself. When I describe my feelings to myself, they always sound a bit silly, and this is good because it reduces their impact and it makes me smile. The more you can smile, or even laugh, at yourself, the better you will be.

I found myself in this situation when I had the great good fortune to meet Edward Barker. He gave me a new way of looking at things and a form of self-hypnosis to practise on a daily basis between my visits. He wrote the formula down on a piece of paper so that I could constantly refer to it when I was alone and feeling afraid. He also taught me that there is no such thing as the perfect solution, that problems have to be accepted and worked through. But knowing you have the best point-of-view available brings some respite from the ceaseless cogitation of a very tired mind. When I felt better, it was much easier to modify and change my ideas into better ones. In the beginning, it was very difficult for me to hold my new points-of-view for more than a minute or two. Those fleeting moments were the start of my eventual emergence into understanding and peace. Time went on – I was able to be at peace for longer and longer periods of time until now it is an almost permanent state of mind. 'Ah,' I hear the pessimist cry, 'So you're not really better?' I am much better than I was, but as I've said previously, mental health demands constant attention to what is going on – and that takes perseverance. Surely nothing is more rewarding than the cultivation of peace of mind which results from practice?

Yoga

Personally, I cannot speak too highly of yoga. To me, it has made the difference between mobility and being wheelchair-bound, between embracing life with energetic enthusiasm and sitting around like an apathetic vegetable. It has also opened up a whole field of spiritual development and self-realisation. When I was introduced to yoga at Tyringham in 1969, it had a very different image from the popularity it enjoys today. People who 'did yoga' were considered to be extremely strange. It was thought to be oriental physical jerks, suitable only for young hippy-types who were totally out of touch with the real world. Yoga was seen as a strange eastern religion, highly dangerous for westerners. When I was looking for a suitable hall for my own group to meet in, a vicar received my request to use his church hall with absolute horror saying, "We can't have *yoga* going on in the church hall. This is hallowed ground!"

Yoga is a practical method of training heart and mind as well as body, and has existed in India for at least 4,000 years. At the heart of eastern spirituality is the belief that one's own consciousness is God, and everything that exists is an aspect of that one reality. This is the unity in which the world lives and moves. Because of our blindness, we cannot see this unity, so our world is made up of a multitude of separate beings, including ourselves. We cannot be aware of our true nature whilst we identify ourselves with the sensations and feelings of the body. We see only the outward appearance, whereas true awareness or consciousness is beyond what we see. We have to stop identifying with the outward forms, and concentrate on the real sense of 'I' – the 'I am' in each individual life for ever being itself. In fact, the study and practice of yoga purifies the body, improves the health and strengthens the mind. Above all, whatever one's personal religious beliefs may be, it intensifies spiritual growth. Everyone, young or old, fit or well, can improve the health of their body, calm their emotions, increase mental alertness, and begin to realise their spiritual qualities through the practice of yoga. However, any great goal in life requires self-discipline, time and perseverance. And if you are controlled by selfish instincts, you will soon give up your yoga practice.

The Asanas

The yoga postures, or asanas, help to promote self-discipline and perseverance, whilst at the same time promoting suppleness, lightness, weight control, greater energy, strength, endurance and control of the emotions. They influence every muscle, gland, nerve and organ in the body, and in this way, the whole being is renovated, the body cleansed, and life expectancy increased. Spiritual awareness is also enhanced.

The asanas take your body through its complete range of movements in a way which stimulates energy rather than consumes it. This is because most of the postures are stationary. When we hold a posture for some time, the blood can be directed to one part of the body, and as blood performs a major healing function, this direction heals, cleanses and renews that particular part of the body. The postures also stretch, exercise and massage the muscles and, most importantly, the internal organs. There is a definite influence on the glands which balance body functions, emotions and mind.

Through holding a posture, the muscles involved are strengthened, so they can easily maintain the many postures of our everyday life: sitting at an office desk, driving, standing, etc. become easier and can be maintained for longer periods. We also gradually learn to blend tension with relaxation so that the tensing or stretching of some muscles in the body is balanced by knowing how to relax those muscles not in use. Thus we become more relaxed, graceful and supple.

The postures also massage the nervous system and have a positive and direct influence on the nervous centres in the body. Posture is part of personality. Every emotion is expressed through movements or postures of the body. There's a great interest at the moment in body language. Think of anger, fear, love, hate, peace, disgust or excitement and you can immediately visualise the body language to express them.

Sometimes emotions or moods have been with us so long that they have become frozen into our body, causing tension and emotional or mental solidification. Athritis is a typical example: as the body becomes more supple, these frozen emotions are released, and a deep relaxation of body, mind and emotions takes place. You also get a literal unfreezing of an arthritic joint.

For these reasons, I have never had more than eight students in my yoga class because many emotions were released during relaxation in the form of tears, or even hysterical giggling, and I needed to be available to comfort and reassure.

There are hundreds of these postures but only a few of them are necessary for the health and the discipline of the self. Most people with a 'fluid' body are also 'fluid' or responsive emotionally and mentally. It is better to start with a mature, receptive mind and stiff joints than supple limbs and a shallow, undeveloped mentality. Joints will loosen up eventually, but a mind that is not ready may stay closed for years. A few postures, practised gently and purposefully, are far more helpful than a great deal of postures rushed through and involving strain.

Yogis (one who practises Yoga) believe that there is no limit to the achievements of someone who knows how to combine the power of bodily posture and the power of the breath with the constructive power of the mind. Personally, I have found the development of mental concentration to be a mighty weapon against ageing when joined with the physical exertion of the asanas.

Finding a teacher

As I recommended in the section on psychotherapy, how important it is to choose your therapist carefully, choose your yoga teacher with great care too. Many untrained and ignorant people have set up as teachers to profit from its increasing popularity, and I have personally encountered two examples of bad and dangerous teaching.

The first was in a class when the teacher literally forced the student's hands to join behind her back, causing her shoulder to dislocate; and the other was when I was asked to take over an adult education evening class. (I am still teaching individual wrinklies yoga and it is still very, very rewarding.) But caveat emptor, as they say. It doesn't matter how many different classes you attend, provided that you find the right teacher for you in the end.

Yoga itself may not be right for you; I had some young active people coming to my class who found it all too slow for their needs, and for whom an aerobics class or workout in the gym was far more suitable. And a sincere teacher will direct such people to an aerobics class, line dancing, or a suitable gym, and not hang on to them for the sake of the class size or financial gain. Every potential student should be given the opportunity to attend at least one class to make their own decision.

Beware of having to pay for twelve classes in advance as a dedicated yoga teacher is more concerned with his or her students' progress than class size, or making money. All that is needed for each student is floor space: the length of the body and the width of one's outstretched arms, a blanket to sit and lie upon, reasonable warmth, an empty stomach (at least an hour since the last meal), patience and perseverance.

The aim is not to see how quickly one can get into the lotus position or the headstand. I have never been able to do the full lotus. I started too late – my hip joints were not sufficiently flexible. But if I were to force myself into the pose, I would probably find myself in hospital having a hip replacement. (It is interesting to note here that hip replacements are practically unknown in India where people sit cross-legged on the floor all their lives, and hardly ever sit on a chair.)

As for the headstand, it took me sixteen years before I finally found myself upside down in this posture, the result of which was utter panic. I was all alone and wondered how the hell I was going to get down again without breaking my neck. Obviously, I did get down and my sense of achievement was unbelievable. I am now blessed with a adoptive granddaughter who calls me 'Supergran' and boasts about me to her friends at school because I can stand on my head.

The benefits of Yoga

Yoga can be used to lose weight, either generally or specifically, to improve the condition of the hair, skin, eyes, figure, posture and balance, to relieve respiratory problems like asthma, bronchitis and sinusitis. Migraine and headaches are also relieved, as are back problems and poor circulation. It also improves concentration, removes mental strain and tension, and enables you to relax properly and stay relaxed under pressure.

The whole body is reconditioned and strengthened and so becomes more agile and younger-looking. I found I became more sensitive, not just to people round me, but my sight improved and my other senses became more acute.

I had already been advised at Tyringham to give up certain foods which were bad for arthritis, and at first, this was a real deprivation. But as I practised yoga, I found these foods becoming distasteful, and more suitable foods like fruit and vegetables becoming preferable. When I go for my bi-annual eye test, it is very gratifying to hear the optician say either, 'No change', or even recommend a weaker lens than I have been wearing occasionally for small print and reading. This improvement started after my first year of doing yoga eye movements and it is sad to see so many of my contemporaries hardly able to walk, to see, to hear, to enjoy food, or even life itself when a short time devoted to yoga, even two or three times a week, would have either prevented or delayed such a decline. However, it is never too late for some improvement to take place. I have taught people in their seventies and eighties, even a ninety-year-old, who have all shown some improvement physically, and an even greater improvement mentally and emotionally.

The most important message of physical yoga – Hatha yoga – is that to control breath is to control the life force – and perhaps life itself. In the yoga schools, or ashrams, and monasteries of the East where the art of breathing has been practised and taught for centuries, strange stories are told of what has been achieved by sages of the past through breath control. Apart from its remarkable healing and reinvigorating powers, it is the key to the mysterious ability to defy gravity and, it is said, the means whereby the ancient wise men could travel through the air with the speed of an arrow. Nicholas Roerich, a Russian philosopher and mystic, who lived in Tibet for many years, claimed to have seen monks travelling through space. Michael Volin, a highly acclaimed yoga teacher, was shown a flat stone protruding from the top of a sheer cliff at an ashram by the South China Sea and was told sages would take off from it for their morning promenade in the air. This does not mean that yoga students could learn to float in the air, but it does illustrate the enormous potentialities of breath control.

Breathing is certainly linked with emotions, thoughts, heartbeat and digestion. It is easy to see how the breathing directly affects the mood. Anger, passion, fear, affection, deep thought, even imaginary situations, all produce a particular type of breathing, so there is a very special connection between breathing and the rest of our being. Of course, there are also just as wonderful connections between the heart, digestion, circulation, brain and nervous system; each cell, in fact, has a special relationship with the whole. Because this special relationship exists, we can take any aspect of our being and through training, influence the whole self. A similar relationship exists between the individual and life in general. We can use breathing techniques to deal with ill-health, nervous tension, unhappiness and depression. When working with our breathing, we are directly confronting our problem, whatever it is. As Wright observed, 'There's no neurotic individual who is capable of exhaling in one breath deeply and easily.' Patients have developed all sorts of ways to prevent deep expiration. They exhale jerkily or, as soon as the air is let out, they quickly bring their chests back into the inspiratory position. Therefore, with any breathing exercises, we must be aware that any difficulty we have in breathing easily and smoothly is a reflection of our inharmonious condition. By disciplining our breathing to right this outer symptom, we are reaching deep within ourselves to the basic causes of our personal unease or disease.

All sorts of excuses and fears will arise to try to dissuade us from continuing, and it is only by gently but firmly persevering that we will succeed. Breathing methods also cleanse the system. Throughout our body are a series of non-physical pathways of energy which yogis call the nadis. They are not the nerves although at certain key points they relate with the nervous system. These points are at the base of the spine, the plexus that controls the bowels and the sexual organs, the solar plexus, the heart, the base of the throat, the centre of the head, and the crown (the Chakras). It may be difficult for some people to visualise or believe that energy can have physical channels, but we can see such energy at work when a magnet causes patterns of its invisible force-field in iron filings; crystals also 'grow' in the pattern of these invisible lines of energy, thus causing their regular and beautiful shapes.

These physical channels are said to be clogged by fine, unclean matter in the majority of people, which causes the mind and body to function far below its possible level. Breathing exercises, done regularly and carefully, act in a stimulating manner on the energy in the nadis and burn up the unclean waste. This shows itself in the form of phlegm, excess mucus, catarrh-clogged sinuses, bad breath, offensive perspiration and constipation. These are all signs that the body is badly clogged and needs cleansing. Together with a wholesome diet, breathing methods will cleanse the whole system, and bring harmony to the body. Deep breathing has repercussions on all the tissues of the body, not just the nadis. There are oxygenating systems which supply each cell with sufficient oxygen to enable it to function efficiently and to burn up waste products. The body utilises food and repairs itself more efficiently, and the psychological value of the yoga breathing techniques is equally significant. Breathing is one of the most obvious movements of a living organism. A baby becomes capable of existing as a individual when it takes its first breath, and death is often only noticeable by a sudden cessation of breathing. Thus the movement of breathing has become synonymous with living because it is so obvious, even in sleep. Like the heartbeat and the digestion, it is spontaneous, and also like these, it can be affected by the ego – that is, our moods and desires can interfere with our natural response to living. Even while sitting still, the position in which the heart would usually beat slowly and calmly, palpitations may occur because of our thoughts or reactions. To control weeping or anger, for instance, one usually holds the breath and grits the teeth, and if one feels guilt or fear about sexual desires, one tenses the abdomen and rectum and holds the breath to keep control.

The source of the breath is the same as that of the mind. Therefore, the calming of either leads effortlessly to the control of the other. To still the breath is to still the mind, and this leads to a meditative state in which we may glimpse our inner consciousness. This is very different from repressing an emotion through tension because we have wrested the control of our breath away from fear and have handed it back to its source which is pure awareness. Remember, that through any of the yoga practices we are awakening the kundalini – a word which is synonymous with the Christian concept of the Holy Spirit or the Buddhist concept of Mindfulness – that is, the unseen, unknown God. Whatever it is called, it is the state of being, consciousness, bliss, that existed before we were born. In other words, before we became aware as an individual. There is much more to learn about yoga breathing techniques or pranayama, and there are many excellent books available on the subject. I would recommend Yoga Over Forty by Michael Volin and Nancy Phelan.

After this brief account of the philosophy of yoga, let us turn to the breathing methods themselves. Remember that these methods are particularly helpful in dealing with nervous tension, emotional disturbance, or an over-active mind. They should be practised after the physical poses of Hatha yoga, and before relaxation. Do not practise them hastily or forcefully; it is better to practise one method regularly for at least three months in the order given before going on to the next. Remember, we never heal ourselves, we never produce our own growing awareness, we only find a way to opening ourselves to the healing force.

The first step is to learn how to breathe fully and easily. There must be no difficulty with either breathing in or breathing out, no jerkiness, no irregularities. The breathing must fill our whole chest, not just part of it. A common difficulty is an inability to breathe abdominally, so to see whether you can breathe in this way, sit upright (well back in the chair) and place one hand on your chest and one on your abdomen, just below the navel. Breathe right out as far as possible and notice whether this is a smooth or a jerky exhalation. Then breathe in as far as possible, without moving your chest, and only the hand on the abdomen should rise. Now breathe in further, causing the hand on the chest to rise – then breathe out, and the hands will lower again, first the hand on the abdomen and then the one on the chest. This may seem impossible the first time, and it is interesting to note here that you are only trying to breathe naturally, not practise a breathing discipline. If you cannot do this, you will see for yourself how tensions and past experiences have influenced your body. However difficult this is, it should be practised daily for five minutes at first, gradually working up to twenty or thirty minutes as it becomes easier. On the other hand, don't give up on the five minutes because it is difficult! Obviously, the hand on chest and abdomen may be dispensed with as you learn to breathe in this way.

When this has been mastered, you can pass on to the next method, which is simply to breathe very slowly without strain. Remember that no breathing exercise is more advanced than another – each one should grow out of the previous one. Again, start at five minutes, and slowly increase, also in a seated posture. This is quite different from the last method; the aim is to breathe naturally abdominally, but to breathe as slowly as is comfortable. It must be comfortable as the aim is to induce a calming of the mind and emotions, and if you are struggling with the method, it obviously defeats its own purpose. So, slowly breathe in, counting to see how long this takes, then exhale to the same count. Just concentrate on the beautiful slowness of the breath. If you have not already practised the previous method, this may be difficult to experience. With practice, you should be able to observe a dropping away of tension, emotions and thoughts.

Sometimes it feels as if something has literally fallen away or as if the abdomen and its contents are dissolving as the tensions drop away.

Eventually, you will glimpse something that can only be described as a quiet peace and bliss. At first, only flashes growing gradually longer. This is only achieved when all efforts and all desires drop away, never by striving. The result upon our nervous or emotional conflicts is one of gradually calming and cleansing, leading towards the 'peace that passeth understanding'. Our personality grows during this practice, but while we may find release from tensions within months, a deep inner peace will only come after several years – like trees, we grow slowly, but there is beauty in it.

The third breathing method given here is one of the oldest and most often used of traditional pranayama, and aims not only to quieten minds and release spiritual awareness but also to clean the non-physical pathways of energy in the body, the nadis (also known as chakras). It should also be done sitting upright. Sitting upright means placing your bottom well back in your chair so that your spine is supported, and your feet are on the floor, with your hips and knees at right angles.

Place the thumb of the right hand on the right nostril, closing it, and breathe slowly in through the left nostril to a count of five.

Close the left nostril with the last two fingers of the right hand and retain breath for a count of ten, pushing the chin hard down on the chest.

Lift the chin, at the same time opening the right nostril and breathing out to a count of ten.

Breathe in through the right nostril to a count of two, hold it to eight, then breathe out through the left nostril to a count of four. Each in-breath counts as a repetition. The breathing is done to a 1-to-4-to-2 count and it can be moved to 2-to-8-to-4, or even to 10-to-40-to-20. It is the repetitions that matter, not the struggling, so find a count which is comfortable, and slowly build up the repetitions. Once you have the hang of it, you can use it as a meditation practice at the same time. As you inhale, imagine that your whole body is being filled with a warm, healing light or the invisible force behind life. As you retain your breath, imagine that all your tensions and problems are dropping away. As you persevere with these breathing methods, you will find parts of your personality letting go, and a release taking place within. This release and the changes it makes on your body, emotions and mind will alter your whole relationship with the world, and help you to reach a union or yoga with consciousness and bliss.

There are very many breathing methods but it is better to practise these three with devotion and dedication, than many methods just for the sake of variety and curiosity. You can practise pranayama for the sake of your health, to overcome asthma, bronchitis, catarrh and sinusitis, to find release from nervous or emotional tensions and fears, or most importantly of all, to develop a realisation of your spiritual qualities. It is a very powerful method that enables you to find that part of your being which is beyond all fears, emotions, opinions, fashions and desires – where the whole universe begins to appear differently to you. The vital part of this lies beyond change and circumstance, and is in the Eternal.

To me, yoga was a great liberation, a literal setting free from the sentence of immobility and its attendant problems of dependence, physical illness, severe pain and frustration. After all, if three eminent specialists had agreed on such a sentence, who was I to doubt their prognosis? But this is the secret of course: don't ever, ever accept pronouncements of physical disintegration until you have breathed your last breath, left your physical body behind, and assumed your spiritual form. Your physical body can then disintegrate naturally and its atoms disperse to be utilised in another form of energy, which is indestructible.

At first, yoga was only part of my physical rehabilitation, but went on to calm my emotions, improve my mental ability and help me to realise my spiritual self. I became aware that my body could either help or hinder my activities and my contemplative life, and therefore to bring it to greater health was to benefit the whole of my life experience. I also realised that all life appeared to me through my emotions, and innate cheerfulness can lighten even physical pain or illness, whilst morbidity darkens even pleasant activities. Therefore, to harmonise my emotions was to see the world in a new light. I became aware that it was my mind that sees the meaning in things, and that it was my mind that directs my body and my emotions – and I can choose whether this direction is positive or negative. And so I reached the following conclusion: while my body is a vehicle, my emotions a response, and my mind that which directs, it is through some other part of me I call my spirit that I can realise a sense of unity with the rest of life and living beings. Without this sense of unity, I am just a disassociated cell in the immensity of life's process.

My spirit relates me to others, not only in the past and present, but also in the future, for it is the breath of the eternal. Thus, I seek to realise my spirit and to know who and what I am. Through purposefully exercising my body, my emotions or my mind, I am bringing them under the greater direction of my will, and see each one – even my mind – as a vehicle of expression and realisation. I realised that none of this would work without persevering. Time and perseverance. Otherwise, what is the point of it, or any new practice? We might hope that it will interest us more than our last sporadic enthusiasm but no discipline of body or mind is even worth beginning unless we decide on perseverance first.

I found that perseverance in the yoga teachings is developed by the practice of yama, which means restraint or control applied to rules of conduct. Why should yama be so necessary at the beginning? We are all the slaves of our instincts, our emotions and our mental concepts. All over the world, we see people of opposing political factions fighting each other to the death. This is not because there is a basic enmity between them as people, but because neither can let go of their opinions. If we are controlled by our instincts, we will soon give up our yoga practice. If I lie, it is because I have not the courage to face up to whatever made me lie, and if I injure someone, I am also injuring or destroying subtle parts of my own nature that are struggling to be expressed – and so on. These rules are not mainly moralistic; they can also awaken latent possibilities within the individual. The practice of yama is difficult, and certainly all I wanted from yoga in 1969 was relief from pain, better mobility, and improved health. So if all you are seeking is a healthy physical condition, you may prefer to come back to the practice of yama later, perhaps when you have read the section on spiritual awareness.

Yama means abstinences, and they are as follows:

> Refraining from violence or causing pain in any way by word or deed, to others or to oneself.
> Refraining from lying, directly or indirectly, by word or action.
> Refraining from stealing, which includes the taking of bribes.
> Chastity, which is not to be confused with celibacy.
> Refraining from possessiveness in any sense.
> Purity in body, thought and action.
> Contentment, a philosophical acceptance of whatsoever life brings.

Austerity – the ability to bear hardship and pain.

The development of inner strengths and mental control, and self-development, which includes the study of meditation.

Devotion to God or whatever you conceive the creative force to be.

These abstinences and observances must be kept strictly by students of ascetic yoga schools, but are obviously not an integral part of Hatha yoga, practised by seekers after better physical well-being. However, a yearning towards them may develop in a student who is practising Hatha yoga regularly and sincerely. My own purpose in the beginning was purely the relief of excruciating physical pain, and a desire to keep moving and out of a wheelchair at all costs. But, subtly and amazingly, I began to feel the stirrings of spiritual awareness, and a growing, almost unconscious, desire to practise the abstinences listed above. Obviously, they are very difficult and no way do I keep them all. I just keep trying.

Spiritual enlightenment is not dependent on intellect or education – in fact, too much of either can be an impediment, because it inhibits the surrender necessary for true illumination. Liberation of the spirit comes only through suspension of the mind; although scholars and others with great mental gifts and attainments are drawn to yoga. A lack of formal education and a sense of intellectual inadequacy are no hindrance. There is something above intellect – something which we can only call intuition in its highest sense, a direct channel to divinity. This – together with sincerity and an open mind, with the possibility for belief and the desire to know – are the essentials necessary for the development of higher faculties. The old ideas that yoga is strange and threatening are dying out, but there are still those who think of it as an oriental kind of physical jerks, suitable only for the young. Untrained and ignorant people have jumped on the bandwagon of its increasing popularity and have set up as teachers; this has contributed to the misconception. True yoga is for anyone who wants it, and age is no barrier. Yoga is not a religion, it is a method of complete development, an attitude to life and all creation, and its aims are the highest and most noble. Whatever your personal religion, you will find in yoga something for yourself, and turn also to your own devotions with increased spiritual awareness and understanding.

The way you approach the postures is important. If you are unconsciously impatient, violent and ambitious, these traits will show in your practice, and the postures will be a strain. You are not trying to show the rest of the class or yourself how quickly you can get into an advanced and difficult posture. It took me 16 years to do the headstand! And I have never been able to sit in a full cross-legged lotus position. I had to cope with watching my younger students go up into a fluid and beautiful headstand before I could, and even endure the sight of a senior citizen do the 'noose' which involves wrapping the feet around the back of the neck. The important thing is to find a comfortable position for you within the asana, and then learn to hold it as long as you can *without strain*. A few postures practised gentle and purposefully are far more helpful than a large number rushed through and strained at. If you practice patiently and allow time for your body to adapt, you will see the spiritual qualities of yama begin to appear. The aim is to find a comfortable but stretched position in the particular posture. When you have found it, relax as much as possible in the pose, breathe as slowly and deeply as the posture allows, concentrate on the posture or pose and make it as perfect as you can.

You can practise at any time of the day, but you will feel stiffer in the morning than in the evening. Remove any tight clothing, and make up your mind to approach your practice with patience, gentleness and perseverance. Use your commonsense and your knowledge of your own body; it would be foolish for a woman of 70 who has not exercised for 40 years to try to force her legs into the lotus position, or for an overweight man with high blood pressure to stand on his head. I would advise a medical check-up for anyone, certainly over 40, before starting any yoga practice. Never force or strain the body; any sign of pain must be a signal to stop. Discomfort, yes – but pain, no. That's your criterion. Slightly uncomfortable – yes, that's OK – keep on going. But pain – that's your body screaming 'No' at you. Do everything slowly and cautiously, with plenty of time for relaxation. If you find your heart beating faster after exertion, lie down and practise deep breathing until it quietens. Think about what you are doing; the constructive power of the mind must be brought to bear on all physical movements, whether breathing, stretching or static postures. If you close your eyes, you can picture your body as you wish it to be, or experience the state of mind you wish to attain. The asanas I perform at least every other day keep me supple and free from locked joints and painful muscles. I must point out that these postures are my personal programme suitable for my body at this particular time of my life, but performed regularly by anyone of any age, they will result in improved health and vitality. However, nothing can take the place of a good teacher, but you will need to shop around until you find a class in which you feel really at home. It is possible to have individual tuition, but obviously this will cost more. If you decide to try my programme, give yourself plenty of time, particularly at first. Study the diagrams carefully and follow the instructions step-by-step. One thing I can predict, and that is an enormous improvement in your general well-being if you practice this programme regularly with patience and perseverance.

Asanas

So first of all, make sure that you will not be disturbed for at least half an hour. Switch off the phone, switch off your mobile, and don't answer the door. Spread a rug or blanket on the floor away from any draught. Have a warm sweater handy for relaxation, and precede the programme by 5-10 minutes of controlled breathing. Demand maximum participation from your body in every pose.

Asana 1

Start with a stretching asana. This is to warm up your muscles. So stand on your blanket with your feet comfortably apart. Bring both shoulders up towards your ears in a shrugging movement, then roll them forwards, then back again, forwards continuously and smoothly, and do not jerk or pause. After three or four rolls, reverse movements, with both shoulders going backwards. Rotate each shoulder separately, as though swimming backstroke. Let one shoulder comes forward as the other one goes back, thus pivoting the spinal vertebra. This exercise keeps the spine supple and sends extra blood to the roots of the spinal nerves. When practised correctly, it brings a very pleasant, glowing sensation in the back and between the shoulder-blades. Excellent for someone who has been sitting at a desk all day!

Asana 1

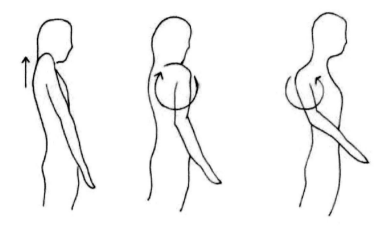

Asana 2

Still with your feet apart, tense your abdomen, stretch up your arms as high as you can, as though trying to touch the ceiling, then let yourself fall forward from the waist. If you are in the first half of your life, your hands will brush the floor. Mine don't! Stretching up gently and slowly, your muscles should be tense; in falling forward, they should be completely relaxed – head lolling, arms dangling, like a rag doll. This is a good way of learning to let go. As you hang there limply, bounce three or four times. Gradually curl yourself upright again, keep the movement under slow control, and your abdomen tightened all the time. All the vertebrae are opened up, and it can be repeated throughout the day. But don't strain – listen to your body, and move only with its permission.

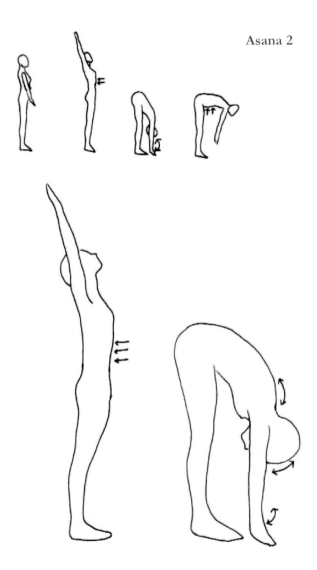

Asana 2

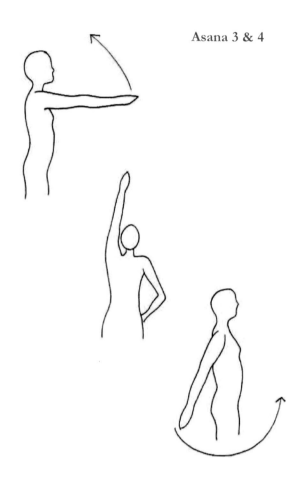

Asana 3

Standing with your feet comfortably apart on your blanket, place your left hand on your hip. Without moving your body, swing your right arm forwards and round in a circle four times. Keep your arm close to your head. Then relax and repeat with the left arm.

Asana 4

Repeat, rotating each arm backwards for four circles.

Asana 5

Bend your elbows so that your fingertips meet at chest level. Move your elbows slowly backwards as far as possible, bounce them three or four times, then straighten your arms out sideways. Press backwards three or four times in that position. Repeat the whole movement three or four times, according to what your body is telling you.

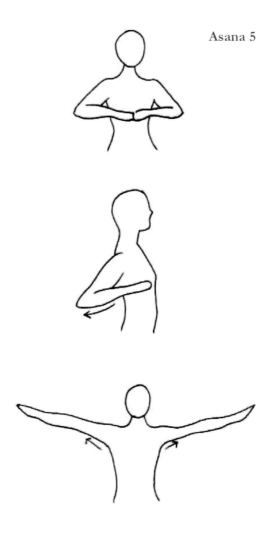

Asana 5

Asana 6

Make your hands into fists and bend your elbows so that your knuckles meet at chest level. Breathe in. As your breathe out, snap your arms straight forward from the elbows. Breathe in as you return to the starting position. Repeat.

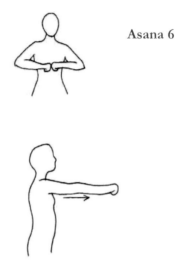

Asana 6

Asana 7

Stand with your arms loosely by your side, and swing both arms round to the right as far as you can go and then swing them round to the left, almost wrapping them round yourself. Your arms should be as limp as empty sleeves. Repeat four times.

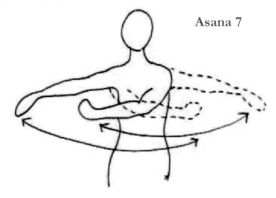

Asana 7

Asana 8

Stand with your right side against the back of a chair. (In all these exercises, when using a chair or piece of furniture, make sure it is solid and won't collapse when you rest your weight on it.) Steady yourself with your right hand. Place the other hand on your left hip. Straighten your left leg and swing it gently forwards and backwards six times. Now swing it out sideways as far as it will stretch comfortably, bring it back and repeat six times. Now move the leg forwards, sideways and backwards in small semicircles four times. And repeat four times with the leg moving backwards, sideways and forwards. Relax and repeat with the other side.

Asana 8

Asana 9

Facing the chair, lightly hold on to the back of it and slowly squat as low as you can. Balance yourself and see if you can let go of the chair without falling. Come up carefully and slowly. This is a good way of balancing the body and the nervous system. Repeat it once or twice if you feel able.

Asana 9

Asana 10

Kneel on all fours, palms flat on the floor. Let your head hang down and keep your arms straight. Your arms, trunk and side form a rectangle with the floor, rather like a perfect cantilever bridge. Raise the middle of your spine, bringing it up into a hump, keeping your arms rigid, and then gently come down into an arch whilst raising the head. All the movement is then in the spine, just like a cat. Do this very slowly and thoughtfully – it's a wonderful tonic for the whole spine. Repeat four to six times.

Asana 10

Asana 11

From this position, gently lower your buttocks onto your heels, or as near to them as possible. Use a cushion if this is difficult. Sit well back, hold your head high, hands on your knees, hold as long as you can comfortably – up to two minutes – and then relax.

Asana 11

Asana 12

Sit back on your heels, use a cushion if necessary, and join your palms above your head. Inhale ⌐– inflating your stomach; exhale – deflating your stomach, and continue breathing in this way like a frog. Raised hands prevent shallow breathing, so that you are breathing deeply and correctly from your abdomen. You can direct the healing power of the breath to any part of the body as you breathe out. This is a cleansing and purifying breath for your whole system. Stop when you've had enough, of course. Relax.

Asana 12

Asana 13

Sit on your heels, and bend forward until the crown of your head is resting on the floor, with your back and buttocks raised. Hold your ankles with your hands. Hold as long as you comfortably can, inhaling and exhaling, peacefully.

Asana 13

Asana 14

Sit with your left leg stretched straight out in front, bend your right leg at the knee, and press the right foot flat against the left thigh. Rest your hands on your knees. Inhale, and as you exhale, lean forwards towards your left foot. Do not bend the left knee. The aim of the asana is to take hold of the left foot and press your forehead to the left knee. I have not been able to do this (!) but if you are relatively young and free from arthritis, you will get there, but don't

Asana 14

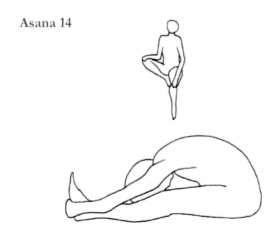

ever strain – you'll hurt your back. Repeat the movement with inhalation and exhalation: inhale when you extend the body, exhale when you fold it. Then change your legs and practise on the other side.

Asana 15

Sit up, and with straight legs, point your toes forward. Lean back on your elbows and slowly lower the top of your head to the floor. Arch your spine as high as you can, for up to two minutes. Come down slowly and relax.

Asana 15

Asana 16

If your neck is uncomfortable lying flat, put one or two thin paperbacks under your head. Slowly stretch your arms above your head, and your feet and legs in the opposite direction. Really stretch your whole body and relax. Bend your right leg up to your abdomen, keeping your left leg straight, and take hold of your right leg with both hands. Press it gently towards your body five or six times. Release the leg, stretch it straight up into the air, and slowly lower it to the floor. Repeat with the other leg. Now bend both legs over your body and hug them close with your arms. Hold up to two minutes. As you progress, you can eventually lift your chin to your knees and hold. (Incidentally, this is called the Gas Ejection pose!)

Asana 16

Asana 17

Still lying face upwards, bend your knees and place your feet flat on the floor, as close to your hips as possible. Now lift your buttocks and lower back as far off the floor as possible, drawing the abdominal muscles up and in at the same time. Then relax. Repeat several times. Stop when you feel tired.

Asana 17

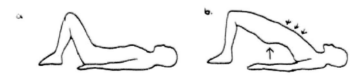

Asana 18

Lying with your knees bent and your feet flat on the floor by your buttocks, stretch your arms out sideways. Drop your knees to the left and turn your neck to the right. Reverse the movement and keep it going from side to side six to eight times. Relax.

Asana 18

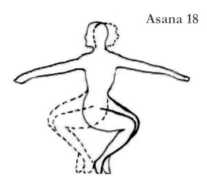

Asana 19

Lying flat, bend your left knee and clasp your hands behind your head. Bring your left knee to meet your right elbow, reverse the movements and keep it going from side to side six to eight times, and relax.

Asana 19

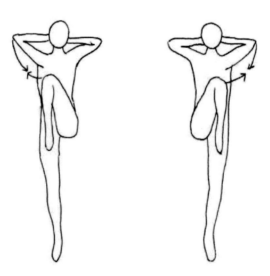

Asana 20

This is a good asana with which to end your practice as it massages the spine and soothes the nerves. Lie on your back, with your knees bent over your stomach. Clasp your knees with your hands and arms. Curve your spine so that the small of your back makes contact with the floor, and rock gently from side to side as you would if you were in a cradle.

Always finish your yoga practice with relaxation for at least five minutes, preferably fifteen or twenty. If you can't stand silence, play some soothing music, although true relaxation can only be accomplished with no sound. Put on your sweater, and lie down with your head supported if

Asana 20

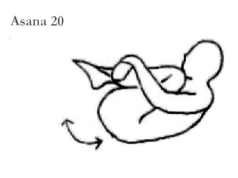

necessary with your paperback. Cover yourself with a blanket, let your feet fall away from one another and place your arms a little way away from your body, with your hands palm upwards if this is comfortable. Close your eyes and practise the breathing exercises. Then relax the muscles of your feet, ankles, calves, knees, thighs, stomach muscles, followed by the muscles of your waist: chest, shoulders, arms and hands. Relax your face, let your jaw sag, relax your tongue, soften your eyes, smooth out your forehead, and relax your spine. If this is difficult, try breathing in, tensing the whole body, then exhaling and letting go.

Now relax your nerves by turning your mind's eye in on yourself. Establish deep and rhythmical breathing, close your eyes and concentrate on the point between your eyebrows. Try to see clearly in colour an object or landscape which pleases you – a tree a flower, a face, or a beautiful view. Concentrate on the ability to see it as clearly as you can. Now identify your pockets of inattention. Close down all the communication between nerves and brain, like a tide going out. Try to think that nothing matters, that you have

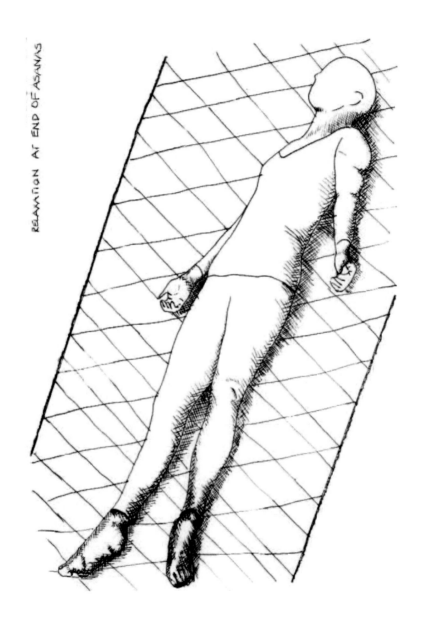

RELAXATION AT END OF ASANAS

Relaxation at end of Asanas (Corpse pose)

completely let go, that your body is growing heavier and heavier, your limbs are leaden, you couldn't even lift a finger, that you are sinking down into clouds of peace, as though going off to sleep. Keep breathing slowly and quietly, five heartbeats to each inhalation and to each exhalation, to relax yourself further. Slowing the breath relaxes the heart muscles and pacifies the nerve centres. Try to detach your mind and send it as far away as you can, leaving behind all your worries, work and responsibilities. Enter your own private space and be there, completely.

When you are ready to leave this relaxed state, move your arms and legs gently, take several deep breaths, stretch and yawn, roll onto your side, get up and gradually resume your activities. Through relaxation, one is able to accept the many things, good and bad, that a full life brings. Through it also, one can initiate changes when they are necessary. Through it, one can drop away many of the things that destroy the harmony of our lives, the things that ruin our relationships with others, or prevent us from giving of our best. Relaxation can help us find wisdom and understanding, in rising to the challenges of our lives. Nervous, ill, harassed or overworked people should all learn to relax, even if you only practise for five minutes a day – it is enough to recharge the body, overcome fatigue, preserve vital energies, and allay ageing.

Taken further into relaxation of the breath and the emotions, it gradually becomes a spiritual experience. In my opinion, the deepest stages of relaxation should be studied as part of the development of spiritual awareness. You won't be able to practise the physical asanas if you have to keep looking back at the book, and you won't relax if you have to keep looking at the book to read what to do while you are relaxing. So I advise making a cassette or a CD of this part in your own voice (if you like it). It's very good actually to hear yourself talking to yourself, because you tend to take more notice than if someone else is saying it to you. If you really can't stand your own voice, then get someone whose voice you do appreciate to make a recording for you. You may the find the prospect of twenty asanas daunting, so start with the pure stretches at the beginning of the programme. Do as many as your feel able, and then gradually increase the amount. Remember, it is not how many stretches you perform but the length of time you hold the position that is important – not to the point of pain, but a certain amount of discomfort shows that you are achieving results. I stretch the muscles and joints of my eyes, hands and feet whilst I am watching TV or sitting at my desk.

Exercises for eyes

I have been known to do the eye movements waiting at a bus stop – once to the great confusion of a man waiting at the same stop in St Anne's. After a few frightened glances at my rolling eyes, he walked hastily (!) to the next stop and seated himself very well away from me when he finally boarded the bus. Never mind! I'm the one who is prescribed weaker lenses every time I have my eyes tested. Worth being considered odd, don't you think? Too many people take to spectacles unnecessarily. Some take to them because they feel they are a fashion item. One day perhaps, feeling tired or run down, you pick up a book or directory and find you cannot focus. Since we are programmed to take failing sight over 40 as inevitable, we automatically rush to the ophthalmologist and have ourselves fitted out with spectacles. This is a mistake because once we wear them, we become increasingly dependent upon them. Your eyes are a part of your body, like your stomach and your lungs. If you are in a low state, you accept indigestion or a bad cold, yet the eyes, ears and teeth are expected to carry on some autonomous life of their own and not be affected by poor general health. Assuming there is no serious physical defect or disease, spectacles could be avoided and good sight retained if the eyes are exercised regularly.

The following exercises not only strengthen the muscles and tear ducts, but also improve the power of focusing. I would repeat here what I said in the chapter on coping with nervous exhaustion – that when you are in a nervous state, your eyes will not be focusing properly. The tiny muscles which focus the lens will be fatigued like the rest of you and you will very often find you have bad sight. So, as I said in that chapter, don't go to the optician because you will constantly have to have your lenses changed. You just won't find a lens that suits you all the time. Far better to relax, do relaxation, do deep breathing, do meditation, and that will help you a great deal more than to keep changing your lenses. Good sight in old age is vital. What a disaster to be cut off, not only from reading and television, but also from faces, and the beauty of sea, sky and garden at a time when these sights are becoming more and more important to us. Don't allow this to happen to you. People say that TV ruins your eyes, but provided you do not overdo it, it need not be harmful. It can even be beneficial if you practise these exercises whilst you watch. Changing focus should also be done when doing any prolonged close work like reading, sewing, drawing, writing, word-processing, etc, particularly working on computers.

Remember too that sun glasses should only be worn in conditions of extreme brightness – on the beach, in snow, a blinding white road in strong sunlight – and even then, the lenses should be prescribed for you. We should not allow ourselves to become like moles without the quality of curiosity or wonder. Now that I rush about less, and am not so occupied with getting and spending, I see the world with new eyes, the minute life in my garden, the butterflies, insects, snails and caterpillars, things growing, opening, developing and dying, the sky, the moon and the clouds, and the Malvern Hills. I use and care for my eyes like a precious treasure which could be lost. As Walter de la Mere said,

> Look thy last on all things lovely,
> Every hour – let no night
> Seal thy sense in deathly slumber
> Till to delight
> Thou has paid thy utmost blessing.

The message of this poem should be important at any age – particularly so, when youth has gone.

I am not suggesting that these eye exercises will cure eye diseases or restore poor sight in everyone but for me they improved my vision, put a stop to deterioration, and even have improved it. They should be done sitting with your hands in your lap, and your neck and your back in a relaxed straight line, not like a sergeant major. Do not move your head, only your eyes. Focus on a specific point, don't just gaze vaguely towards it.

If these movements cause your eyes to ache, or are difficult to do, your eye muscles are weak and you are in great need of the exercises.

Exercises to strengthen focus

Stretch out your arm with your forefinger extended. Look at the tip of your finger and watch it as you slowly bring it back to the point between your eyebrows. Stretch out your arm and finger, watching

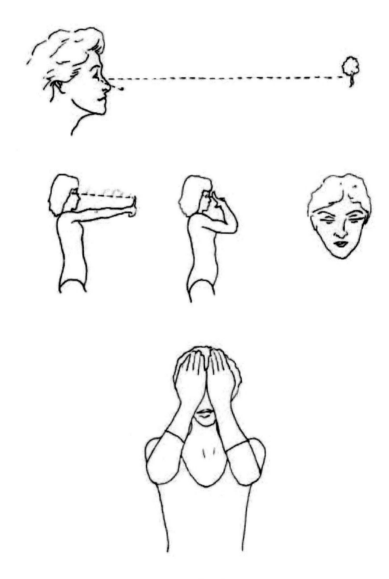

Exercises for the eyes

the tip of your finger all the time, and repeat once more. Close and squeeze your eyelids together to cleanse your eyes and massage them.

Now put these two exercises together, looking from the distant object to your extended finger, watching your finger move to touch the point between your eyebrows, out again, and then to the distant object. Squeeze your eyelids together and blink several times.

Finish by placing the palms of your hands over your eyes to exclude the light completely. Visualise yards of soft, black velvet or a night sky. Lastly, take a moment to appreciate the gift of sight and send your loving thoughts to those who cannot see. Any position which brings blood to the head, and any movement involving stretching the neck and increasing circulation to the optic nerve, can contribute to the health of the eyes. If you have any doubts about performing these eye exercises, then do consult your ophthalmologist first; this is important. Remember that no therapy will do you any real good if you approach it with doubt or misgivings of any kind, or even if you think it's a bit strange. Healing begins in the mind.

Exercises for the hands

If you have arthritis, these exercises may hurt, but persevere and one day you will find it does not hurt nearly so much or maybe perhaps not at all.

Flap your hands limply up and down from the wrists like a child waving an exaggerated goodbye.

Shake your hands vigorously from the wrists away from your body, as though shaking off drops of water.

Separate your fingers, and keeping them slightly bent, move them individually as though playing the piano in the air.

With bent elbows, press your palms together hard in a prayer position in front of your chest. Now push your joined palms as far as possible, to the right and then to the left. Keep your head and shoulders still. Repeat three or four times. This one is very good for preventing or controlling the development of osteoporosis.

Clench your fists hard and draw them back to shoulder-level. Now fling your arms forward and spread out your fingers at the same time. Repeat three or four times. This is an excellent way of ridding yourself of tension too. Hold the person or situation giving you

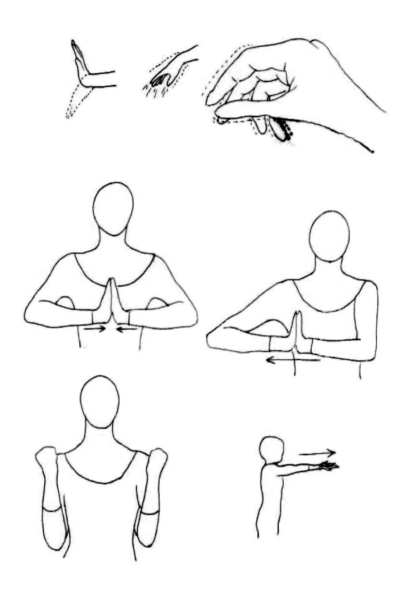

Exercises for the hands

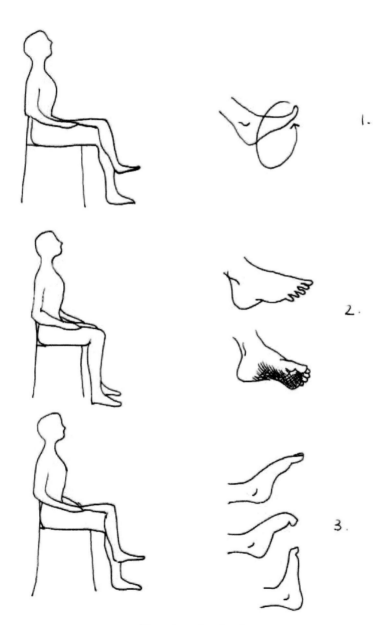

1.

2.

3.

Exercises for the feet

grief in your fists and throw them away literally. I give a good yell at the same time. Wonderful!

Exercises for the feet

Take off your shoes and socks and sit in a chair, with your neck and spine in a relaxed straight line. When you sit in a chair, always put your bottom well back in the seat, so that you are not resting on the base of your spine; it's a very bad position to assume. Your knees and your hips should be at right angles with your back in a really straight line. Now, cross your left leg over your right knee. Incidentally, this is the only time you should cross your legs, as it restricts circulation and can cause varicose veins and other leg and ankle problems. (Cross your ankles instead – it looks much more attractive as well as being harmless.) Now imagine your big toe is a pencil. Circling your foot from the ankle, slowly draw as large a circle as you can in a clockwise direction. Repeat anti-clockwise slowly. Repeat with the right foot crossed over the left knee. Repeat with both feet as many times as you are able.

Place your feet parallel and about 10 cm (or 5 inches) apart. Lift all your toes off the floor and try to separate them. Place them back on the floor, keeping your toes as widely spaced as possible. Grasp the floor with your toes, keeping them straight and not scrunched up, and lift the inside edges of your feet to raise your inner arches. Hold for 15 seconds and release.

Exercises for cramp

Sit with your back and neck in a relaxed straight line. Cross your left leg over your right knee, and stretch out your foot as far as you can. Now curl up your toes as if you were holding a pencil with them, and pull your whole foot backwards. Relax, and repeat with the other leg.

All these exercises can of course be done more than once.

Exercises for the neck

Another useful set of exercises that can be done while you are sitting are for the neck. The range of movement in the neck is amazing: 180 degrees of rotation, and almost as much in its nodding up and

1.

2.

3.

4.

down. Then there are all the many combinations of the two. The neck is like a delicate suspension bridge between the shoulders and the skull. There is much more movement here than anywhere else in the whole spine. If these delicate movements are disturbed by straining or jolting the neck, or by the effects of arthritis on the vertebrae, there can be many manifestations of discomfort and indeed excruciating pain. Obviously, there is local pain, but there can also be pain in the face, head, or even migraine. The head can feel muzzy and detached; there can be blurred vision and dizziness, ringing in the ears, depression, unstable emotions, impaired hearing, difficulty in swallowing, sinusitis, painful teeth – to name but a few. A 'pain in the neck' is often related to your emotional state, and waxes and wanes as we pass in and out of stressful experiences. I often ask my patients, "Who or what is being a pain in the neck to you at the moment?" Anxiety, fear, worry, anger, 'nerves' all make for a painful neck. The way to keep the neck fully supple with normal, pain-free movement is to demand maximum participation of the neck and thorax area through careful and intelligent stretches. These are the neck movements I perform daily, usually while watching TV or stopping occasionally whilst reading, writing or cooking. Waiting for food to cook is an excellent time to do all sorts of yoga practice.

So –

Sitting with a relaxed straight back, pull in your chin without tipping your head forward, hold, and feel the stretch in your neck. Repeat this movement ten times.

Sitting with a relaxed straight back, pull in your chin as far as you can. Now bend your head back as far as possible. Move your head from side to side by moving your nose one centimetre to the left and then to the right. Do this slowly and carefully.

Sitting or standing with a relaxed straight back, drop your head forward and feel the stretch at the back of your neck. Clasp your fingers together at the back of your head, elbows bent and dropped forward. Press down very gently with your fingers onto your head and release. Repeat five times. You should feel a stretch all the way down your spine.

Sit on a chair with your feet on the floor. Place the palm of your left hand underneath your left buttock. Tilt, not turn, your head towards your right shoulder, and bring your right hand up and over your head. Spread your fingers wide and reach as far down the left hand side of your face as you can. The weight of your right forearm is lying along the upper left crown of your head to reinforce the stretch. Hold this position for fifteen seconds and release. Then repeat three times. Then change sides, with your right hand underneath your right buttock, and your left arm reaching up and over your head tilting to the left, and repeat another four times.

Relaxation

The yoga poses and breathing work will promote a certain amount of relaxation in your body and mind, and this can be used to attain a state of pure harmony and peace. Being relaxed is a blessed thing: it is reminiscent of a beautiful ship riding easily through the roughest waves. Certainly it is moved by the billows, certainly it responds sensitively to each wind and current, but at the same time it can choose its course and hold its own against them. Through relaxation one is able to accept the many things, good and bad, that a full life brings. One can also initiate changes when they are necessary, and drop away many of the things that destroy the harmony of our lives – things that ruin our relationships with others or destroy our ability to give of our best. Deep relaxation can help you find wisdom and understanding in rising to life's challenges. When we are ruled by our passions and appetites, emotions or vanity, selfishness or sexual desire, we will not be wholly satisfied with ourselves. It is only when we become whole in some degree that we enjoy the feeling of relaxation; it is not just a practice – it is also an experience.

Learning to relax is not any easier than learning any other skill: how to play a musical instrument for instance – it demands time, attention and devotion. To attain significant success in this realm may take years; even after 25 years of practice I still find deep relaxation quite difficult when I am tense or upset, which of course is precisely the time I need it most. However, even a little practice will give you enough skill to help you through the stresses and strains of everyday living. In learning to ride a bicycle, you may never win races, but at least you have a means of transport. Taking this analogy further, whilst you are learning, there is always the possibility of falling off. You find how frightened you are of hurting yourself and how little control you have over your body, but you usually continue in spite of these difficulties because you see that other people have succeeded in spite of them. Many patients and students begin to practice relaxation blithely believing that heaven lies around the corner and that they will have no problems. Relaxation is the logical precursor of meditation, but because so many 'worldly' people have seen the enormous possibility of financial gain in offering immediate bliss – for which you only have to go on a weekend course, read a book, or go to their classes (in exchange for quite large amounts of money, of course); a number of their victims end up disillusioned, and extremely cynical about the whole process.

In fact, heaven does lie literally 'just around the corner' of deep relaxation, but there are a number of pitfalls and obstacles along the way which the self-styled money-motivated healer fails to mention. Only a thoroughly honest teacher like Bunyan will mention the Slough of Despond (despondency and laziness) and Worldly Wiseman (reasoning based on prejudices, ignorance and fears) so that you are aware of the difficulties you face. When you learn to relax, you come face to face with the very parts of your nature that are holding you back from the experience. Once again, you encounter the process of Facing referred to in the section on Help with Nervous Problems. In facing the parts of your nature that are preventing you experiencing a state of pure being, harmony, bliss, you will come up against them very forcibly.

During your early years, you may have felt bitter and resentful because you were not born into different circumstances, with better educational opportunities, room for fulfilment, and most importantly, parental affection and security. These feelings of resentment and bitterness may have become so much a part of your nature that you are no longer consciously aware of them. You can also be quite unconscious of the way this underlying attitude is colouring your life, altering your relationships with others, and shaping your future. It may not be bitterness or resentment; it could be insecurity, fear of failure, sexual difficulties, depression, feelings of inferiority – a host of attitudes that we attach to ourselves like parasites. It could be a whole host of negative feelings, and in attempting to go beyond them or no longer be conditioned by them, we experience something like the force of gravity. In other words, gravity is almost unnoticeable until you try to resist it – even jumping in the air is a tremendous effort, and thrusting up and away in a spaceship causes such stress and drag that it can lead to unconsciousness. So that to thrust against this force, one has to take special precautions, but success can achieve weightlessness and a totally new view of the whole universe. Therefore you can expect negative parts of human nature to come up and hit you, and to experience them in all their power instead of hardly being aware of them. The harder you push against them the stronger they will seem, and in this practice you will usually feel as if you are getting worse before you get better. Here again, you are experiencing the process of Accepting, described in the chapter on Nerves. Sometimes such feelings will arise during the practice of relaxation itself, and you will see the reasons for them. But more often they will come up out of the blue, and cause you to wonder whether relaxation – Facing and Accepting and Floating – are not all a load of rubbish and best left alone, along with all the rest of the holistic mumbo-jumbo. They answer is to press on with it as best you can, and not succumb entirely to your bitterness, despair, hopelessness or whatever is threatening to overwhelm you, because what you bring forth from within you will save you.   Sometimes, as I have experienced personally in the past, it is quite impossible to overcome the strength of your feelings. I have dealt with this extremity by telling myself gently, 'This is a healing process; I am seeing my unconscious moods coming to the surface. All I can do is to recognise them and press on until it has all come out of me.' Here again, we are dealing with the feeling of floating, as mentioned in the chapter on Nervous Exhaustion. These feelings are not my real and deepest self, but something that will pass. How long this process goes on will depend on how much of your past emotions, thoughts and actions you have to work out, and how you personally handle the situation. You will be tempted to push it all back into unconsciousness or, at the other extreme, you may feel overwhelmed by it all. The ideal is neither to suppress nor to sweep away, but to watch with as much detachment as possible – not detachment of the stoic, forced kind, but arising from the practice of relaxation itself. In practising relaxation, we have to recognise that tension is as vital to the life of the body as relaxation. The heart tenses, then completely relaxes, and so does the chest during healthy breathing.   Even waking and sleeping express this rhythm of action and rest, as do consciousness and unconsciousness, energy and inertia. Life is a balance of opposites – a marriage, or even a contest, between them. Birth and death are the major poles, with the smaller opposites of our life in between. Relaxation is the balance and because of this, you will notice a balancing of your personality as you practise.   This process was shown quite clearly in my class by a somewhat reserved and very scientific intellectual becoming much more intuitive, more emotional, more rational, and actually beginning to read metaphysical literature. Another student, who was already highly emotional and irrational, eventually found a more intellectual, reasoning nature coming to the fore. And similarly, our whole nature responds.

The process of discovering one's real and deeper self is so interesting, enlightening and, most of all, rewarding. However, in most cases, learning to relax deeply will be like climbing a mountain. Sometimes the views are wonderful and an elevated view of the world is gained. But it is hard work! Paradoxically, the hard work is in learning to do nothing, give up all effort, and just be still. Once in this state, there is no effort attached to it at all. But getting there often requires all that we have. Even if you experience the total liberation of deep relaxation, it is only a glimpse – a fleeting recognition – of another level of being. When we are no longer practising the discipline, the feeling is largely lost, and only the fragrance of it remains. We may still be nervous, irritable and thoughtless, insecure in everyday life, although in deep relaxation it will seem as if you have risen above all the causes of these negative emotions that are embedded so deeply within you. For a time, they have ceased to exist, but in coming back to your usual self again they've reappeared. But the vision of what you have seen will remain in your memory and at least you will be aware that *it is* possible to exist in a different way. Even if you only experience deep relaxation once, it will have changed you in many subtle ways. You can forget it or distort it, but you will never be quite the same again, because you now know your fuller self, your consciousness *can* exist in a radiant, clear and joyful state beyond the bounds of the body and its senses. You will see also that many of the things in your life to which you attach so much importance can now be seen from a totally different point-of-view. You may seem unchanged outwardly and even to yourself, but every strong experience changes us slightly, and if you have the self-discipline to continue your practice, the trail you are making will widen until it becomes a road to self-understanding where you are at peace with yourself and the world.

With the actual practice, you will find it much more effective to make a recording, either using your own voice or asking someone whose voice you find soothing and attractive, to make it for you. Don't forget to leave a space between each instruction, giving you time to completely relax. Begin with the primary exercise, to recognise the tension and relaxation as it occurs throughout your whole being. Lie on a blanket or a carpeted floor, put a pillow under your knees and another under your neck. Make sure you are out of draughts and use a blanket if it's necessary – you can't relax if you're cold. Or, if you haven't time to lie down, sit well back in a straight-backed chair with your feet on the floor. Do not sag in the chair – be erect. Do not worry if this is difficult in the beginning as practice will make it more comfortable and all the time you are strengthening your spine. The body should be completely unrestricted by belts or tight clothing and remove jewellery and spectacles. Do make sure that you will not be disturbed for half an hour. This is the suggested programme of relaxation:

Sit or lie for a few moments letting thoughts of recent activity die down. Resolve firmly to keep your attention on the practice during the half hour. Think of it as a friend for whom you are waiting. Don't force anything. Close your eyes gently, and be conscious of the weight of your body. Be careful not to press down or tense up any part of your body. Breathe in your own time without trying to control your breath in any way. Complete eight cycles of inhalation and exhalation. Now tense and straighten your arms and legs; hold for a slow count of five, then let them drop back by the force of their own weight, and relax. Stay in that position for another slow count of five. Repeat the cycle three times, as this will help you become aware of the exact feelings of relaxation and tension. The next step is to isolate this sensation in each extremity.

Put your right hand lightly on top of your left arm, slightly below the elbow. Clench your left hand into a tight fist, and feel the muscles of the left forearm tensing. Loosen your fist, put your right hand above your left elbow, then tighten your left fist again. Now you can feel the tension in your upper arm as well. This demonstrates how even small movements create very far-reaching tensions. Repeat with the left hand on the right arm. Repeat three times with each arm, holding the tensing position for five seconds and the relaxing position for five seconds. You can count the seconds by saying 'One thousand and – ', so it's 'One thousand and one, one thousand and two', and so on, up to five.

Now place your right hand on top of your right thigh and straighten your leg, and you will feel the muscles becoming tense. Hold the leg out for five seconds, then let it drop back of its own accord. Relax for five seconds, and you will feel the muscles letting go. Concentrate on keeping your arm and leg muscles loose. Let your body weight take over; don't press down and don't lift up any part of it. Now place your left hand on top of your left thigh and straighten the leg for five seconds. Let go as before, and relax for five seconds. Repeat this three times for each leg, ending with complete relaxation.

Now concentrate on your shoulders and lift them up as high as you can, towards your ears. Hold for five seconds, let them go for five seconds, repeat the cycle three times. Now feel your arms, legs and shoulders go absolutely loose.

Now concentrate on your head and neck. Press the back of your neck against the pillow or the back of the chair and hold for five seconds; feel the muscles tighten. Release the pressure and gently wag your head from side to side until your neck feels loose. Keep your eyes lightly closed as this will heighten your feelings of relaxation. Repeat this tensing and relaxing of the neck three times. Take a minute to check your arms, legs, shoulders and neck, and let go into complete rest.

Now wrinkle your forehead as if you were feeling apprehensive and hold for five seconds, then let loose for five seconds. Frown, lowering your eyebrows, hold for five seconds, then let loose for five seconds. Now imagine having a completely smooth forehead; then wrinkle and frown again three times. Finally, rest for a minute, concentrating on relaxing the forehead and keeping it smooth. Just imagine yourself in a mirror with a completely smooth forehead.

Now clench your teeth and feel your jaw muscles tense for five seconds; open your mouth a little way and then relax naturally. Let your jaw go slack, and keep it slack for five seconds. Clench your teeth once more and hold. Repeat this tensing and relaxing cycle three times. Rest for a while and now feel the relaxation in every part of your body.

Now push strongly with your tongue against the roof of your mouth and hold for five seconds, and you will feel your throat muscles tighten as you hold. Now let your tongue drop and feel the difference of the relaxation. Hang loose for five seconds, and push up again. Repeat three times and finish in a complete relaxing position.

Now squeeze your eyes tightly shut and hold for five seconds. Let go and rest with them gently closed for five seconds, then repeat the cycle three times. Finish with complete and total relaxation of the whole body.

For the best results, you should practise this relaxation at least once a day, and after a month you will find that you are really aware of the tensions which exist in your body. You may notice some tension in your arms and shoulders whilst driving for the first time, or how stiffly you hold yourself when meeting strangers, or even while you are just sitting still. Slowly, these tensions will drop away – if you practise of course. I had a patient once who was a hotel receptionist and suffering constant headaches. After probing possible emotional and/or psychological causes of her headaches, it became clear that she was maintaining constant welcoming smiles which were causing extreme tension from her jaw through her temples and up into her scalp muscles. By consciously relaxing the muscles in this area every hour, the headaches disappeared and have not returned. She had thought she must have had a brain tumour – the pain was so constant and so severe. The yoga poses and meditation will, if practised, help enormously to make you conscious of your body and what you are doing with it.

When you have performed this primary exercise in relaxation for some time, you may have a glimpse of the wonderful peace it can bring. Some people find themselves floating, blissfully relaxed, warm and soft. A few find that pent-up feelings of grief and misery break through, and let them go in tears. These tears should be allowed to flow until they are all released and you are free. But it is not easy. Paradoxically, the hard work is in learning to do nothing, to give up all effort and just be still. Once you are there there is no effort at all, but getting there requires all that you have. But you will have seen for yourself that your consciousness can exist in a clear and joyous way beyond the bounds of your body and its senses. You will also see many of the things in your life to which you attach so much importance from a totally different point-of-view.

The next step in practising relaxation is to relax the emotions. Start by passing your attention over the body, starting with the legs and moving upwards without actually tensing or relaxing the muscles themselves. When you reach your head, keep your attention there, and wrinkle your brow as much as possible. Imagine it is wrinkled because you are feeling apprehensive. Use any existing worries that you have – financial, physical or social – to deepen this feeling of apprehension. Allow your whole face and body to be influenced by this mood. Now gently drop it away from your face and body as if it were a muscular tension. Using your face and forehead again, express fear in the same way. You will probably find that fear pulls your forehead tight and smooth, and the muscles in your temples tense and hard. You see where the headaches come from! Now drop the whole feeling of fear away gently into relaxation.

Now express anger in the same way, and drop it. Then pain, grief or any other emotion you may be experiencing. Some emotions are so much a part of you that they are engraved on your face and body like an emotional dirt; whilst you wash yourself frequently to remove physical dirt, you seldom cleanse this inner grime of fears and apprehension. Restlessness is only in your thoughts and emotions. One of the origins of daily prayer is that it makes us clean again, and in harmony with life. As the Bible says, 'Be still and know that I am God.' And in the Desiderata, 'Go placidly amidst the noise and haste, and remember what peace there may be in silence.'

Taking care of the body

Now remember: it's no good reading about all these stretches; you have to do them! If the programme seems intimidating, try one or two asanas and gradually add to them. Every other day, or even two or three times a week, is better than nothing, and you may find, as I did eventually, that you so enjoy your practice, it becomes a daily and eagerly anticipated pleasure.

We are in a physical body, so we must take adequate care of it. Most people spend more time and money on their car, yet our body is a much more miraculous machine than any car, computer, jet plane, whatever. It also has to last a lifetime; you cannot throw it away and buy a newer, more up-to-date model. What we eat, how much we exercise, and adequate rest, are the clues to physical well-being. Sufficient relaxation is important too, because a stressed mind will influence the body in a negative way, however healthy your diet and your exercise programme. Most middle-aged people have had the experience of suddenly meeting an old school friend after many years and finding them unrecognisable. Sometimes the change has been wrought by hardship, illness or suffering. But quite often it is the result of prosperity. In these strangers with their florid complexions, thinning hair, gross stomachs and thick neck, we seek in vain the slim young girl or handsome young man we knew.

The sad thing is that it need never have happened. These men and women are the victims of their own ignorance and lack of discipline. The story is usually the same: in youth, they were active and fond of sport. Their appetites were good, they ate well, and their stomachs digested whatever they consumed. With increasing age and prosperity however, physical activities diminished – sport was given up, they drove instead of walking, but the eating went on, bigger and better than ever. The slim girl has now married and has children, she goes to coffee mornings, birthday parties, barbeques, dinner parties – all occasions for eating fattening foods. They cook for their husbands and children, tasting as they cook, cleaning up their children's leftovers, eat at the cinema and whilst watching TV. They drink more alcohol, they put on weight, at first with resentment, then with resignation, and finally with apathy. They take ever-larger sizes in clothes, give up active games because they are short of breath, even stop going to the beach because they look ugly in their swimsuits. They sit about more and often eat as a consolation for their discontent.

The men, active swimmers and surfers, footballers, cricketers, athletes and rowers, gradually became spectators rather than participants. They married, they dropped out of sporting circles, stayed at home with their families or took them for picnics in the car. Some might do a little gardening, slowly following the motor-mower across the lawn, or at the beach they might dip briefly into the sea between sunbathing. But for the most part, weekends would be spent entertaining friends, with dinner parties, Sunday brunches, barbecues and beer, drinks on the patio. On weekdays, there were business lunches to fill them up at midday, a few drinks after work and perhaps a few more at home, then a substantial dinner followed by TV and a few snacks. The conclusion is logical: less exercise + more eating = excess weight and all its attendant maladies.

It is ironic that, by the time most of us can afford to indulge in rich living, our bodies cannot accept it. We cannot take liberties with middle-aged digestions which, if abused in youth, are starting to show signs of wear and tear. In any case, we need less food as we get older. With decreased physical activity, we burn it up less quickly, and it goes to fat, and every other day we are warned of the dangers of excess weight. We are told that it puts a strain on the heart, that it contributes to coronary occlusions which are less common in countries where the population is not so well fed, that animal fat builds up cholesterol in the arteries and leads to strokes. The remedy is regular exercise and a suitable diet, well-balanced, health-giving meals – not in fad and freak diets which are as bad as over-eating. There is nothing so wearing as the health food crank who fusses endlessly about his or her diet – cannot eat this and cannot eat that, constantly switching to new and wonderful, and usually unpalatable, discoveries. Most freak diets are useless for keeping weight down, and can result in malnutrition, indigestion, haggard faces, scrawny necks and bad temper. Steaming, saunas, violent exercise and starvation diets are not only foolish but dangerous for many middle-aged people, and usually the first large meal puts back most of the weight so painfully removed. Dehydration diets are completely unrealistic apart from their bad effects on the kidneys, because the weight increases again with the first cup of liquid taken, and the lined, sagging faces and necks that result destroy any illusion of youth given by the hard-won slender body.

Most middle-aged women know they cannot afford to get thin too suddenly, but too many men overlook this fact. A healthy man in his fifties, alarmed by talk of coronary occlusions, recently embarked on a drastic diet, together with steam baths, and lost several stone in a very short time. From the back, he looked much younger – but his face, which had previously been firm and fresh, suddenly fell into hundreds of tiny lines, adding years to his age. If you are overweight, you must reduce carefully and slowly, through exercise and diet. At one time, it was a belief that exercise had no effect on weight, but this idea has now been completely disproved. Tests have shown that most people do not gain weight when they exercise, but put it on when they stop, although eating exactly the same amount of well-chosen food. Yoga asanas, through their effects on the glands, not only reduce the weight and keep it down, but redistribute it over the body, creating greatly improved proportions, whilst at the same time keeping muscles and tissues firm and preventing the unsightly flabbiness that usually accompanies loss of weight.

Diet

Probably no aspect of life has such a dramatic influence on health generally, and on arthritis in particular, as what we eat. There are a number of specific nutrients which can greatly assist in checking and sometimes overcoming the symptoms of arthritis. Conversely, there are foods which irritate and aggravate arthritis. These can include either highly acidic foods or foods to which the individual is sensitive or allergic. We are all genetically unique, and certain people need far more of certain nutrients than others, and this requirement manifests itself in the particular pattern of symptoms. The requirement may be for any of the nutrients, for instance, minerals, vitamins, amino acids, which the body requires for normal functioning. With regard to arthritis, we would normally be concerned with a particular group of nutrients which is involved with the health of the ligaments, tendons, cartilage, muscles and bones. So let us look at each of these groups.

Exercise must be supplemented by proper diet. This doesn't mean giving up all normal foods, as some people imagine, but it does mean giving up all those things which you shouldn't have been eating in the first place. All diets are improved by eliminating white bread, white sugar, sweets, artificially flavoured drinks, alcohol, chocolate (sorry!), cakes, biscuits, pastries and fried foods, which are all rich in calories, but nutritionally low, mostly indigestible and bad for the teeth. On the other hand, unsalted butter and the much-abused potato are not only valuable nourishment, but contain less calories than many other foods. One three-ounce potato has 72 calories; one slice of chocolate cake has 215; a dessertspoon of butter has 53 calories; and a two-ounce glass of brandy or gin contains 110. We must have sugar to give us energy but we should get it from honey or from fresh or dried fruits, which also purify the blood. A small dessertspoon of honey, taken at breakfast time each morning, destroys the craving for sweets and chocolate, yet it contains only 32 calories compared with 96 calories in the same amount of sugar. If you take sugar in tea and coffee, eat sweets and cakes, you must consume a great many spoonfuls during the day.

The three main dietary principles are: selectivity, moderation and mastication. Select good and nourishing food, do not overeat or take anything to excess, and chew thoroughly, remembering that mastication is the first stage in the digestive process, and if it is rushed or skimped, the result will be dyspepsia, no matter how excellent the diet. Moderation also means commonsense, not going to extremes. You will improve health as well as figure by avoiding artificial or over-processed food, by increasing your intake of vegetables and fruit; aim for at least five portions a day, eating them raw whenever possible, and by sometimes substituting eggs, cheese or oily fish, pulses, nuts or tofu for meat. Do not eat more than two or three eggs a week because of their high cholesterol content. It is not necessary to become entirely vegetarian but meat once a day is more than enough, especially when you are over 40. Fish or chicken could be used instead of the heavier, richer, beef or pork. I personally do not eat meat because I object to the overuse of growth hormones and antibiotics, and the sometimes dreadful conditions in which the animals are housed, transported and killed. I have also proved that my arthritic joints are more inflamed and painful when I eat red meat. There is an idea that a vegetarian diet is weakening, but there have been many successful vegetarian athletes and swimmers, and no one would suggest that the vegetarian gorilla is a weakling!

Fresh fruit at breakfast, fruit juices, fresh and interesting salads – not gloomy, unimaginative mixtures of tinned peas, wilted lettuce and pale, flavourless tomatoes – should all be eaten every day, and salads should not be abandoned in winter. A fresh, green, crisp salad of some kind should be served every day – an oil and lemon juice dressing will make it more interesting. Yoghurt is an excellent food and it is worth overcoming any initial dislike. Make sure that it is made from cows that graze on organic grass; also make sure that probiotic bacteria are added and minimal amounts of sugar. For anyone who is allergic to dairy produce, it is now possible to buy yoghurt made from soya milk. For a light summer lunch, fresh fruit salad of whatever is available with yoghurt instead of cream, honey instead of sugar, and roasted almonds is delicious, slimming and sustaining. And yoghurt with honey or fruit makes a light breakfast, particularly for those people who are in the habit of rushing off immediately afterwards. This of course is a very bad practice. All meals should be eaten in peace, especially breakfast, which can set the mood for the whole day. A large meal of bacon and eggs, bolted down under pressure, with family arguments going on, soon develops into a hard lump, a feeling of nausea or some other disagreeable symptom. Heavy meals late at night are also unwise, and are a common cause of insomnia.

Being overweight increases your risk of developing a host of serious conditions such as heart disease, some cancers, diabetes and, of course, osteoarthriris (OA). If you have been diagnosed with OA are also over weight you will suffer more than slimmer people with the disorder; the extra pounds can cause further damage to your joints and worsen pain and stiffness.

In 1992 it was found that just by losing 11 pounds over a ten year period, overweight people could reduce their risk of developing OA of the knee by 50%. But there's much more to weight control than just calories. Recent studies show that eating foods rich in certain vitamins and nutrients can slow down the progress of OA and ward off its symptoms. Some particular nutrients seem to help protects the joints from damage – something that even drugs cannot do.

Healthy eating involves much more than counting calories. The idea is not only to lose weight if you need to, but also to eat the right *kinds* of food: those that are low in fat and high in beneficial nutrients such as fibre and vitamins. Faddy diets come and go, but there is a simple straight forward way to control and check what you are eating. It involves recognising the groups into which certain foods fall, and eating the right amount fo each group.

In the pyramid-shaped illustration you will see the largest group at the bottom; it consists of bread, cereals and other complex carbohydrates (NOT carbohydrate in the form of sugars).

Above them come fruits and vegetables, then meats, fish, milk and other dairy products. The smallest group is made of sugary, fatty foods.

The number of portions of each group that you should eat daily is indicated by its size and position in the pyramid. Later we will talk about the actual size of the portions and how many of each you should eat on a daily basis. Many people are not aware that they need

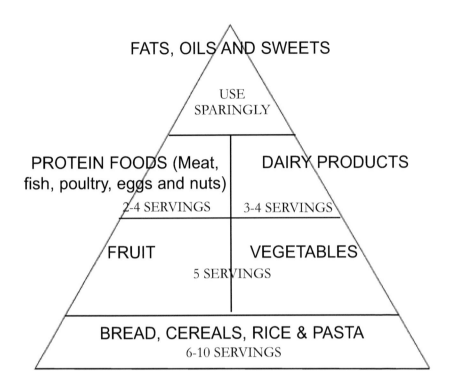

FATS, OILS AND SWEETS

USE SPARINGLY

PROTEIN FOODS (Meat, fish, poultry, eggs and nuts)
2-4 SERVINGS

DAIRY PRODUCTS
3-4 SERVINGS

FRUIT

VEGETABLES

5 SERVINGS

BREAD, CEREALS, RICE & PASTA
6-10 SERVINGS

fewer calories as their metabolism slows down and they also become less active.

The largest group in the pyramid consist of starchy carbohydrates – bread, cereals (not just the kind in packets), rice and pasta. Carbohydrates are the foundation of a healthy diet and should make up at least half the calories in your daily intake. Contrary to what you may believe these starches are not fattening – provided you leave off the butter and other high fat toppings such as full fat cheese and sour cream, or sugary jams and spreads. Also pasta and other starches have the great advantage of filling you up so that you do not have room for snacking on chocolate, toffees, biscuits and cakes! A single portion can either be one slice of bread, three tablespoons of cereal, a bread roll, bap or bun, one small pitta bread, naan bread or chapatti, three crackers or crispbreads, a medium-sized potato or half a cup of cooked rice or pasta. Eat whole grains that are high in fibre. Most fibre leaves the body undigested, being good for bowel function and being undigested, the body doesn't absorb the calories it contains.

The next largest group in the ideal diet is composed of fruit and vegetables. Both are nature's attempt at diet food – low in fat and calories and rich in flavour, fibre, phytochemicals and antioxidant vitamins – all especially important for anyone suffering from OA. 406 fl ozs (125-175 ml) of pure fruit juice, a quarter of a cup of dried fruit, half a cup of berries, one medium banana or other fruit is equal to one serving. Half a cup of cooked or raw vegetables, one cup of leafy raw vegetables or ½ cup of cooked pulses (peas, beans, lentils, soya beans), one medium onion, ½ pepper, one medium apple, two carrots, four broccoli florets, 3 ozs peas, ½ an avocado, 3 sticks of celery, ½ a grapefruit, 1 medium tomato, 14 button mushrooms, 2 medium plums, 5 fresh asparagus spears, 6 baby sweet corn, 1 baby cauliflower, 1 heaped tablespoon dried fruit, 7 fresh strawberries, two 2-inch mango slices, 2 pineapple rings, 1 peach, 3 tablespoons fruit salad, all also count as one potion (www.doh.gov.uk/fiveaday).

It is much better to get your nutrients from whole or fresh food rather than supplements. Fresh food contain a host of other beneficial substances, such as phytochemicals, that can be crucial to reducing arthritic symptoms. Fruit and vegetables are the best source of antioxidants which help to reduce the chemicals formed during metabolism that can damage cartilage and possibly cause inflammation.

To maximise antioxidant intake eat:

1.   Red grapes rather than green or white

2.   Red and yellow onions instead of white

3.   Cabbage, cauliflower and broccoli raw, or lightly cooked

4.   Garlic – raw or crushed

5.   Fresh and frozen (not canned) vegetables

6.   Microwaved or steamed vegetables, not boiled

7.   The darkest green leafy vegetables

8.   Pink grapefruit, not white

9.   Whole fruit rather than juices

10.   Fresh and frozen juice (not canned)

11.   The deepest orange carrots, sweet potatoes and pumpkins

Dairy Foods

The third food groups includes dairy foods – milk, yoghurt and cheese – as well as meat, fishes, pulses, vegetables and nuts. As we progress further up our nutritional pyramid, the fewer the number of daily servings is recommended.

Dairy products provide most of the calcium in our diet; they also provide proteins for growth and repair, and are important for women in staving off osteoporosis. In addition, they are our main source of vitamin D which, although not an antioxidant, is crucially important in the treatment of OA. To limit your fat intake, try to have low-fat or non-fat versions of dairy foods such as semi-skinned milk and low-fat yoghurt.

Portion sizes. Try to have 2-3 portions a day. A single portion is ⅓ pint milk (7 fl ozs) or a small pot of yoghurt, 4½ oz cottage cheese or fromage frais, or 1½ ozs cheddar cheese.

Protein Foods

Lean meat, poultry, fish, pulses, eggs, nuts and the processed vegetarian alternatives are your best sources of protein and also supply you with B vitamins, iron and zinc. The lower fat choices in this category are pulses or fish, and you can cut the fat off meat before cooking. With poultry, light meat is lower in fat than the dark meat, by about 50%, and the fatty skin should always be removed. Only moderate amounts of protein-rich foods are needed in a balanced diet.

Portions. 2-4 portions a day. A single portion consists of 2-3 ozs (55-85 grms) cooked lean meat, 4-5 ozs (115-140 grms) white or oily fish (not fried), or 5 ozs (140 grms) baked beans, or 2 ozs (55 grms) nuts. For vegetarians – 1 egg of 2 tablespoons of peanut butter counts as 1 oz (25 gms) meat. (Both have a high fat content, however!)

Fats, Oils and Sweets.

This is the smallest group of foods and should be eaten sparingly. These foods are very rich in calories, but contain very few of the body-building nutrients the other food groups contain. Examples include fat-filled foods such as butter or margarine, and sugar-rich foods such as sweets, soft drinks or sugar and fat rich biscuits and cakes. Tempting and calorific foods are a major stumbling block to your weight-loss efforts!

Portions. No more than two portions a day and preferably fewer. A single portion is 3 teaspoons of sugar, a heaped teaspoon of jam or honey, a Danish pastry, 2 biscuits, a small bar of chocolate or half a slice of cake.

Meat, full-fat dairy products, nuts, oils and puddings are responsible for most of the fat in our diet. Gram for gram fat contains more than twice as many calories as carbohydrates or protein (9 calories in a gram of fat, against 4 in a gram of carbohydrate or protein). To make life even more unfair we now know that calories from fat are more efficiently stored as fat in the body than calories from carbohydrates or protein. On top of this, a diet high in fat, especially from animal products, harms the body in other ways, such as raising blood cholesterol levels and increasing the likelihood of developing certain cancers. However, the body does need a certain amount to provide fat-soluble vitamins and essential fatty acids. These are required for the development and function of the brain, eyes and nervous system. But the amount actually needed is small – only about 1 oz (25 grms) a day – much less than we consume in an average Western diet. The best sources of essential fatty acids are natural fish oils and pure vegetable oils. But when vegetable oils are hardened (hydrogenated) to make margarine and reduced fat spreads, they can be changed into transfats, which are as unhealthy as saturated fats.

By shopping wisely you can significantly reduce the amount of fat and the percentage of calories that come from fat, in your diet. For instance, pretzels and potato crisps are both salty snacks – but 1 oz of crisps contains more than 11 times more total fat than 1 oz of pretzels; 3 ozs tuna in brine or water contains three times less calories than 3 ozs tuna in vegetable oil.

Try to keep your fat intake to between 1 and 5 portions per day. A portion can be 1 teaspoon (5 ml) of butter or margarine, 2 teaspoons low fat spread, 1 teaspoon cooking oil, 1 tablespoon mayonnaise or sald dressing, 1 tablespoon cream or a single serving packet of crisps.

General Nutrition

Then there some general rules about what you should eat:

First of all, do remember that digestion begins in the mouth – so your food should be eaten slowly, and chewed thoroughly, and for this, you need a good set of teeth, so check regularly with a dentist – these days it really doesn't hurt, honestly.

Avoid foods that are very hot or very cold.

Prefer simple meals as these are easier to digest than those with a lot of sauces and accompaniments. Avoid combinations of certain food that seem to produce indigestion in your particular case; sometimes protein and carbohydrate cause indigestion – for example, very popular ones like bread and cheese or fish and chips. Sorry!

Avoid fried and roasted foods as these are difficult to digest because the digestive juices have to penetrate a fatty layer before they can actually get at the food. In any rheumatic condition, the following pattern of diet will lead to an overall reduction in pain and improved function, especially if accompanied by the other methods outlined here. As we are all beautifully different and individual, it is difficult to be specific about desirable eating patterns. Listen to your body, and if you get indigestion after a mix of certain foods, then don't mix them again! If you feel bloated after a meal, you've obviously eaten too much! So listen to your body – your body's far more intelligent than you are about what it wants and what it needs, and how to cure itself.

Healthy Suggestions

Of course there's no need to be stupid and make your life a misery, and in the process bore everybody to tears about what you're eating and what you're not eating, and how your arthritis is. And I must say that I do have the occasional glass of wine and the occasional square of chocolate, or an ice cream on a stick.

So don't be stupid because life isn't worth living if you go as far as that! Replace tea, coffee, chocolate and cola drinks with herb teas, dandelion coffee and fresh vegetable or fruit drinks, or low-salt yeast extracts or spring water. I have a juicer and I find it the most wonderful piece of machinery in my kitchen. I juice fresh vegetables and fresh fruit and they are absolutely delightful.

I also drink Malvern water, because I am fortunate: I am blessed with a dear friend who delivers it to me fresh from the Malvern spring, but I boil it well because I think this is a precaution one needs to take these days – after all, there are sheep on the hills and there is the possibly of tetanus. When it's boiled well, I cool it and put quite a thick slice of lemon in a glass, pour on the water, cover it and put it in the fridge. And it is nectar – and it doesn't cost anything apart from the slice of lemon.

Avoid vinegar, pepper and curry, and processed, pickled, smoked, preserved and tinned foods. Frozen foods should be limited, and especially if they've been commercially frozen; look at the side of the packet – you'll see all sorts of additives and some of them are quite harmful.

Also, it's advisable to limit plums, all the berries and citrus fruits because they are so very acidic. The diet should consist of at least 50% raw food in the form of vegetables, sprouted seeds (but don't use sprouted seeds if you have *rheumatoid* arthritis – which is very different from osteoarthritis), dried seeds like sunflower seeds, pumpkin seeds, linseed, etc, nuts, whole grains and some fruit.

Drinks should be as indicated above. If of course your digestion is getting weaker as you get older, and you can't take two salad meals a day, then put the second salad through the juicer and drink it. This diet is designed to minimise the chances of continued deficiency. It should also reduce the acidity and toxicity of the body, which is so prevalent in arthritic and rheumatic conditions. With this diet, the self-healing mechanisms of the body will be given the best possible chance to carry out their task of repair to damaged areas and organs.

Cleansing Day & Fasting

As we are speaking of ridding the body of poisons or toxins, I'd like to say a word here about fasting. Fasting is nature's way of resting, and even repairing a body that has been overtaxed and overworked. It is nothing to do with starving, which is to be deprived of necessary food. Fasting is undertaken voluntarily, either because the body cannot tolerate food as in serious illness when the whole mechanism is engaged in fighting for survival, or because it is desired to get rid of accumulated impurities. All animals, when they are ill, turn away from food; it is only so-called civilised man who forces himself to eat when he would be much better off fasting. An occasional one-day fast can do no harm, as long as the person is not already very much underweight, and provided the fast can be done in suitable circumstances. Don't try to have a day's fast while you are working. Rest as much as possible and go to bed early. Keep quiet, conserving all possible vital energy – not talking, watching television or even reading too much. You should take only spring water or fresh fruit juice and a mild bulk laxative like Lepicol or Fybogel at the end of the day will help to get rid of impurities. The day after the fast you will feel fitter, younger, and more energetic, and you will also look so much better.

Sometimes I have what I call a cleansing day, and during that day I drink only vegetable broth or have a cleansing rice meal which I will now describe. For the broth, do try to use organically grown vegetables. Look around – you can usually find them somewhere. If this is not possible, then scrub vegetables very well before you use them. Then, into four pints or 2¼ litres of spring water, place four cupfuls of finely chopped beetroot, carrots, thick potato peeling, parsley, courgette and leaves of beetroot or parsnip. Don't use any sulphur-rich vegetables like cabbage or onion which might produce gas. Simmer this for five minutes, or perhaps a little more if you like, over a low flame to allow for the breakdown of vegetable fibre and the release of nutrients into the liquid. Cool and strain it, using only the liquid and not the leftover vegetable content. You can put this on the compost heap. Don't add salt as this broth will contain ample natural minerals, and provide nutrients without straining the digestive system. Also, it is alkaline and neutralises any acidity in the body. Drink this broth at intervals during the day, but drink just what you want – don't overload your digestive system with it, because this, in a way, is its rest day. Alternatively, use a juicer for a mixture of fruit and vegetables.

The other thing I take when I have a cleansing day is a rice meal, and for this you boil three ounces or 75 gm of brown rice (organic, if you can get it) until it's cooked according to the instructions on the packet. Grate a raw carrot (wash it carefully first) and chop about two tablespoonfuls of watercress. Drain the rice when it's cooked, and add one teaspoonful of a non-salty vegetable extract and also add the grated carrot and chopped watercress. Stir it round together, and if you add a little toasted sesame seed oil and stir that in, it really is very appetising. You can eat that three times a day in place of your normal meals, and you will find that you feel really cleansed the next day.

Allergy

Another point I should mention here is the fact of allergy, because one of the most important contributions to our knowledge of arthritic conditions has come from practitioners dealing with allergies. They have shown that, by the removal from the diet of foods which cause allergies, many arthritic conditions can be improved. In attempting to find out which foods produce allergies in patients, many practitioners use a period of fasting to clear the body of all toxic substances. You shouldn't fast on your own; you should be under supervision.

The practitioners then reintroduced foods, one at a time, to gauge the body's reaction, and in this way they can build a picture of undesirable foods which should be avoided. Sometimes those foods that cause reaction can be re-allowed by using a 'rotation' diet. The allergy-producing foods may be consumed on infrequent occasions, say, once a week. Eliminating dairy produce and refined carbohydrates (for example, white flour and sugar) from the diet, will remove some of the foods which most commonly cause allergies. By employing short and regular fasts, cleansing days, and by using nutritional supplements, the likelihood is that food sensitivities or allergies will be further eliminated.

However, it may be that a commonly eaten food continues to irritate the joints, and this may show up after a cleansing day or a fast when the particular food is reintroduced. If such a food is identified, then it should be used sparingly in the diet. It is also useful to identify other foods belonging to the same group as the one which caused the allergy. These should also be rotated so that they are not used more than once in five days. In general, a combination of all the factors discussed above – namely diet, detoxification and replenishment of deficient nutrients – provides a framework for alleviating arthritic conditions of all sorts.

In addition, exercise and hydrotherapy are enormously helpful. I am very fortunate to have a hydrotherapy pool ten minutes' walk away from where I live, and I've just been there this morning. Gliding into that beautifully hot water and exercising in the water create a tremendous improvement in the small amount of arthritis that I now have.

To sum up therefore, the control of arthritis depends on eating the right food which mainly means cutting out sugar and an excess of carbohydrates, exercise or movement of some kind, and the right psychological attitude. Do go to a practitioner in the first place who will work out a programme for you as to what you should eat, and what are the best movements for you to do.

Drinking

There is no doubt that the most sensible western meal arrangements are those in countries like France and Italy, where breakfast is light, the main meal is at midday – with plenty of time for eating and digesting, even taking a siesta – and where a lighter meal follows this in the evening. The body must be kept supplied with adequate fluids; water is the best drink of all. Spring water is available to everyone and is better than today's tap water which contains traces of all the drugs prescribed to people, contraceptive pills, and the like – not to mention the strong chemicals used to make it 'safe'. Personally, I don't drink with food; I prefer to drink an hour or so beforehand or afterwards. In this way, the digestive juices are not diluted, thus becoming inefficient in breaking down and acting upon the food. If you cannot swallow your food without swilling it down with a drink, then you are not chewing it properly, which is another cause of indigestion. (You might check on your teeth here; they may be the culprit.) Fresh, not tinned, fruit or vegetable juices are also excellent, and everyone who possibly can should buy a juice extractor. With this simple machine, all kinds of fruits or vegetables can be squeezed together. Fresh grapefruit, for instance, is not only delicious but definitely has healing power. (Note however that grapefruit should not be taken with statins.) The juice should be made as it is needed, not stored in the refrigerator where it will gradually lose its vitamin content. Cultured buttermilk is nourishing and not fattening, because buttermilk is a food as well as a drink. Cow's milk is not so healthy because it has been heat-treated and contains growth hormones and antibiotics which have been given to the cows. An excellent substitute is a drink made with 50% yoghurt and 50%

water, preferably spring water of course, and sparkling if you like a little bit of a kick to it. And this is whisked up like a milk shake. This drink is popular in the East where it is known as ayran and one can work and travel long distances on little else without hunger or fatigue, especially in hot weather.

Alcohol, with its high sugar content, puts on weight; it is also of course an artificial stimulant, which can become a habit. It is a drug; taken to excess, it ruins nerves, complexion and digestion because it is a form of poisoning – hence the term 'intoxication'. High blood pressure, cirrhosis of the liver, and mental degeneration are just a few of the detrimental effects it can cause, not to mention the weakening of will power and character. But there are of course many social occasions in western life when it is difficult to avoid alcohol entirely. If you can take a drink, there is little harm in doing so; in fact, in moderation, it can lift the spirits and relax tension. Wine, which contains less alcohol and less calories, is better than spirits as it has been made from grapes which have ripened in the sun, and absorbed its life-giving properties and its Vitamin D. In central Europe, where alcohol is considered as much a part of the poor man's diet as bread, spirits are rarely drunk and drunkenness is uncommon.

Smoking

There has now been so much publicity given to the direct connection between smoking and cancer, chronic bronchitis, emphysema and coronary disease, that it seems hardly necessary to raise the subject. Tobacco is a dangerous drug, like all the other substances with which people systematically ruin their health. For anyone who is health-conscious, to smoke is a contradiction in terms, and a waste of effort. It is hardly worth exercising if you follow it by inhaling lungfuls of poisonous nicotine. As an illustration of the degree of saturation reached by a smoker's system, a yoga student of mine who had been a heavy smoker for years and broken the habit, told me that even six months after his last cigarette, his skin still sweated nicotine when he took a sauna bath. He said the sauna smelled as if someone were smoking in it. Nicotine in the bloodstream affects digestion, the condition of the skin, and particularly the nervous system. It lifts, and then it lets down. It soothes the nerves, then irritates them into an urgent craving for more. Its apparent benefits are in fact destructive, for the stimulation is false, dragged from an already weakened reserve and never replenished. Eventually, the whole store of vital energy is gone, and premature decay begins. Like any narcotic, it feeds upon itself and its victim, who grows increasingly dependent upon it.

The most effective cure is hypno-therapy. No one has ever really been cured of smoking by artificial means. They may stop smoking temporarily, but if a critical situation arises, the victim will probably start to smoke again. Personally, having been a smoker and given up over 45 years ago now, and also having treated other people for nicotine addition, I understand the difficulties involved.

Arthritis

Osteo-arthritis is not so much a disease of the body as the result of general wear and tear on the joints. Rheumatoid arthritis, on the other hand, is an auto-immune disease, having elements of allergy in its make-up, and it needs rather more complicated strategies to cope with the pain, inflammation and immobility that is engendered. But the self-help methods outlined here can be of some relief. The medical care of arthritis is mainly palliative, and the number of drugs used can have dangerous side-effects, like cortizone or some anti-inflammatory remedies. Bulizolidin and Opren were discredited because of the deaths they caused and were withdrawn from the market. Surgery does some brilliant joint replacements, particularly of hips, knees and fingers, but cannot be extended to all the many joints in the body that become painful and inefficient. Prevention is of course the best method of dealing with worn-out joints, but when we are young, when even 30 feels like the end of life as we know it, who gives a thought to a balanced diet, using the body well, practising yoga and learning techniques to cope with stress? Who would ever spend money on check-ups with a osteopath or chiropractor, when there are clothes, computers, clubs and holidays in the sun competing for our hard-earned cash? If you are a parent, now is the time to make good nutrition and good posture a habit with your child, even if you have to nag. They will thank you later when they have more sense! All arthritic changes in joints are degenerative and can be caused by ageing, wear and tear, posture, occupation, poor nutrition, allergies, injuries, infection, being overweight, inflammatory factors and hormonal alterations. It is advisable to have a simple blood test to determine what kind of arthritis you have. I was found to have osteo-arthritis, so since I am writing about the remedies that specifically helped me, I will concern myself with osteo-arthritis only.

In the main, I have managed the osteo-arthritis in my joints by practising yoga, eating 'friendly' food, and using various stratagems to calm the emotional stresses and strains of my life. You will find details of these practical steps in the relevant chapters. As you will have read in my autobiography, I also experienced a spontaneous healing of the arthritis in my hip which seemed to me to be a result of my increased spiritual awareness. I found too, on a purely practical level, that disassociating myself from the problem by not referring to it as 'my' arthritis has helped. Thus it becomes a situation outside myself with which I can cope as my advisor rather than as sufferer. (We are talking here about osteo-arthritis, not rheumatoid arthritis; this is an entirely different situation.) The joints that suffer most are those that bear the weight of the body – that is, the spine, hips, knees, feet, and the weight-lifting joints like the hands, wrists, elbows, neck and shoulders. At first, the only sign will be some degree of stiffness, and little or no pain, but pain will increase as the damaged joints are forced to perform tasks which are becoming more and more difficult for them.

The theory that our forebears moved about on all fours is given credibility by the fact that, in this position, the spine is a perfect cantilever bridge with adequate support and shock-absorbers. Move that horizontal position through ninety degrees and the spine becomes an unstable skyscraper. This upright position is the major reason for the development of arthritis. So the cultivation of an easy, balanced posture is essential in order to relieve the stresses and strains on the joints that this upright posture imposes. It is interesting to note how opinion varies about posture – from the ramrod straightness of the sergeant-major, through various more relaxed interpretations as in yoga, to what I consider to be the most beneficial of all, namely, the postural teachings of the Alexander Technique. Years of slouching, tension and laziness have caused all of us to fall into bad habits which cause harm, mentally, physically and emotionally. How you stand, sit or lie expresses how you feel about yourself and the people around you. I'm not writing in detail about the Alexander Technique in this book. There are many excellent books available if you wish to pursue it further; but it has been of such value to me that I must make some mention of it en passant.

The Alexander Technique encompasses a whole philosophy of co-ordination and movement, but concentrates on getting rid of stress and bad posture. It is based on a series of gentle movements that teach us to sit, stand and move the way we are anatomically designed to do so. It is adjusted to our individual needs and not based on rigid rules. It is advisable to find a teacher – make sure he or she is the right one for you – who will explore areas of tension in your body and give you a feeling of poise, increased awareness and physical well-being. The basic movements include letting the neck be free, letting the head go forward and up in relation to the torso and neck, which widens and lengthens the body. This widening and lengthening relieves the pressure of gravity, not only on the joints but also on all the internal organs. It can and does relieve indigestion, constipation, respiratory and throat problems, simply by giving room to the organs concerned to perform their function correctly. Bad habits, like hunching your shoulders when writing, carrying a bag on one side – for instance, the dreaded shoulder bag – playing a musical instrument, etc. are corrected by a good teacher of the Alexander Technique, and the resulting relaxed activity is performed with greater ease and comfort. If you are concerned about the cost of these lessons, once you have learned the technique – and there are 8-20 half-hour sessions – you do not need the teacher any more, and can go on to incorporate what you have learned into your daily life. In other words, it becomes a learned habit. But unlike many habits, it is of the utmost benefit for the rest of your life.

What is taking place in the osteo-arthritic joint? There is a sheath of smooth, polished cartilage lying between the bones of the joint. You can see it in a joint of meat quite clearly: there's a shining blue-white material covering the end of the bone. This enables the two bones of the joint to glide evenly over one another like a well-oiled ball-and-socket joint in machinery. A good example is the hip joint where the rounded end of the thigh bone glides easily around in the socket of the hip or pelvic girdle, enabling you to move your leg in any direction: back, forward, sideways, and in a wide arc. Think of the amazing leg movements from the hip that a ballet dancer can make whilst working at the practice bar. As osteo-arthritis progresses due to wear and tear, this smooth cartilage wears away, so that the two bones themselves grind together, and are exposed to wear and pressure. As a result, bits of cartilage and bone become irritated, then inflamed; so the body, sensing the problem, tries to protect the area by cushioning, splinting or repairing the damaged area. The body attempts to reinforce the cartilage, and this causes inflammation and pain. As the cartilage wears away, the underlying bone becomes very irritated and attempts to deal with the injury by forming cells to make new bones. These grow larger as the cartilage wears away and become the visible bony lumps often seen clearly on the hands of elderly people. This bony outcropping alters the shape of the bone, and causes more and more restricted movement of that particular joint. This restrictive movement creates pain and stress if you attempt to use a badly affected arthritic joint. So you will have waves of inflammation which will aggravate the wear and tear process even further, whilst at the same time your body will be making desperate attempts to splint and rebuild the damaged joint surface.

The splinting is done by the local muscles tightening up, which prevent any large movements of the joint. At the moment, it is painful for me to turn my head to the right as the large muscle anchoring my head to my neck on the left side has gone into spasm in an effort to keep my neck still whilst repair work is being done in my cervical spine. Some hope of keeping my neck still with the garden and the house, albeit small, to cope with on my own! So there's a vicious circle of pain and damage repeating itself over and over again, and it is not until the joint reaches a totally damaged state that there is any loss of pain. But unfortunately, by this time, there is loss of movement too.

There is a brighter side to the prognosis: the joint may never deteriorate to this totally damaged state if you are practising the gentle movements of yoga, practising the Alexander Technique in your movements and eating health-promoting food. The changes then may be minor, and you may hardly notice any limitations in the movement of the joint. Radiographers will tell you that most adults over 40 show some osteo-arthritic changes in their necks, but the majority of them will be completely free of stiffness and pain. From this, we can deduce that the body's own miraculous process of repair and new bone growth can be successfully achieved.

Now, as the naturopaths tell us, if we are eating the right food, exercising, and in a healthy physical and psychological environment, the body has its own awesome wisdom, and will protect the worn joint surfaces from greater destruction. If osteoarthritis is dealt with in the first stages, and the body is assisted in its repair work, there is every chance that the amount of damage can be limited, thus creating a virtually symptom-free state. This may mean losing weight, improving posture, and reducing emotional and occupational stress. It also means that the nutrients necessary for repair are included in your diet, and that you keep your circulation and muscle tone in tip-top condition through exercise.

Whatever you do, don't think, 'I mustn't do that any more.' When your knee feels tight as you squat, or one arm won't go as high above your head as the other, when your hand hurts after doing the ironing – take it as a kindly warning and do something about it; don't just passively give way to ageing. Of course, the ageing process is inevitable, and whatever you do or don't do, the tissues will age. The older we get, the less elastic they become, which means they lose stretch. The skin around my eyes alas is wrinkled and crêpy, and the tissues around my joints will be losing their elasticity in the same way; I'm glad I can't see these as well! But I am conscious of a loss of stretch; I register a sore elbow, shoulder and neck after lifting bulbs from my garden, and replacing them with bedding plants; so I put off the ironing, thus sparing the joints from doing things they don't like. After a few days, everything settles, inflammation subsides, swelling reduces, and things seem normal. But that's the problem: things will never be quite normal again. The joints are not quite as free as they were; some parts of the joints are still closed down and, like us, having gained a quiet life, do not want to give it up! If I try to push the joint where it doesn't want to go, it will complain loudly and painfully. Now, I can do one of two things: either let the tight and unco-operative joint have its own way, and protect it from any movement at all, or I can make it do the ironing and maybe some cleaning as well, after I have done the gardening. This latter course can cause an angry, painful reaction, because I have pushed the joints too far, or it can relieve the painful spasm if I only do enough movement to coax the tightness back into normal useful function. So sometimes activity is the right thing to do, sometimes the very worst. If you do too much too quickly, the joints will lock tightly in order to go back to the self-healing process mentioned earlier. Pain-relieving drugs may be necessary in desperate circumstances, and they have their place, but don't become dependent on them, take them in moderation, and listen to your body.

Yoga has all the answers. The original yogis knew how joints tighten, and which movements old or damaged joints find hard to do. So there is a complete range of yoga stretches which are capable of rejuvenating each joint of the skeleton. Yoga is the most simple way of keeping the joints young and supple, of releasing the skeleton and counteracting its kinks and bends. In time, all the soft tissues of the body are loosened, even blood vessels and nerves. Elasticity is restored, and the smooth, gliding function of the joints. The stretches promote a more vigorous blood supply which flushes the whole body, and the skeleton is cleansed and rejuvenated. Allied with the Alexander Technique, you should be able to keep yourself mobile and relatively pain-free, because pain is a valuable warning in the first place, to alert you to a fault in the machinery of your body. But after you have taken the right action, it should gradually diminish and eventually cease altogether. Regular brisk walking or jogging or swimming will also improve your general circulation, not only of the blood but also the flow of the lymphatic fluid which helps rid the body of toxins.

When I had an attack of gout in 1984, I was told that I would be immobile for six weeks, and that having had this initial spasm, I would suffer periodic attacks of gout for the rest of my life. As I had a speaking engagement in Torquay five weeks hence, I decided to take matters into my own hands, and the most effective treatment I found was soaking the affected foot in alternate bowls of very hot and very cold water. The hot water should be very hot, but not enough to scald the skin, of course. The cold water should be very cold, with ice floating in it to maintain the low temperature. The timing of this treatment is important: immersion in the hot water should last for three minutes, and in the cold for one minute. Alternate this for 10-15 minutes, finishing with the cold treatment. This stimulates the local circulation and reduces swelling and inflammation in the joint. I was able to hobble within three weeks, limp in four, and was pontificating on the Torquay platform in five – complete with expensive hair-do, smart frock and cutaway tennis shoes discreetly hidden behind the lectern. This method is ideal for either acute or chronic joints which are stiff, swollen, painful or inflamed. A small joint, such as a finger or a wrist, can be treated under the hot and cold running taps, but two bowls allow for greater immersion and also save water at the same time. If the joint cannot be immersed – for example, the hip joint – then towels can be dipped in hot and cold water, lightly wrung and placed over or around the affected area for the same periods of time – that is, three minutes hot and one minute cold, for 10-15 minutes. Gently moving and stretching the affected joint during the hot and cold therapy is beneficial.

During my visits to Tyringham, I was introduced to the seaweed bath. It involves adding a measured amount of dry, powdered seaweed (available from health food stores), a bath of warm water, and relaxing in it for 10-20 minutes. It was prescribed specifically for me for hypertension, but having continued to take these baths at home, I have noticed a lessening of arthritic pain and stiffness as well as a reduction of blood pressure. The seaweed relaxes stiffs muscles and draws the toxins responsible for arthritis from the body. It also induces a profound feeling of relaxation which is essential for the relief of arthritic joints.

Swimming of course comes under this heading because it gives joints the opportunity to move and stretch in a weight-free environment. I have found my weekly swim invaluable: it enables me to tone weak muscles, to stretch tight joints, and lessen the pain of sensitive, inflamed tissues in warm water. Very often, I feel too tired to undress when I arrive, but after a few widths, I emerge invigorated and renewed, not only ;physically but mentally and emotionally as well. Later on in the day, I experience a feeling of quiet calm and enjoyable lassitude – 'As if of hemlock I had drunk' – and sleep deeply and soundly, a much better alternative to swallowing tranquillisers. Information regarding hydro-therapy facilities can be obtained through local health authorities or CABs (Citizen Advice Bureaux), and there are some heated pools in most centres of population.

Massage is very useful and you can do this for yourself. Apply a light lubricant oil or cream to the painful area, and stroke the muscles and soft tissues in the direction of your heart. This method is very useful for knees and elbows, wrists and hands. It also has the advantage of not putting precious time aside – you can do it whilst watching TV or at other moments during the day – at your desk, waiting for the vegetables to cook, or the washing machine to finish its cycle. Pressure can be applied by using your fingers and thumbs, and this pressure gradually disperses the excess fluid which is causing the joint to swell. If this causes pain, you are pressing too hard. A tennis ball can also be used by rolling it rhythmically across the tight congested tissues, and this accomplishes quite an effective massage. This method is particularly useful for difficult-to-reach areas, like the spine and the muscles of the lower back, pelvis and hip. You put the ball on the floor, lower the affected part of the body onto it, and gently move the affected area over the ball. A smaller ball, such as a squash or golf ball, can be used on areas such as the forearm, legs or thigh, by gently pressing the ball into the muscles and rolling it about. The ball can also be used to keep the feet supple, and with a good, strong arch. Rest your foot on the ball and roll your foot to and fro; this stretches the ligaments and muscles under the foot.

I am so grateful to the people who taught me to do these movements, as I can still walk three miles, maintain a good balance on my toes, sit back on my heels, and squat comfortably to garden, when the prognosis in my forties was immobility and a wheelchair within a year. This is why I am writing this book, in the hope that it will help more people to take matters into their own hands and defy disease for as long as possible.

Exercise

Exercise can reduce the risk of heart attacks, and increase the chances of survival if you suffer one. It helps slimming by burning up the energy in food, and works off the tensions of everyday living. It can help to keep you in a healthy state of mind, and cut down anxiety and depression. Above all, it promotes general fitness of the whole organism. There is no scientific definition of fitness, but as those who are fit will vouch, it is more than the mere absence of illness or disease, more than simply feeling well; it is a manifestation of positive health, the physical expression of vitality; it is having the capacity to cope with the physical demands most people face each day, and having a little extra left in reserve.

Here is a simple fitness test to try at home. Stand with your feet together in front of a step, eight inches or 200 mm high. For three minutes, step up and down at the rate of two complete movements every five seconds. A complete movement means one foot up, the other foot up, then one foot down, the other foot down. Stop at once if you begin to feel remotely uncomfortable. When the three minutes are up, sit and rest for exactly one minute. Then take your pulse. If you are fit, it should be more or less back to normal. Check your fitness level according to the accompanying table.

Pulse rate – beats per minute		Fitness level
MEN	WOMEN	
Under 79	Under 84	Very fit
80-89	85-94	Fit
90-99	95-109	Unfit
100 plus	110 plus	Very unfit

Three basic components of physical fitness are suppleness, strength and stamina. Suppleness means flexibility or mobility of the neck, trunk and limbs. The more supple you are, the more easily you can move your joints without discomfort. Suppleness exercises stretch and loosen the various muscles that work the joints. The joints themselves are tightened and toned up, whilst the ligaments that support them are shortened and strengthened. Suppleness allows us to twist and turn, and bend and stretch, without strain or sprain. It is an important component of fitness especially for elderly people whose muscles easily stiffen, making it difficult to cope with ordinary activities, such as getting out of bed, bathing, dressing and doing housework.

Strength is simply muscle power, the maximum force that a group of muscles can apply to an action. Strength is needed for pulling, pushing, lifting and shifting. Strength of forearm muscles gives a strong hand grip; strong shoulder muscles make light work of lifting children or loading shopping into the car. Elderly people need to maintain the strength of their limbs so they may get in and out of chairs or the bath with ease. Strength is developed by exercising muscles against resistance – for example, by weight-lifting, press-ups or bicycling. Broadly, the more resistance the muscle meets when it retracts, the more its individual fibres are brought into play. Muscles that are regularly exercised against resistance respond by becoming bulkier and stronger.

Stamina means staying power, and is the fundamental component of fitness. It is the capacity to keep going without gasping for breath or going weak at the knees. Any activity involving the rhythmic contraction of large muscles, such as those of the legs, requires stamina. Running and swimming are good examples. They are sometimes described as 'aerobic' from the Greek words for 'air' and 'life' because the working muscles need a plentiful supply of oxygen. This puts an extra demand, not only on the heart, lungs and circulation, but also on the muscles themselves which must be able to extract oxygen from the bloodstream rapidly and efficiently. All these functions can be improved by exercising energetically and regularly.

So why bother to be fit? For many people, the words 'fitness' and 'exercise' conjure up visions of agonising physical exercising in the school gym or the loneliness of the long-distance runner. In fact, far from being a chore, the whole point of exercise or fitness is to increase your enjoyment of life, because keeping fit means taking regular, moderately vigorous exercise. It is important to choose something that gives you an incentive to continue. So don't choose something that you loathe! You might just hate swimming or you might hate playing tennis, so choose something else. Apart from the physical benefits of exercising, research has shown that it can help to relieve anxiety and depression. Athletes describe the natural 'high' that they get through vigorous exercise, and that is an apt description of what happens in their brain. Scientists studying this effect found that exercise seems to stimulate the release of certain natural hormones – called endorphins – within the brain which mimic the effects of morphine and have a pleasurable and pain-suppressing effect. Being fit can also help to combat degenerative diseases. Inactivity can lead to problems ranging from muscle and joint stiffness to obesity, or from palpitations to an increased risk of heart attack. Regular, moderately vigorous activity, with at least twenty minutes of stamina-building exercises twice a week (preferably more often) reduces the likelihood of these conditions.

The first and most crucial step to fitness is getting started. *You* have got to make the decision. Obviously, it's going to mean extra effort; there's no lazy way to get fit! That's a contradiction in terms. But that does not mean that you have to launch yourself into a vigorous physical training programme. The essential thing is to start gently and build up gradually over the weeks. You can take the first steps to fitness by making a few changes in your lifestyle. First of all, use your legs! Walk more each day, to work or to the shops. Use the stairs instead of the lift; get off the bus a stop or two before your own. A brisk walk for five or ten minutes is an excellent introduction to fitness, and each day put a little more effort into your walking. Use the stairs, as I say, more than the lift or the escalator. And climb more hills! Spend at least five or ten minutes each day doing some activity that makes you moderately breathless. Even standing still is better for you than sitting or lying down.

Stop smoking: cigarette smoking reduces stamina because, a few minutes after you smoke a cigarette, the very small air tubes, the bronchioles in the lungs, shrink – almost doubling their resistance to the flow of air breathed in. This leads rapidly to breathlessness during exercise. Smoking raises the heartbeat by 20-30 beats a minute, which reduces stamina. Nicotine in the bloodstream also silts up the arteries with fatty deposits, reducing the flow of blood to active muscles, including the heart, thus increasing the risk of thrombosis. The fewer cigarettes you smoke, the more good exercise will do for you, but exercise cannot cancel out the effects of smoking.

Lose excess weight; exercise helps you to lose weight but staying slim helps you to benefit more from a fitness programme. The more surplus fat you lose, the more comfortable you will be when exercising, and the less likely to injure yourself.

There are many groups which meet regularly for aerobic, aquarobic, weight-training, etc. and this is a good way to start. You will not only have professional advice and supervision; you will have support, companionship and an incentive, all of which are lacking in exercises performed alone. You can also have a jolly good laugh in an exercise group, and this is perhaps the best medicine of all.

Meditation

The dictionary definition of meditation is 'think about', 'ponder', 'engage in thought', 'muse', 'cogitate', 'dwell upon mentally', 'plan', 'design', 'intend'. And then 'ponder' is defined as 'weigh carefully in the mind', 'think over', 'consider deeply', 'reflect upon', 'examine carefully', 'value', 'estimate', 'deliberate', 'muse over'. And 'muse over' can be defined as 'study' or 'reflect on in silence', 'dream', 'engage in reverie', 'wonder at'. So that the definitions after 'ponder' and 'muse over' in relation to thinking about God, the infinite, the Creator, is to become aware of the sacred nature of existence. As William Blake wrote: '

He who sees the infinite in all things, sees God.' And, 'If the doors of perception were cleansed, everything would appear to man as it is – infinite. For man has closed himself up, so that he sees all things through narrow chinks of his cavern.'

Blake saw existence as the descent of the Spirit into matter, and was illumined by it. He said, 'The tree which moves some to tears of joy is, in the eyes of others, only a green thing which stands in the way.' So that, in the beginning, meditation is essentially an intellectual practice in which we focus or concentrate on a particular theme: it may be a visual image, or an episode concerning the life and ministry of Jesus (or one of the other great spiritual teachers) or one of the parables. For agnostics, it may be an abstract piece of reasoning, for people trained in the Eastern religions, it may be a constantly repeated phrase or sound which is called a mantra. The object is always to focus the discursive mind on one particular theme to the exclusion of all else. But prolonged concentration, except on vast and intricate subjects, is very difficult and we soon become bored and tired, and our minds start to wander. For instance, if one concentrates upon a rose, one can think about the perfect symmetry, colour and scent of the flower, but even these are soon exhausted.

But if one stops analysing it, and merges one's consciousness into the whole rose, one's identity or self can be absorbed into the rose. In this way, the rose and the observer become one; the effort of concentration, with its fatigue and tension, go and a feeling of release and relaxation takes its place. This is a stage which can be reached by everyone through the dedicated practice of meditation. Some reach it easily – others have more difficulty. The final stage is when the rose or the tree, or whatever it may be, is transcended and one is in contact or communion with the reality which lies behind all things. This is an induced mystical experience, and will never come of its own accord; it only comes by divine grace. You can meditate for ever, but you will never reach this stage as long as you seek it selfishly. Whoever lives selfishly is finally disappointed, no matter how successful he has been; but he who lives in awareness of life's eternity, is never crushed by the circumstances of the moment. There has been a cloud of witnesses through the ages who have demonstrated this to us. Sectarian religions may become stultified and eventually disappear, but the striving towards the spiritual or super-conscious level will never be thwarted.

We reach these levels by psychological means and spiritual help. Psychological techniques help us to understand ourselves, and so to rise to a fuller life and a greater maturity. These include training the will, and analytical procedures, and the creation of an ideal model which possesses the qualities lacking in ourselves. The aim of all these techniques is to heighten our response to the world around us, to become more consciously aware of other people so that we may relate to them positively, detach ourselves from our own problems, and see them in a new light. But of course, in spite of all this knowledge and expertise, we may still fail to solve the problems of personal integration. St Paul knew this problem very well: the good he wants to do, he fails to do, whereas the evil he tries to avoid seems to recur with unfailing regularity. He finds that the Spirit has one law, the flesh another. And the latter nearly always triumphs, no matter how well-intentioned his motives. This is the human tragedy, because most of us really mean well. We use scientific and idealistic political measures, we want to lift mankind out of ignorance, vice and disease through education, morality and health. But something always seems to go wrong, no matter what methods or political theories we use, something always seems to go wrong, as it always has gone wrong; reactionary regimes follow revolution, and the revolutionaries have imposed just as tyrannical a regime as their predecessors.

Any attempt to change society from the outside will fail – not because society itself is healthy: it is, after all, full of corruption – but because those who want to change it forcibly are fighting their own psychological battles, and so projecting their own conflicts onto other people. The most profound psychological understanding will not help us while we are still imprisoned in our own personality and are using our will on a personal level. It is only when our consciousness expands to see beyond the personal level to the trans-personal – in other words, to a level that involves all other people and all other created things and binds them into a coherent whole, rather than numerous separate entities, that some hope of a change may occur. Mere transformation of the environment without the transformation of the personality does little lasting good. Peace cannot come until we are at peace with ourselves. This peace is not a state of blissful inactivity resembling sleep; it is conscious, purposeful, willed activity in harmony with the activity of the universe which, after all, is a manifestation of the will of God.

Just stop for a moment and look at your thoughts. You will find that your mind resembles an ant-heap, or a monkey hopping frantically from branch to branch on a tree. It is chaotic, confused, repetitive and certainly most undisciplined. This is your habitual mind that automatically reacts with anger, desire, fear, jealousy, blame. It is like a candle flame in a draught, flickering whichever way the breeze is blowing, but underneath this unstable, shifting, scurrying morass of thought, lies a lasting, deathless awareness or innermost mind, which is absolutely untouched by change or by death. This is the true and innermost essence of the mind which Christians and Jews call God, Sufi mystics call hidden essence, Hindus 'the self', Sheba, Brahmin and Vishnu, and Buddhists call 'Buddha nature'. How sad that religion is used as an excuse to make war when at the heart of all beliefs is the certainty of a fundamental truth; and life is a sacred opportunity to realise this truth as we evolve.

The chaotic morass of our thoughts and emotions hides this fundamental truth from us like clouds hiding the sun. Sometimes the clouds are blown away, and the sun is revealed to us, shining in a clear blue sky. So, during the practice of meditation, thoughts and emotions may be shifted to reveal to us a glimpse of the innermost nature of our mind. Sometimes the glimpses may be fleeting and hardly recognised. But with perseverance, they will grow stronger, bringing freedom from negative emotions, from greed and selfish desire, and an awareness of the purpose of life.

Three of the major problems in contemporary society are noise, hurry and crowds. Carl Gustav Jung once said: 'Hurry is not *of* the Devil: it *is* the Devil.' So if we hope to go beyond the bedlam of our modern world, we must be willing to go down into the silence, the inner world of contemplation, to find the inner place or space where we can be completely at peace in the stillness. Most of us are victims of the pressures of modern urban living. Everyone reacts to the stressful situations in their lives in different ways, to maintain a delicate balance between themselves and their environment. Some react efficiently and appropriately, especially when we are young or the stress is short-lived. Others are destroyed by complex events in their lives over which they have only partial control. We know that stress contributes to cancer, hypertension, coronary thrombosis, skin diseases, digestive disturbance, chronic bronchitis, and many more physical diseases. Unresolved emotional stress can alter the balance of a person's sanity which may result in suicide.

However, let us not forget the benefits of stress. The challenge of competition makes us seek perfection in love, work and sport. But when the body overreacts to stress, that stress may become habitual and eventually causes irreversible change. This self-destruct programme will result in physical or psychological illness if it is allowed to continue over many years. As well as reducing pollution, noise levels, overcrowding and long working hours, we can benefit from psychotherapy, relaxation techniques, yoga, jogging, walking, working out and other physical disciplines. Secular meditation too can overcome stress within the body, and calm the mind. It is a technique of deep relaxation by which the mind is taken to the source of thought, the pure field of creative imperatives. The conscious mind is expanded and its power increased, and the body gains more energy. In this way, we can make full use of our mental potential and there is also a cumulative growth in calmness, alertness and efficiency, and a decrease in any craving for drugs, including tobacco or alcohol. The physiological effects of stress are minimised by the deep relaxation of the body during meditation.

Most of us fill every moment of our time with noise or boring tasks, or frantic activity. Anything to ensure we are never left alone or in total silence. We fear silence and solitude; we have no inner security

– only the fragile support of our worldly identity: our name, our life story, our partner, home, job, friends, financial status, and so on. But these are all in the 'outer' and can be taken away from us at any time, leaving us lost, bewildered and terrified. The modern world feeds off anxiety and depression, fostered by consumerism which trains us all to be greedy and to see money and the acquisition of possessions as the only goal worth striving for. Our lives in fact 'live us' – we feel we are swept along and we have no choice or control over them. More than 10% of the population of this country suffers from some kind of mental illness. Our minds cannot stay still for even a moment or two without distraction. We reach for the radio, the TV or the CD player, a book, a telephone, a bar of chocolate, a drink – anything to fill the terrifying abyss of the mind in silence.

No wonder Aldous Huxley taught that this world is the hell of another planet. Certainly, living in a big city in today's world is close. Our minds are so restless and fragmented that our thoughts are scattered everywhere and there is no-one at home. So my personal definition of meditation would be that meditation is 'bringing the mind home'. You do not have to control the mind, neither do you have to try to be peaceful. In fact, you do not try to do anything. When I am meditating, I am content simply to be. I sit quietly and allow my mind to rest. I don't question whether I am in the right posture, or if I am doing it right. I simply am. My ordinary mind is no longer there. There is only a natural spaciousness and a deep unshakeable peace. There is nothing at all to do. But, you will say, I sit down and endeavour to be peaceful, and my mind is like an ant-heap, my thoughts run riot, and are wilder and more insistent than ever. This is a good sign; it means you are becoming quieter and are realising just how wild and uncontrolled your thoughts have always been. Don't be put off by this; just watch these thoughts tumbling one on top of each other, like the water tumbling over the Niagara Falls, seemingly uncontrollably. After a while, as your meditation practice is perfected, your thoughts will become like a deep river, slowly winding its way to the sea, then finally it will become the sea itself, still and calm, its surface disturbed by only the occasional ripple.

Do not make the mistake that I did, of thinking that when you meditate, there should be no thoughts at all, and then, if thoughts or emotions arise, think that you have failed. There is a Tibetan saying: 'It's a tall order to ask for meat without bones, or tea without leaves.'

And while your body is alive, your mind will have thoughts and emotions. Going back to the analogy of the mind as an ocean, the ocean has waves, but – the waves go back into the ocean. So be tolerant towards your thoughts; they are the very nature of your mind, and will dissolve back into it provided you do not react impulsively to them. For instance, during meditation the thought may arise: 'What shall I have for my supper?' If you react to that thought with, 'What have I got in the fridge?' or 'Will I have time to cook it before I go out?' or 'I don't really feel like eating that at the moment; what else can I have?' then you have lost it and you might as well leave the meditation and get up and prepare your supper anyway. The trick is to stop, 'What shall I have for my supper?' right there and not continue to speculate on the subject. This is where concentration on the breath, a candle flame or a mantra can really help.

Ask any random group of ten people what the word 'meditation' means to them, and the chances are that you will get ten different answers: 'It's another word for prayer,' or 'It means to think deeply about something,' or 'It means to empty your mind,' or 'It's sitting down and seeing beautiful pictures in your mind's eye,' etc. So, to begin with, I must make very clear what meditation means to me – and of course my definition may not be the definitive one. One Tibetan master described meditation as 'Mind suspended in space – nowhere'. It is like a jar of muddy water: the longer we leave the jar without shaking or stirring it, the more the particles of dirt will sink to the bottom, letting the natural clarity of the water shine through. The natural state of the mind is bliss and clarity, and if you can only leave the mind alone, your thoughts will settle just like the mud in the water, revealing the mind's true radiance. This awareness of deep peace does not happen overnight; like any other learned experience, it takes time to become a priest, a doctor, to learn to play the piano or to speak Chinese – and these are easily attained compared with the ability to meditate. You have to practise all your life. But when you begin to understand where meditation will lead, it will become the most important thing in your life, to be undertaken with enthusiasm, perseverance, and most importantly, self-discipline. Like all these therapies I am suggesting for self-help, only you can do it, and it has to be practised at least twice each and every day. Days when you are tired, dispirited, disenchanted, ill, days when friends and associates are making fun of you and labelling you as some kind of nut, days when you tend to agree with them! – it is only by practising daily, if only for a few minutes at a time, that you will eventually notice a gradual improvement in the quality of your life as a whole. In this stillness and silence you will find your true self which you have lost in the restless confusion of living in the world today. To me, meditation is the true practice of peace – a deep, inner peace, free from distractions and restless thoughts and endless activity. It allows for no violence or aggression, so that spread worldwide, it could lead to total disarmament.

The inner reality of the spiritual world is available to all who are willing to search for it. If you doubt this statement, have you ever taken even ten minutes to investigate whether or not such a world exists? Like any other scientific study, we form an idea and then experiment with it to see if the idea is true, or not. And if our first experiment fails, we do not despair, or label the whole thing a fraud. We re-examine what we are thinking, perhaps adjust our ideas, and try again. We should at least persevere with the concept as diligently as we would in the field of science. The fact that so many people are unwilling to do this is not because they are unintelligent but because they lack self-discipline, or are prejudiced, or both. Human beings seem to need someone else to speak to God for them, and are content to get the message from God second-hand. The history of religion is the story of an almost desperate scramble to have a king, a mediator, a priest, a go-between, then we do not have to change (for to be in the presence of God is to change), and we also have someone else to blame if things go wrong. This is why true meditation – being in the presence of God – is so threatening to us because it calls us to enter into the living presence of God for ourselves; it tells us that God is speaking to us and wants us to listen, right here and now, to the directions being given to us. But why not? If God is alive and active in our affairs, why can't that voice be heard and obeyed today? To me, this close communion with God is the ultimate end of meditation. Longfellow caught the vital nature of this experience when he wrote:

Let us then labour for an inward stillness,
An inward stillness and an inward healing.
That perfect silence when the lips and heart are still
And we no longer entertain our own imperfect thoughts and
    vain opinions,

But God alone will speak to us.
And we wait in singleness of heart, that we may know His will
And in silence of our spirit that we may do His will and do that
    only.

What a counsel of perfection, you may say! And how utterly unattainable in the chaotic world in which we live. I believe that true Meditation is an encounter with the Divine. If you believe that we live in a universe created by an infinite personal God, who delights in our communion with him or her, you will meditate as a communication between the lover and the one beloved. I do not refer to God as either male or female; to me, God is a pure presence or spirit, and to give this purely spiritual presence a human, sexual identity seems to me to be somewhat naïve. I prefer Creator, Divine Love, Pure Consciousness, the Infinite – whatever. But not him or her. I feel that human beings are given a sexual identity because we are creating other bodies that more souls may enter, so that sexuality is purely concerned with creating other houses for other souls in which to dwell; and once you get that out of the way, then everyone to me is pure presence, and whatever goes on below the waist doesn't really matter!

A lifetime, or perhaps even many lifetimes, of practice may not result in the realisation of true meditation, but the discipline of regular short periods of quiet reflection will bring an increasing awareness of peace, love, understanding and forgiveness, not only into our own lives but also into the lives of everyone round us. If we hope to go beyond the bedlam of our modern world, we must be willing to go down into the silence – the inner world of contemplation – to find the inner space where we can be completely at one with God, whatever we conceive Him to be, and be completely at peace in the stillness. If you are an atheist or an agnostic, do not dismiss meditation; try some of the suggestions I make regarding preparation, concentrating on the breath, an object like a candle flame, a sound, or an exercise in visualisation. This will improve the quality of your life in every way and may – just may – bring you eventually to the state of purer awareness which is the ultimate goal.

There is a prophecy in the Old Testament book of Amos, that the time will come when there will be 'a famine in the land – not a famine for bread and not a thirst for water, but a famine of hearing the word of the Lord'. That time has come to pass, I think, and it is now.   All the master-teachers of meditation, and indeed the physicists, the scientists, are trying to tell us that the universe is much larger than we know, that there are vast regions still unexplored, but just as real as the physical world we inhabit.   We are in fact being called upon to be pioneers of the spiritual frontiers, and this is all very, very exciting.   Eastern meditation stresses the need to become detached from the world.   There is an emphasis on losing individuality and merging with the cosmic mind.   There is a longing for release from the burden of the pains of life, and to be caught up into the effortless, suspended bliss of Nirvana.   Personal identity is lost in the pool of cosmic consciousness in an escape from the miserable wheel of existence.

Transcendental meditation has the same roots, but in my opinion, in its western form, it is meditation for the materialist because there is no need to believe in the spiritual realm in order to practise.   It is a secular method of achieving inner tranquillity.   The transcendental meditation student in the West – I stress, in the West – learns to sit down and close his or her eyes for two periods of twenty minutes each day, during which he or she leaves the stress battlefield and wills himself into a state of 'restful alertness'.   He or she does this by concentrating on the silent repetition of a word called a mantra – a soothing meaningless sound, assigned to him by his instructor.   Whether because of the mantra or not, most beginners learn quite easily how to ease into quietness, their hands and feet feel heavy and tingling, and their minds idle, so that thoughts float.   It has been proved scientifically that, during meditation, there is a marked reduction of oxygen consumption which is the prime measure of the body's metabolic rate.   This reduction is greater during meditation than after six hours' sleep; the concentration of acid in the arteries, a chemical produced by anxiety, drops four times faster in meditation than in simple rest.   Galvanic skin resistance, another positive measure of relaxation, increases fourfold in some cases, and all these effects persist beyond the twenty-minute period.   So secular meditation is in fact a medical technique reducing high blood pressure and consequently the risk of strokes and heart attacks.   Many transatlantic businessmen use this kind of meditation to hold down blood pressure whilst accentuating the winning streak, and encourage serene but profitable decision-making.   So, even if you do not join the transcendental meditation group, you can meditate in this way, repeating a simple word of your own choice – like peace, joy, love, strength, well, order, calm, plenty, sleep, still, serene, etc. One syllable like OM or AAH also works well. Just sit quietly and go through the preparation of a comfortable position, no distractions, concentration on the breath, probably gazing at a candle flame or a flower, and your word or sound should float into your head almost unbidden.

I started to meditate in a very simple way because I was in such a state of stress, I was sure I was going mad! But after 25 years of practice, I now feel a true communion with God or the Infinite, during which I receive clear and exact answers to most of my earthly problems. There is also a strong sense of the spiritual presence of my husband, and flashes of blissful awareness of the unity of all creation. So there is not just a perception of the birds in the cherry tree outside my window: the birds, the tree and I are all one, and there is an end of isolation. These flashes of blissful awareness or at-one-ment do not occur very often or last very long, but when they do, I know in some indefinable way, the changeless unity and harmony of the universe. When the brief encounter has passed, I am filled with great joy, happiness, gratitude, and an incredible peace which fills me with a loving compassion towards all my fellow human beings.

So, there are many levels of experience in meditation; in fact, it is experience with different levels of awareness. It is impossible to learn to truly meditate from a book; it is like riding a bicycle or swimming; a few basic instructions can be given regarding posture or movement, etc. but we only learn to meditate by meditating. Do not think that, because you are setting aside certain times of day for practice, that you are finally meditating. This work of meditation involves the whole of life; it is a 24-hour-a-day job. The whole of our day is in fact preparing us for our specific times of meditation. If you are constantly involved in frantic activity, it will be impossible to be quiet at the moment of inward silence. A harassed mind cannot meditate. We need a sense of balance, and an ability to be at peace through the activities of the day, an ability to rest and take time to enjoy beauty, an ability to pace ourselves. Unfortunately today, people are judged by what they earn or produce. So if we expect to succeed in meditating, we must pursue our goal with ruthless determination, and maybe cut down on our appointments and social activities.

In earthly terms, I am now considered to be old, and one of the great advantages of age is that I have time to meditate. I no longer have to earn a living in nine-to-five terms, and can always avoid social invitations by pleading fatigue. Actually, I have more than sufficient energy to do the important things like walking, swimming and writing, watching my garden grow and the moon behind my cherry tree. But I can 'do' old if necessary, particularly if it gets me away from the chattering classes!

Certainly, I would not have been interested in meditation when I was younger. My social calendar and my work were much more important than what I would have described as sitting down cross-legged and becoming rather strange. How I wish I had tried it years and years ago, particularly when my problems were at their height.

So – how do we get there? You must believe that this is the most important goal of your life, a goal that demands enthusiasm, perseverance, much thought, and most importantly, discipline. At its highest, meditation is enlightenment and communion with the Infinite. It also brings tremendous relaxation, peace and bliss along the way. With time, patience and discipline, your mind will gradually become more and more pliable so that you can become the master of your own mind and use it in the most beneficial way. Normally, we waste our lives in endless activity, in intense anxious struggle and competition, in acquiring money and possessions and an endless social whirl. Meditation is the exact opposite. It is a state free from competition, from care or concern, from anxiety and a struggle to forget, and free from ambition. We are neither fearful nor hopeful, accepted or rejected. We are released from all the emotions and thoughts which normally imprison us. We are free to float in stillness and in silence, in a state of what I would call 'calm abiding'.

When you begin to meditate, you will probably feel your thoughts are more like an ant-heap than ever, and are really running riot. One patient said to me, "My mind is like a hamster, going round and round on his wheel, faster and faster, getting more and more frantic with every turn." "Don't worry," I replied. "This is a good sign. It doesn't mean that your thoughts have become wilder. It means that you have become quieter and are now able to see how noisy and uncontrolled your thoughts have always been." In Asian meditation instruction, these thoughts are always described as arriving 'one on top of another, like a steep mountain waterfall'. Gradually, as you persevere, your thoughts become like the water in a deep, narrow gorge. Then like a great river winding its way slowly down to the sea, until finally the mind becomes like a still and placid ocean, ruffled only slightly by the occasional ripple or wave. Don't make the mistake of thinking that no thoughts or feelings whatsoever should arise during meditation. Rising thoughts can only improve your practice. As long as you have a mind, and are alive, you will have thoughts and emotions.

So, whatever thoughts and feelings tumble through your mind, be patient, and allow them to settle back into the mind, just as a wave comes and goes in the ocean. The ocean has waves, but is not particularly disturbed by them. They rise and go back again because they are part of the ocean. In the same way, your thoughts and emotions are part of your mind, rising up and dissolving back again into your mind. Be compassionate and understanding with yourself, as a Tibetan master said: 'Be like an old wise man, watching a child play.' So, when you change your attitude towards disturbing thoughts and feelings, your mind will change. When you become tolerant, unbiased and compassionate, your thoughts and emotions will change too. When you have no difficulty with them, they will have no difficulty with you.

Thoughts will come and will go, and as you watch them dispassionately, you will see that there is a gap between each one, infinitesimal and almost imperceptible. But when the past thought is past and the next thought unformed, there is a gap, a glimpse of pure, unadulterated mind. So your work in meditation is to allow your thoughts to slow down in order to make these gaps more apparent. You will have many negative thoughts and many troubling emotions. Any of us in human form cannot escape this: to be human and alive is to be vulnerable to pain on every level of being. I find that the more deeply I am upset by various random happenings in my life, the more difficult it is for me to meditate. The stream of troubling negativity seems continuous and overwhelming.

So, whatever thoughts and feelings tumble through your mind, let them! Don't wallow in them like a sea of self-pity, or feed them with more negativity. Just watch them coming and going, like waves in the ocean, or like small clouds in the sky which obscure the light of the sun as they pass across it. The ocean is not disturbed by the waves because they are itself. And the clouds do not obscure the radiance of the sun; in fact, they are gradually dispersed by its warmth. So be like the ocean, watching your own waves, or the sun, looking down on the cloud, knowing that those waves and clouds are passing and ephemeral.

As you practise, you will find that the meditative state gradually becomes a part of you. You will feel more and more at peace with yourself and your world. More and more free from the desire to possess, either people or material things. You will be content with what you need rather than with what you desire or want. Your ego and its greed and fear will gradually dissolve, leaving you free to live your life in wisdom and calm abiding. This is the true purpose of practice – to let us glimpse and eventually return to our inner awareness that we have lost in the frenetic distraction of our lives as we live them today. It is said that consciousness goes through a stage of tormented restlessness after death. Are we not already experiencing this agony in the cities of the modern world? Sometimes when I meditate, my mind settles into pure being straightaway, and I am content simply to be. I just am. Other times, my mind is so moody, so obsessed by imagined hurts and painful emotions, that being calm and still, restful and joyful, seems a total impossibility. Secular meditation relies heavily on practical formulae. After all, western civilisation is fascinated by technology and machines. But true meditation relies on the dedication of the creative way in which we practise. Mind and body are interrelated, and there is a direct connection between the posture of the body and the state of the mind. If your mind is calm, you can sit effortlessly. If you are tense and anxious, you will be physically uncomfortable.

Unless you are an advanced yoga student, you will not be comfortable sitting cross-legged on the floor. So sit on a chair with a straight back, with your buttocks well back in the chair, and your feet firmly planted on the floor, or crossed at the ankles. Feel strong and serene like a mountain, so that your mind is free to soar and to fly like a bird. Straighten your back by taking a breath, and as you let it out, feel as if you are pinning your abdomen firmly to your spine. This will relax the natural curve at the base of the spine and lessen your tension. Then touch your breastbone lightly and push it up, which will straighten your shoulders and balance your head comfortably on your neck. Fold your hands loosely in your lap or rest them on your knees, palms upwards. Some people prefer to close their eyes; if you are easily disturbed by outside events, it is a good thing to close them and look within. Gaze at the point between the eyebrows. Shut out life but be open and at peace with it. Some people start by closing their eyes and opening them again once they have calmed down. Personally, I light a candle or gaze at a single flower or a crystal or a magnificent picture of the resurrection of Jesus, in which he is surrounded by a wonderful prismatic aura. Meditation is a highly personal activity, and you should feel intuitively what is right for you and not be influenced by any dogmatic instructions. Once you have become calm and tranquil, gaze into space as if it were a limitless ocean. As your gaze expands, you mind will expand and fill with a limitless compassion, wisdom and understanding for all living things upon the earth, including yourself.

The next technique which fosters a meditative state is to itemise and give up present fears. With your palms down in front of you, put these fears into words. For example, 'I let go of my anger and resentment towards X.' Or, 'I let go of my fear of going to the dentist tomorrow.' Or, 'I let go of my anxiety over paying the bills this month.' Or, 'I let go of the frustration I feel about my immobility and my arthritic pain.' Whatever is on your mind, place your palms downwards and release it. Try to see a picture of it disappearing in some sort of cloud, like smoke or steam. Colour it bright red if it helps! Then turn your palms upwards, as a symbol of your desire to receive help from the universe or the Infinite; see your palms filling and overflowing with love and healing.

Another powerful method which leads to a meditative state is concentrating on the breath, which I have described in the chapter on breathing. When you meditate, breathe naturally as you always do, and focus your attention on the 'out' breath. As you exhale, let go and release the negative thoughts and emotions as you release them when you put your palms down in the exercise. Put the two exercises together if you like. Each time you breathe out, and before you breathe in again, you will notice the gap, like the infinitesimal gap between each thought. Rest in that gap, and as you breathe in, stay there instead of thinking about the 'in' breath. Don't concentrate on the breath entirely; give about three quarters of your attention to becoming quiet, relaxed and spacious so that you and the breath gradually become one.

Do not feel that these breathing techniques are mandatory. You may find them claustrophobic. Always listen to your own inner voice, and let it decide what is best for you. We are all amazingly different, like snowflakes – no two of us are alike. So do not feel obliged to follow any of these suggestions unless you are at ease with them. I mentioned watching an object as an aid to meditation. Personally, I find resting my sight lightly on a flower or a crystal invokes a feeling of inspiration. The picture of Christ however is particularly powerful because he connects me directly to my inner self. Of course, it can be any master: it could be Buddha or Zoroaster or Mohammed or Allah – any master who particularly appeals to you.

The technique of reciting a mantra or sound can change the state of your mind from nervous fragility to calm tranquillity. The word mantra means that which protects the mind. When you chant a mantra, you are charging your breath and energy to work directly on your body and mind. The sound used can be a single syllable, as in transcendental meditation, or a phrase that particularly appeals to you. Some of mine are 'Make me an instrument of thy peace,' 'Go placidly amidst the noise and haste, and remember what peace there may be in silence.' Repeated slowly and quietly, and giving deep thought to the meaning may be a powerful preparation for meditation. But the true aim is not to pay attention to your thoughts but to let them float through the mind without following them up with more thoughts; just leave them in your mind like an ant-heap or a hamster scrabbling round and round on its wheel. When your mind slows down, and begins to rest in the gaps between thoughts, you are glimpsing Meditation, and your work now is to let your thoughts slow down, and become more and more aware of these gaps.

When you arrive at this state of vibrant peace, just remain there quietly without grasping at it to make it stay. Once you say, 'This is meditation and I must stay in it,' you've stopped meditating and you are out on your ego. As you continue to practise meditation, it will gradually become a continuous living experience so that you slowly lose the terrifying emotions, hopes and fears of physical existence, and come closer to wisdom, generosity, kindness and compassion. There will be no more barriers between you and others; you will have come home to a true and blissful at-one-ment with the whole of life.

The human brain and body together is a magnet because it is part of the earth. We are inseparably connected with each other, the earth and the cosmos. So that when there is turbulence in me, then that turbulence is not confined to me; it will eventually affect you and the earth's magnetic field as well. So, if there are earthquakes, you can make a connection between what happens in human consciousness and what happens in the earth's consciousness. We are part of the earth, because we are made from its dust; we are made from recycled earth. We are waves in the vast ocean of consciousness. Vedanta says, 'It is our duty to be peaceful because when we are not, we disrupt cosmic harmony.' So for the sake of humanity, we need to find that place of perfect peace inside us.

There was a very interesting study done on the collective practice of meditation, to see exactly what was happening during the process. If all the readers of this book were to meditate together and had oscilloscopes attached to their brains, eventually everyone's brainwaves would be in tune, so we would be connected at one level, like a flight of birds which all turn together, or a school of fish which swim together. When we are in a state of inner peace – that is, when we are not filled with rage and anger which basically come from fear, our serotonin levels in the body go up. Serotonin can be measured by its metabolite in the urine. So when people are depressed, they take Prozac which is supposed to increase serotonin levels and eventually they feel more able to cope, are happier and more contented, and therefore more powerful.

An experiment was done where 7,000 people sat down together and meditated. The observers of the meditation were looking at the meditators' brainwaves, using oscilloscopes. They were also looking at the levels of serotonin in their bodies by measuring serotonin metabolite in their urine. All the brainwaves of the meditators became coherent, and the levels of serotonin metabolites went up. So, they were creating a coherent energy field, giving an absence of fear, and a positive feeling of power. This was not surprising to the scientists conducting the experiment; what really blew their minds was when they measured the serotonin levels in people on the street outside who were not meditating. And these people's serotonin levels went up also! So what the meditation group was doing influenced not only themselves but also what was happening outside them on the street.

So just imagine what could happen to the world if large groups of people all over the planet meditated regularly. Patanjali, who was a great seer and lived 2,000 years before Christ, said: 'When we are firmly established in non-violence, all beings round us cease to feel hostility. This is why retreat into silence is so valuable – both to oneself, and also to the world in general. And a retreat of this kind literally means silence: no television, no telephoning, no reading, as well as no conversation, because silence means just silence: no oral or written communication. Not only is there a process of mental and physical regeneration, but the soul and spirit are in total harmony with all creation, not only with other human beings but also with birds and animals. You are connected with the mind of the cosmos, so even if only one or two percent of people reach this pure state of being, it influences the entire population.

If we could reach the state of going into spirit, then things like the Twin Towers, the Spanish train explosion, 7/7 in London, or the goings-on in Baghdad, Palestine, Israel and Kosovo simply would not happen. It is strange, is it not, when tribes which are large enough to be called nations go to war? People wear uniforms, kill one another, and are given medals and honour for that killing. Kill someone without wearing uniform and the excuse of nationalism, and you go to prison for murder. But it's the same thing! There is now evidence that the causes of criminal behaviour begin even in the womb. If you have a single mother in a high-rise flat in inner London, with very little money, no family around to help and support, she will be surrounded by the sights and sounds of violence, gang warfare, drug addicts, guns going off, cars exploding, sirens and screams; and every time she hears or sees one of these upsetting events, the baby in her womb reacts to the increase of adrenalin in her blood. Even when the baby is born, he will experience a stress reaction every time he hears a door bang, a siren wail, a scream or a shout. Scientists now call this reaction 'free-floating rage', and it arises for no other reason than that the child has been programmed for violence before it was even born.

But of course, there can be the flip side to this. Buddhists sing songs to a baby before it is born, and a particular African tribe names the baby at the moment of conception and they then sing songs to it throughout the gestation period in the womb. When the baby is born, it is welcomed into the world with its own particular song. And afterwards, at every ceremony in its life – its birthday, various initiations, adolescence, puberty, marriage and the day of death – that special song is sung. So, whenever that person is stressed or upset, they don't go out and kill someone or mug someone; they don't take Prozac; they sing their song! If you play music or recite poetry to an unborn child, if the mother meditates or practises yoga, if there is loving conversation between the man and his partner, you can see on an ultrasound picture that the baby responds by smiling.

If you make a sudden loud noise, the baby will put its hands to its ears. If a mother talks to her child in the womb in a loving way, using its name, it will respond to its name at the moment of birth. These children are also highly cognitive, perceptive and responsive. So this is what we can do with meditation in general, and enlightenment is the only solution to violence. Making laws is obviously a non-starter; prisons are more full of people these days than they have ever been, and crime is on the increase.

About meditation in general, do not make judgements about your meditation. Sometimes you will feel you have attained a state of bliss, sometimes you will feel that nothing at all is happening, sometimes you will be thinking about an argument you have just had with someone. Sometimes you will be thinking about your bank statement or maybe just how badly you need to go to the bathroom. Don't judge; whatever your human feelings, your meditation of itself will have great value. True meditation of course allows the mind to make unlimited flights of speculation regarding the nature of the mind of God, or whatever you conceive God to be. (The power of that mind, the love of that mind, the wisdom contained in that mind, the substance which comes from that mind out of which small things are formed, the instant availability of all the elements of that mind to the one who is open and receptive to it, until we become as conscious of the presence of God as we are of the presence of warmth, of light, or any other element with which they have become familiar.) Meditation can be a process of association with the Divine Presence – a direct communication and conversation with the mind of God, and many questions are answered and much valuable instruction received for the future conduct of our lives.

God and Living Alone

You may feel like skipping this chapter. I shall not blame you if you do. But before you reject it, I would remind you that I was once the most neurotic of people, and faith in God has been, and still is, of the greatest help to me.

God

At some time in our lives, we may have learned that there is an old man up in the sky called God. This old man is very like our own father in one of his terrifying moods. So he also has to be pacified; he knows all about you and can send thunderbolts and lightning that can kill people. So it is absolutely necessary to keep in his good books. The adults in our lives will say, "God doesn't like naughty little girls who tell lies, and he will punish you. You are wicked and worthless, and you must do as we tell you, or else…" We have heard about hell in a vague and fearful way, and we are suitably chastened. If we work with these theories in a constructive way, we revise our ideas about God as we grow older, and God becomes a Being, a force of great love and compassion who does much to fill the emptiness within us.

Growth of Spiritual Awareness

I would describe my own spiritual journey as a journey home – a home infinitely more wonderful than anything I could imagine. Along the way I experienced glimpses of the changeless unity and harmony in charge of the universe, and managed to arrive above the clouds of unhappiness, fear, self-pity and insecurity, into a new kind of knowing, a different state of consciousness. This mystery has to be experienced rather than be explained. Reason and intellect have to be discarded because the ultimate meaning of our existence cannot be defined in human terms. The mystery has to be felt before the journey can begin. But once experienced, it compels us towards itself relentlessly. One awakens drunk with joy. Francis Thompson expresses the inevitability of making the journey home in The Hound of Heaven when he says:

> I fled Him, down the nights and down the days;
> I fled Him, down the arches of the years;
> I fled Him, down the labyrinthine ways
> Of my own mind; and in the mist of tears
> I hid from Him, and under running laughter.
> Up vistaed hopes I sped; and shot, precipitated,
> Adown Titanic glooms of chasmed fears,
> From those strong Feet that followed, followed after.

This may sound dramatic but it does express the inescapable nature of ultimate realisation. This spiritual journey is one of continuous learning and purification; it goes on for the whole of this life and perhaps for many more. The path has never been more difficult or more impossible than it is in today's society, where greed and ignorance feed the sad fantasies of success and power which together are destroying the planet. The hope is, that an increasing number of the human race will seek this path of enlightenment in order to save it from disintegration and annihilation. I see more and more proof that this is happening in the world today: more and more ordinary people – as distinct from the people in power – are making a leap of faith and taking a stand against exploitation, oppression, cruelty and unfairness. Personally, I prefer the American word 'regular' instead of 'ordinary'. 'Regular' implies consistency, normality, harmony and conformity, not casual or capricious – whereas 'ordinary' conveys an impression of the commonplace and mediocre.

So it is these 'regular' people who are now beginning to determine events through the collective voice of humanity rather than the so-called leaders or politicians. In 1990, Sir George Trevelyan said to me, "Watch out for the year 2000. At the moment, we are sitting astride the fence which is highly uncomfortable, but around 2000 the discomfort will become so great that we shall have to jump down, either on the side of spiritual progress or on the side of evil and destruction."

Madam Blavatsky, who founded the Theosophist movement in 1930, forecast that, during the last 25 years of the millennium, and up to the year 2011, there would be an immense spiritual revolution which would transcend any other revolution and cause a total shift away from previous perceived thinking. She prophesied that the leaders of this spiritual revolution would be 'regular' or 'ordinary' people, musicians, motor mechanics, teachers, taxi-drivers, artisans, etc. who would speak up with such a loud voice that bureaucracies would begin to fall into line with this shift in consciousness. As Victor Hugo said in Les Misérables, "There is nothing more powerful than an idea whose time has come."

This shift in consciousness can be seen clearly in the past 25 years, in the fall of the Berlin Wall, in the ending of apartheid in South Africa, in the dismantling of communism in Russia, the overthrowing of petty dictatorships in Eastern Europe, the growth of the organic movement, even in no smoking in restaurants and public transport. Whoever thought that taxi-drivers would ever display a 'No Smoking' sign in their cabs? During the past 25 years, there has been an increasing number of teachers, not just of spirituality but also about taking responsibility for ourselves and our lives on the physical and emotional plane. And here again, many of these teachers have been 'regular' people: Louise Haye was a dancer, Marianne Williamson was a nightclub singer, Dean Ornish was a preacher, and Wayne Dyer a schoolteacher. Unfortunately, there are very few true teachers or masters of truth; the West particularly is full of charlatans, because it is very difficult to check the authenticity of someone who calls himself a 'master'.

Personally, I am wary of anyone who makes such a claim; I know at least two so-called 'masters' who regularly exploit their students, both financially and sexually. Unfortunately, such exploitation is only too easy when we are overwhelmed by personal tragedy or failure, or deeply unhappy. In such a state, we will cling to anyone who seems to us to offer support. A true teacher or master is, above all, kind and compassionate and certainly does not steal either money or sexual favours. They do not manipulate or abandon their students, and give unstintingly of their time or energy in order to share their wisdom. They are more concerned with the truth of the teaching than with demonstrating their own charisma, and so have true humanity. To me, the late Sir George Trevelyan and Krishna Murti are shining examples of true teachers. As Krishna says to Arjuna in the Bhagavad Gita, "There is the path of wisdom and the path of ignorance. They are far apart and lead to different ends. Abiding in the midst of ignorance, thinking themselves wise and learned, fools go aimlessly hither and thither – like the blind led by the blind. What lies beyond life shines, not to those who are childish or careless or deluded by wealth."

My first experience of this different state of consciousness came to me when I was about 16. I had been consistently unhappy since being uprooted from my foster-home when I was three. I was walking through some beautiful Leicestershire countryside, with a calm blue reservoir, bounded by green hills and peaceful meadows, the sun shining from a blue sky, a swan soaring majestically over my head. I was so immersed in my own misery that I saw nothing of this; all that registered was my deep emotional pain, the prison in which I had lived for so many years; I was no longer aware of a world outside.

I sat on a stile, gazing idly at the water, and then suddenly the walls of the prison collapsed around me. I felt, with absolute certainty, the changelessness and unity of everything. The burden of self-pity, self-absorption and unbearable unhappiness just fell away; reason, imagination and all mental activity died down, words failed as, for the moment, I stopped thinking. It was as if I'd just been born, brand-new, mindless, innocent, with no memories.

This experience had a profound effect on me, and although I did not realise it at the time, was the start of my journey. It was a glimpse of the goal; it imbued me with a deep and profound longing for this nameless something, this union of human and divine, which the mystics call absolute being, cosmic consciousness or cosmic mind, the godhead, unconditional being, the nature of mind, spiritual awareness, etc. Actually, it is impossible to define in words, because words are of the world, and this wonder and bliss is not. It is ineffable.

At least, this experience showed me what I was thinking, although it was to be another forty years before I even began to do the dedicated and effortful work which the spiritual journey demands. I had been a dilettante member of the Church of England since I was ten, and was confirmed when I was eleven. For me, this was far too young an age to make such a important commitment; I didn't really understand the promise I was making – in fact, my real reason for going to church was to be eligible for the youth club which was the only possible place for me to meet boys. Since it was connected with the church, my aunt felt that we would be so rigorously supervised that there could be no possible hanky-panky. Also, I have always loved singing hymns which, combined with some innocent fantasising about a rather handsome member of the choir, made Evensong an attractive experience. Certainly, there was no vestige of the spiritual. In fact, for many years I thought God's name was 'Father Ed Witchart' – owing to learning the Lord's Prayer like a parrot, and saying "Ah! Father Witchart in heaven. Hello! Ed be thy name."

I was married in church, because in those days, it was the thing to do. Registry office weddings were highly suspect at that time, and certainly confirmation that something nasty was lurking somewhere in the background. My husband and I went to Evensong from time to time, but to me it meant very little apart from belting out the hymns and holding my husband's hand during the sermon.

The only closeness I felt all this time was to Jesus. When I was three, I went to the small chapel Sunday School in the tiny village where I was fostered. And on the wall was a beautiful picture of Jesus surrounded by children of many colours and sizes, some in his arms, and all protected by him in one way or another. Underneath was the caption, 'Suffer the little children to come unto me.' Feeling so desperately unhappy and unloved at that time, this picture soothed and comforted the depths of pain and loneliness inside me, and certainly planted the seeds of my present deep and abiding affinity with Him.

When my husband died, I became a total atheist. After such a cruel and loveless childhood, such a life-threatening blow seemed to prove to me the total absence of any benign or loving power: everything seemed to be unremitting darkness, and deep and terrible agony. I remained in this spiritual wilderness until my son was adopted in 1966, and for the second time in my life I seriously considered suicide. Later, when I was threatened with severe changes in my work situation, as well as losing my home at the same time, I was truly desperate. But as I know now, it is in meeting and solving life's problems that we embark on this difficult journey of spiritual awareness: the trick is to hear God in the whisper, not wait until He sends the earthquake.

At this cutting-edge of despair, and through a series of apparent coincidences, I discovered The Unity School of Christianity, and this is where my journey started. I began to read and study widely. I attended a twelve-week course on 'The Interpretation of the New Testament' and my horizons expanded. I became increasingly and avidly interested in this man who claimed to be a human manifestation of God walking the earth, offering us this truth which sets us free from our misery and our pain.

You really have to work to find out the truth about Jesus: there is so much confusion. There are so many forms of Christianity – the Roman Catholic Church with its dictums and dogmas, its heavily robed bishops, its priests, its ornate church buildings and its rituals; then far away westward, the Celtic Church with its hermits and faith; and many, many other permutations of Christianity in between.

But none of these is very enlightening about Jesus Himself. And it was the man I wanted to disentangle from all these archaic institutions built around Him. The Gospels are confusing, because three out of the four don't say the same things about the same story; whilst St John seems to be more of a philosophical interpreter of what Jesus said, rather than stating His actual words. Scholars say that Mark's was the first gospel to be written, and that Matthew's and Luke's are based on Mark's, but changed what they considered to be offensive. Mark said that Jesus was angry when the disciples turned the children away, but Matthew and Luke don't mention His anger. Personally, I warm to a manifestation of God who is capable of showing strong human emotions like anger, otherwise how can He ever understand me?

Only Luke tells the story of the Virgin Birth. Maybe he thought Jesus would be accepted more readily as a god if He had been born to a virgin; there were many myths of gods being born to virgins in Greece and Egypt at that time. Women were beneath consideration: if they were menstruating, they were not allowed into the Temple. This barbaric custom was carried through into Christianity for centuries. Women could be divorced at any time with no compensation. The Gospel writers were horrified by Jesus' attitude towards women in general, and prostitutes in particular. He entered into serious discussions with them, and He allowed a prostitute to massage His feet and lavish kisses on Him. I think the fact that such a story was recorded shows that it must have happened.

Jesus showed a warmth and understanding of mankind in general that was not demonstrated by His Jewish kindred or even the Essenes amongst whom it is thought He spent most of His adult life. Even this monastically pure and spiritual brotherhood were outraged by His behaviour towards women. The Jews were expecting a Messiah superior in every way – a great leader inspiring reverence and obedience, with a strong personality able to overcome all things. They did not expect Him to break the Mosaic law and say, "The Sabbath was made for man, and not man for the Sabbath." Nor eat with law-breakers, and say, "I came not to call the righteous, but sinners to repentance."

However, His famous saying came originally from Jewish literature. The first commandment from the Sermon on the Mount can be found in Deuteronomy, and the second – about loving one's neighbour – is in Leviticus. I don't suppose He thought for one moment that He was teaching anything other than the established Jewish path; but with His experience, His knowledge and authority, He injected new life into the old teachings.

Such wise sayings as 'The kingdom of heaven in within you' and 'My Father is greater than I' have been part of Greek, Egyptian and Buddhist teachings for some time, but there is still much more originality in the real Jesus which was proved when, in 1945, a large jar was dug up in Nag Hammadi. Inside the jar were 700 pages of Coptic – Egyptian Christian Gnostic works – written by groups of Gnostic Christian sects living between the two centuries after the birth of Christ. The Gnostics synchronised peacefully the beliefs of unorthodox Jews, Greeks and Persians, and based their good and moral lives on gnosis – knowledge of the true nature of things. This greatly troubled the Christians of that time; St Paul was especially opposed to Gnosticism.

In spite of this, many Gnostics were devout Christians. One highly significant document found in the jar at Nag Hammadi turned out to be another gospel: the Gospel of Thomas. This gospel is truly authentic, written at the same time as the traditional Four Gospels, either rejected by the Church as heretical or, more likely, kept secret by the Gnostic sect which probably used it as the basis of their practice. To me, this gospel shows the real Jesus, full of profound and mystical sayings, transformed by a new and moving language. For instance, Jesus said,

If they say to you, 'From whence have you come?' – say to them, 'We have come from the light, the place where the light came into existence, through itself alone.' If they say to you, 'Who are you?' – say, 'We are his sons and we are the elect of the living Father.' If they ask you, 'What is the sign of your Father who is within you' – say to them, 'It is a movement and a rest.'

The place where the light came into existence seems to echo what Eckardt calls 'the spark in the soul which neither time nor space touches, and through itself alone seems to be about the mystery, the source and the origin'.

The final phrase, that the sign of the Father within is both a movement and a rest, reflects the letting-go of Taoism which says, 'The way to use life is to do nothing through acting. The way to use life is to do everything through being.' A wonderful understanding came to me on hearing the disciples' question: 'On what day will the rest of the dead take place?' And, 'On what day does the new world come?' 'And He said to them, 'That rest which you are awaiting has come, but you do not recognise it' – meaning that life is rest when I stop myself seeking, when I forget myself and merge with all life, a true at-one-ment and a wonder of existence to which I have not yet opened my eyes.

Another time, the disciples asked, 'When will the kingdom come?' And He answered, 'It will not come by expectation. They will not say, 'See here' or 'See there.' But the kingdom of the Father is spread upon the earth, and men do not see it.' In other words, there will be no sudden arrival of the Kingdom that will transform the earth; instead, we must open our eyes to that which is spread before us, and see the wonder of God's Kingdom in all creation. He says again, 'I am the light which is over everything. I am the All; from me the All has gone forth, and to me the All has returned. Split wood, I am there. Lift up the stone, and you will find me there.' As the completed All as enlightenment itself, Jesus is present everywhere – in wood and under stones. 'In all things, I am scattered, and from wherever you wish, you collect me.' Wonderful! And, 'Let him who seeks, not cease from seeking until he finds, and when he finds, he will be troubled; and when he has been troubled, he will marvel, and then he will reign over the All.' This is a wonderful description of the journey; so often there is a time of doubt, stress, confusion, trouble – but there's also wonder and marvel which carry us forward, and without which, we cannot make progress.

In Thomas's Gospel, Jesus also says, "If those who lead you say to you, 'See – the Kingdom is in heaven,' then the birds of the heaven will precede you. If they say to you, 'It is in the sea,' then the fish will precede you. But the Kingdom is within you and without you. If you will know yourselves, then you will be known; and you will know that you are the sons of the living Father. But if you do not know yourselves, then you are in poverty, and you are poverty.' It is rare indeed to find this teaching in the churches. He said the Kingdom is within and all around you – but you are a part of it now, so if you make the effort to know your true self, which is beyond the range of the ego, you will find this Kingdom, and you will be one with God. This means finding an awareness which is deeper than the emotions, and a sense of timelessness which is beyond the intellect. So we have both to reach up and reach down for enlightenment. There is a great difference between knowing *about* God, and being able to say, 'Now I *know*' or 'This is *it*'. And without such knowing, we are trapped in superficiality, swayed every which way by all the different opinions we hear.

Jesus seems to me to state this very clearly. But it is only Buddhism and some independent spiritual teachers who give their followers any practical exercises to further their awareness of the true self and its close relationship with God. This was the Jesus I was looking for, a man who was the embodiment of enlightenment and who saw the sacredness of everything, even wood and stones. He was not conventionally Jewish; He would challenge any of the old laws if He thought they were spiritually destructive. He helped a woman on the Sabbath, and was frequently found in the company of the outcasts and people who were poor, mad or sick. Totally committed to God as He was, He felt the luminous presence of God directing all His actions. The sole purpose of His teaching was to show everyone how they could share this enlightenment. To me, he affirmed that life was for living. The narrow-minded called Him a glutton and a wine-bibber, particularly when the wine ran out at the wedding and He made an even better brew.

I find this person infinitely more attractive than the usual solemn, unsmiling, somewhat sickly, conventional portrayal – so holy and so pious that any close personal relationship with Him would be blasphemous and totally unthinkable. There is still a great mystery about Jesus however, and this mystery has inspired some of the greatest art, music and literature ever created – where He is shown

313

more as Christ the Way rather than Jesus the sociable and welcoming man.

Many Catholic Christians believe that Jesus Christ contains the whole explanation of existence, not as an historical figure but as the spirit of the universe – what we call the cosmic Christ. Being both a scientist and a priest, Teilhard de Chardin expresses this cosmic sense well in his book Let Me Explain:

Once we make up our minds to take the words of revelation literally, then the whole mass of the universe is gradually bathed in light. And just as science shows us that the lower limits of matter, and the ethereal fluid in which everything is immersed, and from which everything emerges, so at the upper limits of spirit, a mystical ambience appears, in which everything floats and everything converges.

However, my own spiritual quest had barely begun. I still felt there was much more to true awareness of this coming home to my real self, this realisation of my own sacred unity with God and the All.

I realised that a great stumbling-block in the way of my personal enlightenment was my usual ordinary self, a self full of likes and dislikes, and worst of all, the intolerant judgements I was making all the time. Just looking at someone on TV would immediately bring forth a judgement. 'Doesn't she realise how fat that dress makes her look?' or 'If he says, "You know" once more, I shall scream.' Or, on meeting a large over-friendly dog walking across the common, 'People shouldn't be allowed to have dogs they can't control,' while scrubbing angrily at the muddy footprints on my clean white trousers.

I saw that I used the same negative energy about upsetting events, mulling them over in my mind, and altering them, so that in my re-creation, I came out of these situations as the victor, with everyone else reduced to the incompetents I felt they were. I would repeat over and over in my mind the clever repartee I could have used, so that my mind became clogged with these excessive remarks, leaving no room for any positive, compassionate, loving attitudes towards my fellow human beings. I realised that much of my time and energy was being wasted in this way and could be diverted into improving myself.

The great teachers all stress kindness and compassion at all times – and this is the key to making life easier instead of difficult. It needs to be extended towards oneself as well, so that when the casserole burns, instead of being angry and frustrated and feeling a failure, one accepts it as a fact: it's happened, and all that can be done about it is to buy a kitchen timer, and rustle up some beans on toast. The acceptance of fact of past transgression against ourselves makes us able to see them more objectively, with less self-pity, and eventually to let them go. Most people behave badly just like the rest of us. I realised that other people's small idiosyncrasies were not really my business. All that is asked of me is to be kind and compassionate and relate to them with warmth and understanding. We always have a choice – to be right, or to be kind. So – choose kind.

I realised that this true sense of 'I' was a mystery to me; I was always too conscious of the people around me and was much too anxious to please and to agree with them. It's very true that if you need or constantly seek approval, you weaken your spiritual strength. I had no confidence in myself or in my own opinion, and was easily influenced by the more self-assured. Consequently, I felt a total lack of control over the apparently random happenings in my life. There is a Tibetan maxim which says, 'When a king is on his throne, his courtiers come to him. But if he gets off his throne and follows any of them, he loses it.'

Hindus speak of God as 'the self', the awareness of which is a feeling of having come home, a realisation of one's own sacred being-ness. After a while, I came to see that the 'I' that was so occupied with people, and their opinions and the various upsetting events of my life, was not only different but also less important than the true 'I' within myself. This is what is called self-realisation. Everyone is the Self, and is infinite. But we all mistake the physical body for the Self – it is consciousness that is the Self, so that no-one is ever away from It.

Once we remove the belief that I am my body, or I have not realised myself, then only supreme consciousness remains. As Simone Weil says in Gravity & Grace,

We live in a world of unreality and dreams. To give up our imaginary position as the centre, to renounce it, not only intellectually but in the imaginative part of our soul, that means to awaken to what is real and eternal, to see the true light and hear the true sounds. A transformation then takes place at the very roots of our sensibility, in our immediate reception of sense impressions and psychological impressions. It is a transformation analogous to that which takes place in the dusk of evening on a road, where we suddenly discern as a tree what we had at first sight seen as a stooping man, or where we suddenly recognise the rustling of leaves what we thought at first was whispering voices. We see the same colours, we hear the same sounds, but not in the same way.

So how to achieve this state of permanent quiet awareness? The obstacles seem too numerous to ever overcome. They live in our human reactions to events and people, our expectations and our insensitivity. For instance, we never really look at things properly, even something as mundane as a table can convey a sense of wonder and of mystery. Touching the wood, feeling the grain, appreciating the lines of its utilitarian form – all give a sense of space and constant admiration. It is possible to live life like a constant sacrament by having a reverence for everything we touch, see and do: embracing a tree, watching fire, admiring the sheen of rain on pebbles, watching the birds, arranging flowers, cooking creatively, watching the moon rise behind the cherry trees in blossom – all the simple significant things of life in which we can see Paradise. Matthew Fox, the Domincan scholar, puts it succintly in Original Blessing:

To live is not merely to survive. Living implies beauty, freedom of choice, discipline, celebration. What has been most lacking in society and religion in the West for the past six centuries has been a *via positiva*, a way or path of affirmation, thanksgiving, ecstasy – of life, not death; of awareness, not numbness; of loving, not control. This growing sensitivity is part of the process of evolving from a person who's controlled by his five senses to someone who becomes multi-sensory and is aware of their intuition, their hunches, if you like; their more subtle awareness.

Before I became aware of this more subtle consciousness, I felt terribly alone in the threatening and purely physical universe. Through the teachings of Jesus and my many other beloved teachers, I am now aware that I am never alone; I am part of an intelligent, compassionate, living universe that is a production of the souls that share it. It is a school where everything that happens to me is a lesson for me to learn, or an experience for my soul to have. I realise my enormous responsibility to this universe and everything in it, because everything I do, say or think, affects not only me, but every other soul that shares the universe with me.

I realise that I have a soul, or a higher self, but as a human being, I also have a personality which is temporary but helps me – but it will die when my body dies. Every minute I am making decisions, choosing what I will do, and these choices are affecting my soul's progress. My personality is deciding whether I will be angry, afraid, lonely, cynical, vengeful, hateful, sorrowful, or full of shame. It is deciding whether to exploit, manipulate or judge others, or to seek power over them. I can also choose to be loving, kind, compassionate, and wise in my dealings with others, but these choices come from the soul, that part of me which is immortal, and not limited to the five senses, like the personality. As I gradually extended my five senses, I began to be aware of the effects that different emotions produced in me, and to recognise that if I could harness my soul to my personality, I would really begin to make progress along this rocky road towards self-realisation – the goal of our existence and the reason for our being on earth.

By this time, I also began to be interested in karma. Most people believe that we have only one lifetime for the soul to evolve and nothing of ourselves lasts beyond that lifetime. I had always questioned the point of babies dying, infants and young children, teenagers, and young people – indeed, my own husband. What chance of soul-progress did they have? So it seems logical to assume that the soul needs to incarnate many times to attain wholeness. I do not know beyond all doubt, but I believe that the soul has no beginning and no end, and moves towards perfection. In a perfected human being, it is impossible to see where the personality ends and the soul begins, because the personality is located in the body, both of which come to an end when the body dies. But the soul goes on, I believe, back to its immortal state of unbounded love and compassion.

I believe there are many incarnations of the soul, each having a different body, with its own unique personality in order that the soul may evolve towards wholeness. During these many lives, we may experience many forms – a mother, a father, a son, a daughter, a teacher, a priest, a soldier, and so on. We may struggle with many emotions (anger, love, fear, loss, jealousy, courage, despair and vulnerability), and we may have very different physical characteristics (strong or weak body, a placid or nervous disposition, a black, brown,

317

yellow or white skin, be physically attractive in the eyes of the world). All these attributes are suited to that particular soul's progress.

Karma is the Indian name of a venerable doctrine which states when we injure others, the injury is inevitably reflected back to ourselves, whereas when we benefit others, that benefit will inevitably return to us. The Indian sages could not understand the perplexing problems with inequality in the character and circumstances of human beings. By intense concentration, they came to discern a certain rhythm at work beneath the incessant ebb and flow of life's fortunes. This philosophy is backed scientifically by Newton's third law of motion: for every action there is a reaction which is equal and opposite.

Science has also discovered that all life is ultimately unitary. The unity of the universe is the fundamental law of its being. All the sciences touch each other at some point, and none can stand alone. The law of evolution reveals that life is a continuation of all that has gone before. We are linked in a long series; we begin as primal molecules, and end as an extremely complex human being. We keep going towards an unseen goal because we feel the need for completion. What a long way we have already travelled from primeval mud to our present selves, but we have to travel further. I think that at the end of the journey we make the sublime discovery that man is no mere cipher, no glorified ape in a dangerous and meaningless jungle, but part of a blessed and divine reality.

Another scientific principle is that energy is indestructible, however much it changes form. In the same way, human thoughts and actions are energies, which are not destroyed but reappear in the form of their effects, not only upon others but also on ourselves. They are like seeds which sprout eventually in the manifestation of time and space. The doctrine of heredity could suggest that the body has had some kind of existence before birth, and similarly so has the mind. In fact, transmissive mental characteristics could have been derived from a former earthly existence. Newton's law of equal returns also appears in the world of ethics. Whatever we do unto others is returned to us in some way at some time. Life pays us back in our own coin. Be sure your sins will find you out. And the good deeds we do foreshadow the good fortune we shall reap eventually. As we sow, so also shall we reap and our misdeeds find us out ...

Living Alone

Life alone need not necessarily be a life apart from other people, as separation due to feelings of inferiority, fear or dislike. It can be a life dedicated to the service of mankind and the development of the individual to the peak of his spiritual awareness. In this state of excellence, he can both commune with God and be the servant of God in the world. 'We should not so much seek the answers as live the questions' (Rilke). I do not believe in blind chance; I think we go through the apparently fortuitous circumstances of our lives as a testing-ground or a place of experience, to further develop our personalities. Some of us need isolation in order to grow in authenticity, so that we become less dependent on the whims and fashions of the society around us. The period in the wilderness does at least help us to get our priorities right; the things we assume to be essential, like the constant company of other people, their approval, our own reputation amongst those whom the world considers important and the number of important people we know, dissolve like a mist of unreality. It can be a revelation in restricted circumstances how simple life can be when social conformity and manners have been stripped away. At first, life seems too unbearable to confront, but suddenly it widens into a prospect of inner freedom – maybe the first opportunity to really be oneself since one was a very small child. This self is in fact a central point within, a secret place which is the foundation stone on which the whole person is built.

To live life in its fulness in the way Jesus came to fulfil life (John 10:10) is to be fully oneself and to flow out to every circumstance and event in one's life with confident anticipation and joy. A full life need not be filled with constant entertainment in order to eradicate boredom and to disguise the gaping void of inner futility. This is in fact a way of escaping and evading the questions of meaning and destiny that lie behind the diverting façade of life. The full life is one in which we are completely open to the present moment, and instead of seeking distractions to cover our fear and inadequacy, we give ourselves to that moment. This is the inner experience that Jesus demonstrated during the whole of His life among us. 'I and the Father are one' (John 10:30). It is impossible to be lonely and depressed when we are relating purposefully to life in whatever circumstances we find ourselves. The need for diversions, hobbies, even holidays and friendships, fade away because all of these are found in and around us at all times. This is not to suggest that when we live the full life we are above personal relationships – far from it: we are in such a deep, indeed perfect, relationship with all things that every part of creation is a friend to us, and everything we do is to the glory of God and the benefit of our fellows. In the words of St Paul, 'The life I live is no longer my life but the life Christ lives in me' (Galatians 2:20). When we need people around us we have a lack that cannot easily be fulfilled. Many so-called friends in worldly relationships flinch from us when we are in pain and distress, because we threaten them with a burden of caring and commitment that they feel unable to carry out. But when we are full of the life that springs eternally from the depths of our being, all those around us are revitalised and renewed by our presence; we are in communion with all life. The fulness of life that comes to us when we are open to all that the present moment can give is like the living water that Jesus spoke of to the Samaritan woman: it will turn into 'a spring inside us welling up to eternal life' (John 4:14). How can we find this life of abundance in which we are so filled with the Spirit of God that we are in eternal communion with all created things? We can be sure of God's grace and presence because of His nature which is love.

But freely available love cannot be demanded or grasped: it can only be welcomed. The inherent courtesy of God is such that He does not force Himself on mankind; if He were to do this, He would annul the basis of freewill that He has given to us. He stands at the door and knocks patiently for admittance. The sovereignty of the human soul to what is His own domain is acknowledged. We in turn must respect the presence of God and treat Him with reciprocated courtesy. If He is grasped, He recedes and we find only a shadow of His presence with us. If there is only one action that the will can take in the soul's communion with God, it is open acceptance. This is the free giving up of oneself to God – heart, soul, mind and strength. All that is now in and of oneself is now also in God, and the two are one. Then we are filled with the divine essence and our life is no longer selfish and isolated, but is indeed the life that Christ lives in us.

It is very difficult to contemplate God when we have not seen an image of what we think of as God. We come close to this image when we are aware of the divine presence in our soul and in the world around us. But even the mystic recognises the enormous expanse of spiritual light that separates the creature from the Creator. St John reminds us in 1 John 4: 20, 'If a man says, I love God, whilst hating his brother, he is a liar. If he does not love the brother whom he has seen, it cannot be that he loves God whom he has not seen.' This means that we must start by devoting ourselves to the things in hand at the present moment, because God shows His eternal presence by the love He bestows on all His creatures. We should be aware of the things that confront us minute by minute in the day's work, give them our total attention, and be grateful for them however humble they may be. This gratitude should embrace the One by whom all things are created, the creature itself, and the gift of being able to respond with a healthy body and alert mind to all the many wonderful things we meet every day of our lives. Jesus tells us plainly that unless we become like children, we cannot enter the Kingdom of Heaven. We have to accept the Kingdom of Heaven like a child (Mark 10:15). A small child does not have such spiritual gifts as charity, wisdom, selflessness, or devotion to God. All these qualities have to be learned in the experience of life. But the child does have the one thing necessary for salvation: an open mind, innocent of dogmatism, arrogance and cynicism. Its mind is clear of subversive thoughts and therefore immediately receptive to the wonders of each present moment. The little child sees everything in the aura of exquisite uniqueness: everything is a new creation. Watch a toddler exploring for five minutes and see the truth of these words. If we as adults are to move towards this heavenly kingdom, we must give up our attitude of bored indifference to the things around us. When we return to the simple receptivity of a little child, every encounter has new possibilities, and the most amazing things in the world are seen to be the simplest, and God is constantly making all things new (Rev 21:5). This is both a glimpse of the ultimate transformation of the world and the confirmation of the never-ceasing renewal of nature by divine love. Thus each moment has its own validity and is quite unlike the one that preceded it to the person that is spiritually aware, and can take each moment as it comes with confidence and expectancy.

A child sees the constancy of God's eternal providence and at the same time waits in eager expectation of some new event that proclaims the unfolding of God's purpose in the world. By a deeper knowledge, we are allowed to glimpse that this purpose is the raising up of all life to immortality, in that through resurrection, there will be eternal fellowship of all created things. Contemplating the present scene consists of two reciprocal actions: attention and blessing. The way of attention means that we must have a receptive and welcoming attitude towards the matter in hand. The way of blessing is the giving of oneself as a living sacrifice to the world around us. We must welcome the world with enthusiasm and then offer ourselves in its service – and none of this is easy. When we bless something, we pour out our inner essence in love and prayer onto it, with the hope that something of the divine may rest on it and transform it. The act of blessing is an inner attitude rather than an outer ritual; if it becomes obligatory to be bestowed on everything and everybody, it soon becomes an intolerable burden. To bless means to send out goodwill to everyone one meets during the day. When the true spirit of goodwill flows out from the depths of one's being to another person, one begins to know him or her, not as someone to be analysed or manipulated, but as a true brother or sister whom it is a privilege to know and to help. In other words, the blessing that comes from God brings a deep fellowship of souls in which all are one in the power of divine intelligence, which leads us to the truth of the situation and illuminates the way of progress to full humanity.

Goodwill is the beginning of a changed attitude to our fellow human beings and to the world. Initially, it shows itself as the ability to respond in blessing to any creature, be it plant, animal or human being – but this must be realised in actions that result in healing the injured and binding up the broken-hearted. If goodwill is not merely a complacent attitude, devoid of commitment to those in need, it will show itself in giving up time and leisure to the benefit of all those who are in difficulties, especially those who are in psychic and spiritual distress. This provides a significant starting-point in the life of anyone obliged to live alone. What might easily turn into a solitary isolated existence can be transformed into a life devoted to others. If you live alone in awareness and contemplation, you will eventually know your vocation in the ministry of healing and reconciliation, because living alone provides an excellent means of being available to many people in need. However, it must be emphasised that this eventual availability is the result of a long, bitter and exhaustive encounter with your inner nature and a slow working out of personal difficulties and inadequacies. But the end is an emergence, strengthened but scarred by suffering, from the depths of dereliction – a testimony that the battle with the dark forces within has been fought and won. If you simply offer yourself to others in order to evade your own inner silence, than you will use people rather than help them. This kind of encounter will degenerate into gossip and mischief-making; this is always a hazard for those of us who live alone, since we have fewer family interests to occupy our time and attention. The way of gossip is the antithesis of the abundant life, because it is a means of escaping from the real demands of life into a secluded realm where one can look down on other people, and criticise their weaknesses with malice and jealousy. When we are dissatisfied and unhappy, there is nothing we enjoy more than reducing other people to our own level of misery. It is such a relief to most of us to know that our heroes also have feet of clay, and that even the acknowledged masters of the spiritual life can be cut down to size by inside information about their private lives. The effect of this attitude does not hurt the victim nearly as much as the one who has cast a stone, because the tendency to gossip, which moves subtly to vicious mischief-making, prevents the spiritual growth of the mischief-maker. When Jesus was disgraced and in the hands of His adversaries, even His disciples wanted to have as little to do with Him as possible during the final hours of his mortal life, whilst the majority rejoiced in the humiliation of yet another alleged Messiah. How delighted they were at His impotence on the Cross! If the summit of all human aspiration proves to be only a flat mediocrity; then we too are exonerated from making any special effort to become a real person. This view of life is parodied in the advice, 'Let us eat and drink, for tomorrow we die' (1 Corinthians 15:32). This is the logical conclusion of those who work to demolish everything that is noble and inspiring – everything that lifts the common man above the limitations of his own ego, and gives him a fleeting vision of true reality.

This true reality is a life of abundance; we give thanks for the blessings that surround us and we bless all the things that we meet. It is hard to bless an unpleasant trait or attitude that disturbs our inner composure and our relationships with other people. But until we accept every part of our personality as ourselves, rejecting nothing and holding everything as equally valuable, we will be at constant war with the aspects of our own nature. Jesus said that we should love our enemies and pray for those who are spiteful towards us, which means that we should not resist evil – and this applies especially to the things in ourselves that are distorted and disturbed. Only when they are brought out and recognised can they be progressively healed and eventually play their full part in our work in the world. This is the way to a peaceful society but we can never impose outer peace on those around us whilst we ourselves are in a state of internal disorder. The psychic rapport that binds us all together in one entity is so weak that we tend to live fragmented lives. We are so often in conflict with ourselves that we cannot respond openly to other people, and the vibes that we give off are disruptive to the peace of the group to which we belong. However, conflict itself is an important part of growth. When everything is smooth and harmonious there seems to be little progress – but true harmony flourishes when conflicts can be synthesised into a new understanding of reality. Conflict becomes demonic in those situations where the opponents seek to destroy each other, but where conflicting points-of-view can be surveyed with detachment, fresh light can be shed on a confusing situation, and everybody involved with the situation can grow in tolerance and understanding. Those who live alone have an opportunity to grow into deeper self-knowledge, which enables them to be agents of reconciliation with those who are so obsessed with their own point-of-view that they are unable to appreciate any other approach to the truth.

Living alone can make the many-faceted diamond of truth more understandable, because it brings with it an attitude of non-attachment to the passing scenes of life and a greater awareness of living constructively. It is an ability to view the wood of life as something greater than the trees of individual desires, possessions and power, and to move beyond to an awareness of all that is worthwhile in the world: its freshness, its beauty, its constant variety, and its day-to-day challenge to move forwards into fresh fields of human endeavour. The person who lives from the inner secret place within is one from whom true healing can pour out, not only onto his fellow-being but also onto all life. This is the inner meaning: we do not have to do anything so much as to be in continued communion with that which is – God, Divine Intelligence, the Infinite, Cosmic Consciousness, etc. – whatever describes this power most clearly to you. On the surface, we all know that personal relationships are the very stuff of life; we were never meant to be alone, even when we are obliged to live alone. But as long as our bond with our fellows is one merely of necessity – that is, in order to escape from loneliness – we shall never know personal freedom, and we shall keep our companions in bondage to ourselves. There is no true relationship between people who are bound in ties of mutual dependence, because each will try to please the other until the situation becomes unbearable and a complete break may be inevitable. This is the love-hate relationship that prevents so many of us from reaching inner maturity. Instead of following diligently their own path to salvation, they are bound in emotional servitude to those whom they both admire and fear, and whose influence is both stimulating and stultifying. It is only when we have learned how to let another person go that we can begin to love that person even beyond the limits of this mortal life. Love and freedom are indivisible. We can give ourselves freely to the beloved, even to the sacrifice of our own life, only when we are a free agent. Even in the depths of a foul prison we can still be free in the secret place of the soul, and from this oasis of liberty we can give support to those around us in love, and to those far away in thought and prayer.

In the Song of Solomon 8:6-7, we read: 'For love is strong as death, passion cruel as the grave. It blazes up like blazing fire, fiercer than any flame. Many waters cannot quench love, no floods can sweep it away. If a man were to offer for love the whole wealth of his house, it would be utterly scorned.' This passage describes the tempestuous passion between two lovers at the height of their relationship, and how wonderful it is to experience. But when the ardour cools, the more enduring tender love warms their souls, so that they can be together in silent communion without the need for constant reassurance of their mutual support. To know this love is the purpose of our life in the world – its origin and its end – the love that God bestows upon us. Its whole purpose is to bring all created things into the furnace of love where their dross is refined, so that their essence may be brought into the divine presence and transfigured. Those who live alone have a special burden of love to carry since they are likely to be free from the demands of a close relationship with one particular person. Therefore they are available to enter into a deep relationship with a number of very different types of people. When what you prize most is taken from you, you are perhaps for the first time in your life free to relate to many things which previously you had dismissed out of hand.

The inner purpose of a life lived apparently alone is to live in the midst of many people whom one previously would hardly ever have noticed, let alone approached, in a spirit of friendship. We seldom undertake renunciation of our own freewill; more often it is thrust upon us. The things of life that are most valued are suddenly taken away and we are left alone; misfortune strikes suddenly and with it go all our illusions about security founded on ownership. The bottomless pit that bereavement exposes is a stark reminder of the vital part one person plays in our life when he or she is gone; our life has no meaning and there is no longer any incentive to do anything any more. All the money in the world cannot give us health – bodily, mental or spiritual – without which we cannot attain true satisfaction in any aspect of our lives.

And the third requirement for fulfilment is the work we do and the material security we enjoy. To live without having work to do is an experience that an increasing number of people are going through as the tragedy of unemployment affects more and more of the global population. Therefore, even if our material wants are satisfied, our worth as human beings is undermined when we have no useful place in society. A person with dignity is closely related to their ability to contribute to the world through service and creativity. Once we have no useful role to play, we undergo an inner disintegration that eventually ruins our personality. But even in an affluent society, the inroads of physical ageing as well as the claims of younger people make retirement from work a social as well as a personal necessity. However, it is important to accept the situation without looking back with regret to the past. A new way of life has dawned and we must move decisively into the future. The secret is to live in the moment and let the apparently menacing loneliness of the future take care of itself. As we progress through this testing life-experience, we begin to realise that we ourselves are not entirely responsible for our own existence. Certainly, we are responsible for our actions but it seems to me that there is a much greater plan at work than we, with our limited vision, can understand. I find I play my part by doing my best minute-by-minute in the ever-changing flux of my life; my more distant needs seem to be provided for in ways that are beyond my comprehension. Obviously, I am not doing my best for all of my minutes – would that I were! We acknowledge this mysterious fact of life intuitively when we believe that all will be well in the end, provided we do our best and trust in God. This is more than a passive belief that God will make everything safe and happy for us. That is childish irresponsibility that could lead to disaster. To trust

God means remembering God's Spirit not only in times set aside for meditation, prayer and healing, but also when we are in the midst of life's battles. To remember God in our work, we need to do everything to His power and glory, and to see the nameless Christ in the face of the stranger we meet in the street and at the place of work. To me, the most convincing and sublime of all the resurrection appearances is in Luke 24:13-32, where the risen Lord appears to a group of disciples walking along the road to Emmaus. He seems to be a stranger who grudgingly imparts to them the teachings of eternal life as they listen to Him in rapt attention. Later, they share a meal with Him, and when He breaks the bread and says the blessing, their inner eyes are opened and at last they see Him as their Lord. When we give ourselves fully to the moment in hand, God is with us also, and our trust in His providence is the height of wisdom. We attain peace, and are able to do the work for which we were called. When our first allegiance is to God His love fills us, and we give that love to all around us.

The most poignant renunciation that most of us have to make follows the death of a loved one. We are stripped of a sustaining relationship with the beloved person and from henceforth we have to live on our own. There is a considerable difference between the life of a person who has always lived alone, either from choice or necessity, and the life of one who has been enclosed in a loving relationship only to be suddenly stripped of it and left on their own. The wrenching apart of an old attachment and the void of loneliness that gapes in front of one can be unbearable. It is well-known that a bereaved person requires at least 2-3 years of adjustment before he comes even remotely to himself again. The removal of a beloved companion renders life meaningless for a considerable time, because to be tolerable, life must have purpose to give it meaning. The human mind cannot tolerate meaninglessness because a meaningless life has a quality of non-existence that seems worse than death itself. Death is the great unknown experience which may conceivably open up a new vista of fulfilment, whereas the interminable misery of a mortal life that is purposeless and devoid of growth can scarcely be contemplated in normal consciousness.

How can we continue to live in such circumstances? This is the valley of the shadow of death so aptly described in Psalm 23 – cold and featureless. But until we know its contours and features as we know our own domain, we have not tasted life fully. The result is a changed person, who lives a transformed life, whose perspectives are no longer limited to human objectives but are infused with divine aspiration. Such a one becomes a servant of God and shows this in unceasing self-giving to his fellow human beings. It is vital to recognise that the past is behind us and that life continues; in relation to bereavement it is necessary to leave the dead to 'bury the dead' and to continue to live a meaningful life here and now in the present. This does not mean forgetting the loved one or never speaking about them. My own husband is as real to me today as he was when he lived and was with me in his physical body half a century ago. Not a day goes by without my making an allusion to him, either mentally or verbally. Indeed, I'm sure my thoughts are of great importance to him and the progress of his soul. But I think he should be allowed to make this progress in his own way, without being constantly pestered by my attempts to communicate with him and to hold him back with me.

Clinging to the past is a very good way of thwarting my own growth and his also. I think that possessive memory can prevent the soul growth of those to whom it attaches itself. We see this principle operating in the world today when a parent continues to keep his or her grown-up children as helpless infants who are still totally dependent. Hence the relationship between parents and children continues to be abrasive until the parents have grown up and realised that their children are individuals in their own right, and not extensions of the parent's personality. They have their own destinies to fulfil, and one of their functions is to guide their parents into an understanding of renunciation which alone will lead to fulfilling relationship with them, the children. When we see our role in this life as one of stewardship of all the world's resources, we are approaching a mature understanding of the meaning and purpose of our very brief and transient mortal existence. The custody we show to the earth's bounty and on those closest to us is the way to regeneration and transfiguration. Of course, the memories of warm companionship and intimate bliss will recur as old associations come to mind: the empty chair, the single ticket, the journey taken alone, and a time of unassuageable grief plunges us into the hell of silent despair. The ache of a soul bereft of its companion is like an unending dirge to which the dark foreboding of the barren future adds its gloom. We know how deeply the wound has penetrated and how far it is from being healed. Indeed, it can never be obliterated;

the scar will always remain, even in the midst of future joy. It is a part of our experience and is deeply engraved on the soul. But our soul's pain is the only way of entering the pain of all our fellow men, as the wounds of Jesus are a testimony to His presence: 'In truth, I tell you, in very truth, the man who does not enter into the sheepfold by the door but climbs in some other way, is nothing but a thief and a robber; but the man who enters by the door is the shepherd in charge of the sheep' (John 10:1-2). Christ as the True Shepherd knows His sheep because He has entered their souls and recognises their troubles. So it is when we have experienced the hell of loss and persevered through the arid wilderness of bereavement. When we reach the other side, or come to ourselves after the illusions of the past have been stripped away, we are able to comfort and heal those who still remain in agony. We are free to enter into the depths of all suffering when we have come to terms with something that is irreparable, like the enforced loss of a loved one or a bodily function or limb, permanently ruined by disease or an accident. No one who is human is foreign to it; it is only those who have been cleansed of all conceit, of all vanity based on physical, intellectual or psychic gifts, all illusions of personal ownership, indeed all clinging to possessions, who can find a place through the small gate onto the narrow road that leads to the life abundant. This is the crucial lesson of loss: the bitter fruit of bereavement which, once tasted, becomes sweet with the promise of universal healing.

'Enter by the narrow gate. The gate is wide that leads to perdition, and there is plenty of room on that road, and many go that way. But the gate that leads to life is small and the road is narrow, and those who find it are few' (Matthew 7:13-14). When we have lost that which seemed to be vital for our well-being – indeed, our very existence – we come eventually to recognise the unassailable reality within ourselves that endures all outer storms. It is like a rock planted deep within the soul on which we can lay our weary heads and rest. When we know this rest, we do not concern ourselves with the unknown troubled future, troubled through the perversity of man's actions in various dark psychic courses; instead, we can live constantly in the present. This is the only way we can contribute constructively to our own future and that of mankind, so that divine peace may begin to calm the troubled psychic currents around us, and so bring release to the misguided minds of men. Ultimately, the mortal mind has to accept its childlike ignorance about the things of eternity, and to rest in faith on the hidden reality of divine intelligence. We cannot recapture that which has passed beyond our mortal limitation, but if we are still and give ourselves wholly to the moment at hand, our loved ones will commune with us in the life beyond death, and what they reveal is both a comfort and strength. Paradoxically, this is also true of those who have lost some physical function, whether sight, hearing or mobility. As long as they fight desperately to retain the power that is waning, they will be imprisoned in their impotence and raging futility against their misfortune. But once they accept their new life of physical limitation with grace and childlike trust, so will new spiritual faculties be revealed in them. These spiritual faculties were always there of course, but were disregarded in the bustle of everyday life where the things of the Spirit amount to nothing. When an athlete is permanently crippled by a serious accident, his old life is over. All that remains are painful though precious memories of past triumphs; but if, like Chris Reeve who played Superman, he proceeds with courage into a future apparently devoid of any further use for himself now that his talents are destroyed, he may develop a compassion for others that was previously eclipsed by his own prowess and reputation. Thus he may devote the remainder of his life to caring for the disabled and the disowned, so that they may attain the bodily health and proficiency that he was obliged to surrender.

The ways of God are indeed strange, but their purpose is always the same: to reclaim the lost, to bind up the broken, to heal the sick, and to bring all creatures to an inner peace. In the same way, it is uplifting to sense the calm, placid behaviour of a blind person whose independence is lost, who trusts completely on the guidance of the sighted, including the wonderful companionship of devoted dogs trained by equally dedicated people who love animals. But, as the outer eye fails, the inner eye of knowledge and love may be opened. When Jesus healed the blind man, He opened both the outer and the inner eye of this witness to God's glory. Those sighted witnesses who questioned the blind man's healing remained spiritually blind (John 9). Living alone can remove the scales from the eyes of the soul so that one begins to perceive wisdom that is invisible to those who skim perpetually over the surface of life. To my mind, no experience of aloneness is more isolating than that of deafness. The blind evoke a ready sympathy that is easily aroused, when any aware person will rush to guide and protect. But the deaf tend to bring out the worst in those which whom they try to communicate: irritation, annoyance, ridicule, and eventually avoidance, is all too often the sequence of events. In addition, the deaf are deprived of the beautiful music that lightens the soul's weary burden. Once again, the way forward is to accept the loss, helped of course by the amelioration of modern hearing aids. When we can rest in our present situation, we are granted new powers of perception. The blind person's sense of touch and hearing become unusually acute, as does the deaf person's sight. Both may be aware of unusual psychic sensitivity as well, so that they can pick up the atmosphere of a place or the attitude of a group without any previous knowledge. This happens especially to those who do not hanker after their past way of life, but go forward with faith in the new situation. It is important to face one's defect, wherever its nature, and to talk about it with someone who is both trustworthy and kind. On the other hand, one should be careful not to overwhelm one's closest friends with constant demands for help, since everyone has their limitations. The best way is to be oneself, with courage, even in the deepest despair – then help is more likely to be offered spontaneously and can be accepted with gratitude and dignity. It is important to remember that he who receives help bestows a priceless gift on the one who has given it. The benefits are mutual as they transcend the tyranny of an egocentric world, dominated by rewards and obligations. The binding force of self-revelation is love. Nothing that lives ever stands still. So now I do not try to make contact with my husband through spirit mediums; it would be sad if we stayed in the same state of self-centred limitation after the death of the body. I feel that the advanced soul has far too fine a spiritual radiance to tolerate the coarse vibrations of a human intermediary. On the other hand, it can make its presence felt directly in the mind with such power and penetration that the beloved knows with a certainty beyond rational proof that life continues after death. This communication has mystical overtones as it lifts the bereaved person out of the prison of past memories and present anguish into a realm of pure bliss, where the divine love pours out eternally in the world of fathomless unity.

We gradually learn that day by day we are renewed inwardly although out outer form may be in decay. It seems that in the loss of physical attributes, following illness or ageing, those of us who are still spiritually attuned are given proof of deeper, more enduring spiritual gifts (1 Corinthians 2: 14-16). When the body dies, these spiritual qualities should be so well developed that you can commune with each other and with God directly through the soul, although we no longer have any physical means of communication. Thus the tribulations of this life that cause such agonies of renunciation bear their fruit in a closed, purified personality; that can be an instrument in transforming the society in which we live. The spiritual body emerges from its physical shell as an organ of extreme sensitivity determined by life's vicissitudes and transfigured in the hell of suffering. Only when it has wrestled with the threat of disintegration and prevailed can it claim freedom, not only for itself, but for all that exists. It works towards this freedom by loving all things and giving perpetually of itself to them. It seems almost pre-ordained that those people who are destined to live by themselves for a long time are unduly sensitive people. This sensitivity has two parts: an extreme response to the happenings of the world and a deep inner vulnerability that makes one flinch with pain at the manifest cruelty of society. This vulnerability is not only affected by outer events however; it also registers the deep recurring pain that has built up from past injuries and traumas, and is in psychic communion with the thoughts and emotions of all people. This intimate fellowship also extends from the living to the dead, so that no part of creation is outside its influence. Whilst finer degrees of sensitivity can be seen in some individuals living a communal life of prayer and service, it is in those who spend much of their life alone that the impact of pain from deeper sources than the merely physical impinges most harshly. They have nobody near them to deflect the pain, or a communal social group, where talking together can dilute the awareness of deeper unrest.

The first kind of sensitivity we feel when we are alone is the impact of memories of the past on our present awareness. In general conversation, these memories can be dismissed from the field of consciousness and allowed to dissipate into the unconscious. In due course, they emerge – usually despised as symbols in a dream – where once again they are rapidly dismissed from memory when we awaken. Inevitably however, their psychic charge becomes so loaded that they have to be acknowledged consciously, examined and, hopefully, resolved. We have to examine our past attitudes and actions, and face up to our responsibilities. We have to acknowledge the unpalatable contributions that *we* have made to the misfortunes that dog our lives, and the potential harm *we* have done to others, not only directly but also at a distance – by our lack of charity, and resentment based on jealousy and fear. The essence of healing is acceptance; we cannot accept the unpleasant perverse side of our nature until we fully accept ourselves as we now stand. The self I try to project is the self I would like my friends and the world to believe in. But such a person is artificial and has no intrinsic life in it. It is only when I face the full force of myself, as I now am, that I can rest in myself and give myself wholeheartedly to the divine. Like the apparently worthless publican, one is more acceptable in God's sight than the outwardly worthy Pharisee (Luke 18: 9-14). It is only when we are totally empty of conceit that we are in a state of openness to God's grace. The conventionally religious man is so full of his own piety and good works that he can hide behind them and thus give nothing of himself away at all. Those who believe they have arrived in Heaven are furthest away, especially when their attitude is based on doctrinal rectitude. How many people really *talk with* God? It is so much easier to parrot the words and phrases given to you by someone else because then you don't have to think. The ones who are in Heaven are those who have lost all concern for themselves in their conversations with God, and their service to their fellow men.

In the life apart from others, there is often no one to help with the pains of self-revelation emanating from the unconscious. Sometimes one can become so submerged with the rising memories of first unhappiness that life can become unbearable. When we awaken from sleep in the early morning we barely recognise these fears below the surface of consciousness, that rise up in such terrifying array that our whole mind soon becomes a seething mass of confusion, resentment and hatred against those whom we imagine are taking advantage of us. Sometimes the need to do something to relieve this inner tension is irresistible, and in the heat of such a moment, we may write an abusive letter or make an aggressive and insulting telephone call. It is so important to do and say nothing precipitate during such a paroxysm of emotional anguish. If only we could check ourselves during phases of tempestuous anger; the amount of emotional debris let loose into the psychic atmosphere would be greatly reduced. A clean psychic environment is a prerequisite for a healthy physical world, a world in which the debris of violence and conflict could be kept to a minimum as we learned to live more peaceably together. To check our emotional imbalances does not mean to deny them, let alone suppress them. To do this, we create a mawkish, hypocritical relationship with others, people against whom the honest personality would rebel and cause psychosomatic disorders which could result in serious bodily disease. The important precaution to take against this eventuality is to go into the silence of our own secret place, where we meet with our own particular awareness of God. If we can become aware of our own shortcomings in His manifest presence, they are cleansed of any malign psychic influence, and we are already in the first stages of healing. This principle applies to bereavement. Certainly, we must leave the dead to bury their dead in order to move forward, but it is just as important not to bury our grief, especially during the first two or three years after the death of a loved one. The first anniversary is an all-important shared occasion of particularly painful times. The pent-up emotions associated with such precious memories must be acknowledged and expressed, either through tears or in the silence of solitude, or in verbal venting to a tried and trusted friend or relative. Psychotherapy or bereavement counselling can help here of course, but do choose your therapist carefully; make sure there is a friendly, sympathetic feeling of ease between you.

The sacrament of each present moment includes not only the outer events of life that we are experiencing moment by moment, but also the inner life of the psyche, of which we are aware continually. Beautiful scenery, for instance, not only evokes an intense aesthetic response, but can also recall a past rapture with someone who has either died or moved away to another part of the world. These two emotional impulses coming together have the effect of a sublime grasp of reality, where the transience of physical beauty is linked with the deepening of eternal life. Because that which is beautiful and noble outlasts its physical form, but remains an inspiration to all who eventually pass along the way.

When we really live in the present moment and give our life to the passing scene, we add our own unique flavour to that moment and that scene, so that both the world and ourselves are blessed. It is in these passing moments of heightened awareness like those following the sensitive appreciation of the transience of all worldly beauty, that we are transported to an awareness of the mystical union that underlies all earthly creation. We know that death is not the end of life, but rather a moment of passage to a more spiritual dimension of reality. This spiritual life is one in which the deep core of inner discontent, with its additional burdens and sorrows of the past, is continuously encountered, explored and transmuted. This journey is also the journey deep into the psyche: the way up is the way down, and Heaven can never be reached until Hell has been recognised and reclaimed. The Harrowing of Hell which Jesus undertook after the Crucifixion was the final work He did on the astral plane before His Resurrection. It is important to note that He was closely involved in the work of Hell right from His baptism when the Holy Spirit descended upon Him and led Him out into the wilderness, which we call the world, to be tempted by every dark force in creation. Each temptation had to be met without flinching, be recognised for what it was, and be embraced in love. All of us are inhabitants of Hell for some period of our lives, and it is only through love that we are cleansed and our purpose renewed. Only that which is explored and accepted, can be changed by the power of love. In this light, there is physical radiance, mental illumination, emotional unburdening, and spiritual transparency. By love alone is the evil brought to the good, and death raised up to eternal life. So the increased sensitivity of the person living alone makes one more able to intercept the dark forces that pervade the cosmos. As we enter the spiritual realm of light, so we can accept all pain and evil, and act as an agent to convert the powerful and negative influence of malice and fear into the warm radiance of recognition and blessing – and this is the very antithesis or pouring out one's anguish and venom on everyone in the vicinity. These destructive emotions cause a general upheaval in relationship and release negative fears and distrust. The power of positive thinking emphasises the importance of our thoughts, not only as they affect our own lives, but also their effect on the psychic environment we share with those around us, and indeed the world. However, the good effected by these superficially articulated thoughts regarding evil and our misfortunes is seldom profound, because these thoughts come from the ego rather than from the depths of the self. It is what comes out of the inner depths of a person that affects him and those around him. 'As a man thinks in his heart, so is he' (Proverbs 23:7). The 'heart' in this case is the deep unconscious layer of the mind which contains many emotional memories of past unhappiness, and it is these thoughts that have to be exposed, relived and accepted before they can be healed – and integrated successfully into the personality. Only then can positive thinking be undertaken in the spirit of authentic belief. Indeed, the

335

end of our spiritual life should be one not so much of thought as of contemplation, when we, receptive and alert and dedicated, are filled with the Spirit of God. It follows therefore, that when we deal with the destructive emotional forces that attack us when we are on our own, we must first frankly acknowledge the agonising pain of emotional upheaval. It should then be lifted up to God in contemplative meditation, so that divine guidance may show us the deeper significance that pain has in our lives. It is then possible to accept the negative emotion in a spirit of creation, and even eventually to love it, for acting as a gateway into the psychic life of the many deprived and underprivileged people in the world. Only then can the great work of faith proceed. If we can neither deny the existence of the pain within us, nor flinch from it, it will cause no psychic disturbance outside us; and if it is blessed in the name of God, its negative emotional charge is neutralised, and it becomes infused with warmth and love. 'Make me an instrument of thy peace,' said St Francis, because he knew that it is only when our inner domain is filled with peace that we can bring peace to the world outside and around us.

This means blessing every circumstance in our life in God's name. Then even a potentially destructive attitude can be transformed so that it ceases to threaten the integrity of the personality and starts instead to bring harmony to those around us. This deep, internal spring of peace is an intimate relationship with the Creator in which we also enjoy boundless communion with all created things. When I know myself in the light of divine love, I know everyone else in that light. This is the second great commandment of course – 'love thy neighbour as thyself' – where I am realising, as well as affirming my identity with my neighbour. In the sight of God, we are all one, since God loves everything He has created. It's not possible to exclude anything from God's love, no matter how evil and destructive it shows itself to be in our lives. The difference between the good and the evil agent, in the subtlest psychic emanation to the humblest physical form, lies in how receptive it is to the love of God. God causes His sun to rise on the bad and the good, His rain to fall on the dishonest as well as the honest. But it is only the good and the honest that are receptive to God's goodness, and able to bring what they have received back to Him with a blessing. The evil ones dissipate and squander all that they have received, and in the end are as deprived as they were at the beginning. But God never stops caring for them, always hoping that their hearts may change and they will turn to love Him and their brethren travelling with them on the road of life. However, not all unpleasant emotional forces come from the depths of the personal psyche. They all impress themselves on the conscious mind but there is a much deeper region of shared psychic experience that proceeds from the collective unconsciousness to assail all those who are particularly sensitive to it. The source of these forces may be the accumulated evil that has existed ever since God's creatures abused the freewill that they were given and acted independently. It can also emanate from the mind of another person, either still living in the flesh or one beyond death and devoid of a physical body, but still functioning in a tenuous type of body which retains past thoughts and emotions, but still awaits healing and redemption. Such assaults on the psyche may cause acute suffering to those sensitive people who live on their own and have no one on whom to lean for emotional and moral support. This can reveal itself in bouts of apparently causeless depression that can be severe enough to threaten suicide. This kind of unpleasant experience is especially liable to happen to those who dabble in the occult. Divine intelligence alone can deliver us from evil, and at the same time care for the souls that have lost their way, and are causing such psychic havoc. Sometimes the sensitive person is given vague intimations about future events, and psychic confessions can wreak havoc on the lives of sensitive people who are ignorant about para-normal phenomena and a tendency of the mind to misinterpret and distort information that it only partially grasps. This situation is not helped by the ignorance and antagonism – the two go hand-in-hand – shown by some psychiatrists and ministers of religion on the subject of psychic phenomena. It follows therefore that the field is dominated by ill-informed enthusiasts who dabble in occultism, and tend to lack proper psychological, theological and spiritual training. Only a psychologically balanced, spiritually experienced and emotionally mature person can have the necessary discernment to interpret psychic communications with authority. Psychic communication is so fleeting, nebulous and unpredictable, that it is dangerous to use it as a guide to sound living, although sometimes it may shatter the most sceptical mind by its accuracy. The important principle to grasp is that God, or Divine Intelligence, is in charge. We may be inspired by spirit to act directly in confused situations, but this spirit does not rule our lives or cancel our own powers of choice. In other words, this power strengthens the human will by infusing it with purpose and confidence, but it does not ride roughshod over that will. He who stands patiently at the door of the soul and knocks quietly for admission does not take over the personality or control the will.

This is the difference between the courtesy of God to His creatures and the power-hungry lust of an intermediate psychic intelligence that uses everything in its vicinity for selfish motives. The Divine raises its creatures to an image of His own nature, as mirrored in Christ, whereas predatory psychic powers reduce all with whom they come into contact to the state of compliant slaves. A determined mind is the first prerequisite to deal with unwanted psychic influence. Even if some of the information appears accurate in the short term, it does not contribute to the person's welfare in the end, when the personality is enslaved and the will is sacrificed to outside forces. The same principle holds true of those who allow their lives to be governed by astrological predictions or the teachings and advice of mediums. All of these have sufficient truth to impress but they do not lead to the full growth of the person. We certainly need to know more about the inner workings of psychic phenomena, for these too are part of God's dispensation, but they are no more acceptable as oracles of truth than the utterances of the worldly purveyors of wisdom who dominate the fields of politics, economics or science. The acid test is always the same: 'By their fruits you will know them' (Matthew 7:15-20). Spiritual teaching alone provides the word of life for it brings with it the unconditional love of God, and inspires the person towards new peaks of endeavour in which they themselves are the master. So, a determined mind will tell all invading psychic influences to depart – but most people want the best of both worlds, so that, although they would like to be free of psychic interference with their independence, they also want to bask in the glamour of psychic communication that boosts their ego and promises material benefits. This was the supreme temptation of Jesus in the wilderness when the Devil took Him up to a high mountain and showed Him all the kingdoms of the world. 'All these,' he said, 'I will give you if you will only fall down and do me homage.' All of us who aspire to true freedom, which is God's service, must respect the reply of Jesus who said, 'Begone, Satan. The scripture says you shall do homage to the Lord your God, and worship Him alone' (Matthew 4:8-10). It must be emphasised that it is not the fact of psychic information that is wrong, but the source of much of this information, because the message of God that lifts up our hearts and sets the captive in us free is also coming from a psychic source, so it is essential to know the source of the information. Once the mind has told all invading psychic forces to leave its domain, it must seal the door of the soul lest they return accompanied by more. Jesus warns us that merely getting rid of one evil spirit is no guarantee against its return accompanied by others even more wicked than itself (Matthew 12:43-45). So that the last state of the victim may be worse than the first. The secret place where we meet with God is protected against psychic assault by communion with God, because where God is allowed in, all subversive powers are excluded by His presence.

But it may be necessary to strengthen the psyche against invasion before communion with God becomes possible, and an understanding of the human psychic constitution is a great help in this process. There seem to be certain areas of the body that correspond with tracts or channels through which psychic impulses connect with the mind, especially in sensitive people, and these psychic centres should be under control so that they do not admit negative emanations indiscriminately. The most important centre in admitting or rejecting strongly emotional charges has its centre in the upper part of the abdomen, just above the navel. If you can fix your mind on this area of the body whilst deeply relaxed, a degree of control over the centre can be made. As you breathe in and out, the sign of the Cross can be visualised on that part of the abdomen. If this simple exercise is practised several times a day for about five minutes, the psychic centre will come under such control that it will no longer allow the indiscriminate entry of baneful impulses. This is in no way a substitute for true communion with God as in prayer or meditation, but it may be a necessary preparation before more profound spiritual devotions are carried out. It is hard, maybe even impossible, to meditate effectively until every part of the psyche is removed from the world and fully attentive to God. Certainly, when one's prayer life is strong, the possibility of attack by extraneous psychic forces becomes small. It is interesting to note that the Greek for 'work together' is more accurately translated as 'intermingle'. This makes the statement more acceptable to a man dying painfully of cancer perhap!. In the end, we have to believe that 'God works all things together for good for those who love him' (Romans 8:28). If we can keep our minds fixed on this moment now, and all that pertains to it, we will be in psychic rapport with the entire created universe immediately. Then our constant solicitude for the world's problems will bring us into a creative psychic fellowship with our fellows and with all we love. We are members of one another at the level of the soul or 'true self', and the closer we are to our own soul, the more authentic will be our relationship with all people, and the deeper will be our knowledge of God. This is the supreme lesson of psychic sensitivity; it may be a great burden, but if we accept it properly it will bring us into fellowship with a vast range of people, and thus lessen the pain of living alone. It is the person who lives alone who bears the brunt of psychic sensitivity because there are fewer distractions in his life to divert his attention to the things of the physical senses. But as these people persist in exploring their psychic sensitivity, there are immense dimensions of spiritual understanding revealed to them. If religion is what a man does with his solitariness, then our thoughts and hopes when we are completely alone reveal our response to the reality of death and the nature of God. 'As a man thinks in his heart, so is he' (Proverbs 23:7). Jesus said, 'Where your treasure is, there will your heart be also' (Matthew 6:21). And the one treasure that outlasts change and survives disillusionment and the exhaustion of age is that eternal enlightenment which comes from God. From the source itself comes inspiration that never dies, everlastingly renewed by the power of God's Spirit. In solitariness, we can move through the superficialities of life on the surface to the ultimate truth that makes us aware of our own inherent nothingness, together with the seed of eternal life that is deeply implanted within us. This seed is the Spirit of God, Christ in us, the hope of being changed into a perfect human being as seen in the likeness of Christ.

Those of us who live alone are not burdened by the demands of others around us. Family commitments can easily take up all our time, energy and inner serenity, so that we who live alone have a responsibility as well as a Heaven-sent opportunity to explore the inner world of the Spirit through the actions of prayer, meditation and contemplation. It is a duty and a privilege to spread the radiance that follows prayer and contemplation into the world around us. If we would only begin to work in harmony with the Divine Presence instead of beating the air blindly in trying to achieve what we, in our stupidity and ignorance, see as our own best interests. 'Unless the Lord builds the house, the builders will have toiled in vain. Unless the Lord keeps watch over a city, in vain the watchman stands on guard. In vain you rise up early and go late to rest, toiling for the bread you eat. He supplies the needs of those he loves' (Psalm 127:1-2). When we and God work together, we build the house that is both the inner sanctum of the soul of each one of us, and also the edifice of the world. Communion with the Divine enables us to stand watch over the world in the presence of God. The prerequisite for this divine communion is silence. Silence is essential before we can really listen to another person, not only to their voice but, even more significantly, to the whole personality that pours out from them. We first grasp the message by seeing, hearing and feeling; then, with the combined powers of intellect and intuition, we begin to communicate at a deeper level with the other person. In the same way, when I am silent before the Creator, in the deepest, formless, most intense way of meditation which is contemplation, I can begin to converse spontaneously with this force and listen to what it is telling me. When we become completely still to the world outside and the mind within us, when there are no noises or images to distract us, a silence descends on us which is a true balm to the soul, not a negative void, but a wave of love that pervades the whole personality and lifts it spiritually to a new understanding of the meaning and purpose of life.

As Blaise Pascal said, "The whole of man's problems stems from his inability to sit quietly in a room by himself." And remember this was a scientist, remember learning Pascal's law in physics?

Epilogue

It arrived on 24th November 2004 - an innocuous handwritten envelope which contained amazing news. The handwriting closely resembled that of an ex-patient of mine in Gloucester, the burden of whose letters was general complaint. So I put it aside until I had showered and had my breakfast, and felt more able to cope.

The contents of the letter shook me to the core: it was from NORCAP, the agency which reunites adopted children with their natural mothers, and it asked for help in tracing the mother of a young man who 'believed that he was related to the Swan family'. I was overjoyed by the fact that the son, who had been adopted in 1966, actually wanted to make contact with me. After all, so far as he was concerned, I had given him away. I wrote back with alacrity, and in due course received a charming photograph of him and his family, and news about them over the telephone from the NORCAP liaison officer. It appeared that he was married to an American; they had two sons and were living and working in Taiwan. All kinds of powerful emotions were triggered by this event, both joyful and sad, and I spent most of Christmas that year in a very tearful state: tears of sadness for all that I had missed of his life for the past 38 years, and tears of joy in the knowledge of his existence, that he was well, successful; and apparently both happy and secure - certainly much more secure and happy than I could have made him on my own. I had seen too much of the misery brought about by single mothers bringing up children alone during my teaching experience, and boys particularly without male influence seemed to suffer more. We eventually exchanged letters and arranged to meet on 9th August 2005, which then seemed to be a comfortable distance away.

I wrote him a letter, saying that I had no aspirations to be his 'mother' in the true sense of the word. I felt very strongly that his adoptive mother, who had lavished so much affection and care on him all those years, should have that title. Again, looking back at my own experience, I realised it was Grandma Manton and Auntie Edie who were my real mothers - certainly not the cruel and inflexible Auntie Alice. After all; it is the loving, caring, comforting person who appears in the middle of the night to soothe your distress who deserves the title of 'mother', not the one who happens to give birth to you. I read an article recently by Werther Huemer putting forward the idea that the mother's role is critical for incarnation, not only physically but also spiritually and psychically. The mother's inner condition determines to a large extent which of the human spirits seeking incarnation can really connect with the child's body. After incarnation until birth, the incarnated spirit influences the further development of their body, until finally a personality - a human spirit with a multitude of individual strengths and weaknesses, tendencies and experiences – opens their eyes into the light of the world. So it seems that the body is really a tool for the Spirit, and that the purpose of being born is for the development of one's own inner being.

My son was very pleased to receive this disclaimer letter and told me subsequently that his adoptive parents were helped considerably by reading it. I felt very strongly that his adopted mother should not feel at all threatened by this potentially menacing situation.

For our planned meeting on 9th August, apart from buying a youthful lavender trouser suit, I was not particularly affected - but, when 1st August arrived, my nerves really started to jangle. What would he think of me? What would I say? Would my gelatinous legs carry me to the meeting-place? Would I even have a stroke, etc, etc? Time of course is inexorable, and the morning of 9th August dawned fine and warm. Somehow I got through the hours until 3.30 pm when my taxi arrived to take me to this amazing meeting. I did my hair about fifty times and tried on and discarded at least half a dozen tops to wear with my suit.

I tottered into the hotel feeling like a puppet abandoned by the puppeteer, and saw a red-headed young man just inside the entrance, together with a slim attractive young woman. They both rose to their feet as I moved forward and he just took me in his arms and held me for some minutes. It was a real feeling of coming home. The words 'flesh of my flesh and bone of my bone' repeated themselves over and over in my mind. We broke apart at last and he introduced me to his wife Barbara, a New Yorker who welcomed me with great warmth and affection. She had all the attractive qualities of American womanhood – articulate, capable, smart and self-assured – and we warmed to one another at once. And between the two of them, the meeting was as if we were very old friends who had been reunited after a long absence. We talked absolutely non-stop for over two hours about their background, their education, their plans for the future, their interests and their two boys – then aged eight and six. We also talked about their life in Taiwan. They appeared to be true citizens of the planet, flying from Taiwan to England, to Greece, to Australia, as easily as I might go from Worcester to London, to Torquay or to Suffolk. They were obviously true children of the 21st century which was great. We went walking on the Malverns the following day, had a pub lunch, and then came back to my house where Barbara took photographs of Martin and me.

His adoptive parents had christened him Martin, so I had to get used to his new name – which has been difficult after calling him Stephen in my mind for so many years. I saw them off with sadness and returned to the solitude of my present life. But it was fine: I felt great satisfaction having held him, touched him and smelled him, and that the circle had been finally squared. I also felt a sense of achievement in having produced such a splendid person – good-looking, well-mannered, gentle and considerate. Of course, most of this was nurture, but at least I had provided the raw material! I did not forget John in all this; most of all, I was reminded of him by Martin's eyes and the shape of his head. I would have loved to have had a telephone conversation with him the next day, to discuss feelings, but remembering the limits I had set myself to remain on the periphery of his life and not make any demands of any kind, I didn't telephone and neither did he.

A succession of friends telephoned however, falling over themselves to ask, 'How did you get on?' – but I was so overcome by memories, emotions and the general collapse that follows an episode of extreme stress that I just burst into tears, and was able only to gasp, 'Fine, I'll speak to you tomorrow,' before putting down the phone and plundering the box of tissues yet further. By the end of the day, I could barely see out of my little reddened eyes.

I didn't hear from him until three weeks later, when I had a postcard from Greece where they were all on a sailing holiday. He said he was overjoyed that we had met, 'Not just because of familial reasons, but you have led an amazing life and developed an amazing character, and are fascinating to talk to.' I realised that I could not expect much in the way of letter-writing but at least he was anxious to keep in touch in future. I realise now the truth of the aphorism: 'Boys don't write - girls do.' Certainly Jane does, bless her! She showers me with cards, letters, phone calls, flowers, on any and every occasion. I also realise that one has to abide by one's choices in life. I chose to have him adopted, and in so doing gave up any rights or expectations of close contact, and I am content for it to be so. I had a sudden phone call from him in December. It appeared they were coming to the UK to spend a family Christmas with his brother who was also adopted later on. Martin wanted to come to Malvern and introduce his children to me. This was a very strange experience: these two small red-headed boys came to my door, seemingly quite unfazed by the experience of meeting 'Daddy's tummy mummy' (as Martin had described me and explained the relationship) and explained the relationship. We went out to lunch and a walk in the woods, and the whole experience was quite surreal. Here I was after nearly forty years with a son, his wife and two grandchildren. Maybe my 'bread on the waters' was coming back as chocolate cake?

The elder boy demonstrated echoes of his maternal grandfather when, after visiting the men's cloakroom, announced in a loud voice to the whole restaurant that there was a naked lady in the men's loo, and also proceeded to make several further visits to enjoy this vision. When they finally left, they piled into the back of the car, and were immediately absorbed in a new Harry Potter DVD on their portable DVD recorder. I don't think their new 'tummy grandma' made much of an impact! However, it was a joy to meet them, and to realise that a part of me goes on.

Since that visit, I have had a card from Utah where they were all on a skiing holiday, and also one from Australia where Martin and his wife were hosting an incentive weekend for sales executives in Brisbane. They had been swimming with dolphins, sand-sledging, cuddling koalas, catching crabs and indulging in far too much good food and wine – a far cry from my life of shopping for food, lunching with friends, exercising in a hydrotherapy pool, seeing patients, and my osteopath and acupuncturist. Not that I am not extremely grateful to be doing all these things at 86; at my age autonomy is perhaps the greatest blessing. So the wheel has turned full circle, and the agony and despair of 1965-66 have turned to joy and gratitude. I have a son, and this indeed is a blessing. Obviously,

I will remain on the periphery of his life, but it is so good to know that he exists, he is well, and most importantly, is an incredibly good husband and father. So what appeared to be disaster, has in fact been for the greater good, and I am so thankful to Divine Will that it is so.

Further Reading

C Edward Barker, *Nerves and Their Cure*

(London: George Allen & Unwin, 1960)

Wayne Dyer, *Manifest Your Destiny*

(London: Thorsons, 1997)

Deepak Chopra, *Ageless Body, Timeless Mind*

(London: Rider, 1993)

Kahlil Gibran, *The Prophet*

(New York: Alfred Knopf, 1923)

Joel Goldsmith, *The Infinite Way*

(De Vorss and Co)

M Scott Peck, *The Road Less Travelled*

(I would recommend this as my star book above all the others)
(London: Rider, 1978)

Sogyal Rinpoche, *The Tibetan Book of Living and Dying*

(London: Rider, 1992)

Dr James Scala, *Arthritis - Diet Against It*

(Foulsham)

Gloria Steinem, *Revolution from Within*

(London: Bloomsbury, 1992)

Michael Volin & Nancy Phelan, *Yoga Over Forty*

(London: Pelham Books, 1965)

Claire Weekes, *Self-Help for Your Nerves*

(London: Angus & Robertson, 1984)

also *More Help for Your Nerves* and *Peace from Nervous Suffering*

Also, any material from *Nightingale Conant (highly recommended)*
Long Road, Paignton, Devon TQ4 7BB
ukccare@nightingale.com, +44 (0) 1803 666100

and *The Seekers Trust*
Addington Park, Nr Maidstone, Kent ME19 5BL
+44 (0) 1732 843589

About the Author

Eileen Swan has experienced many difficult times. In building a healthy, fulfilling life for herself, she has aquired a remarkable ability to help others who think they 'Can't go on'.

At the age of 85, Eileen continues to teach yoga and to work as a counsellor. She lives in Malvern.